The War Scientists

For Colin Soleim and Owen VanderBilt,
who are smart but not lethal

The War Scientists

The brains behind military technologies of destruction and defense

Thomas J. Craughwell

METRO BOOKS
New York

Contents

Introduction

The first weapons were almost certainly sticks and stones, and these of course were not invented but were found objects. The "inventive" part came about when our prehistoric ancestors realized these things could be used to hurt and even kill. The first "war scientist" was probably the man who discovered that while hitting someone with a stick was good, stabbing him with a pointy stick was even better. And so the spear was born, and from it developed two other staples of warfare— the bow and arrow, and the sword.

For most of human history most weapons technology served at least a dual purpose. The spear, and the bow and arrow, and later the musket and the rifle, made it easier to hunt game, but they were also effective in killing off enemies. We know from carved reliefs found in Egyptian palaces and temples that pharaohs used their chariots, the prototype of the tank, to chase down lions and to chase down Hittites. In the same way, dynamite can reduce a city to rubble, but the engineers who dug the Suez and Panama canals found that it was also useful in clearing away rock and earth.

Of course, there are weapons that have no alternative benign function. The Gatling gun and its successor the Hiram gun fall into the same category as Greek fire and the atomic bomb—they serve no purpose except to kill. Yet Richard Gatling believed his weapon—which could fire 400 rounds per minute—was a

On May 6, 1940 the famous aviation designer Igor Sikorsky set a new record for the duration of a helicopter flight at 1 hour, 32 minutes, and 25 seconds in the VS-300. An assistant holds a sign showing the old record.

lifesaver. In a letter dated 1877 he wrote, "It occurred to me that if I could invent a machine—a gun—which could by rapidity of fire, enable one man to do as much battle duty as a hundred, that it would, to a great extent, supersede the necessity of large armies, and consequently, exposure to battle and disease greatly diminished." Today we read Gatling's words almost with disbelief—how could he have been so naïve? I imagine that 130 years ago the friend who received the letter probably thought the same way about Gatling's statement as we do. But deadlier weapons have never turned humankind away from war. Chemical weapons, biological weapons, nuclear weapons; no matter how much the world recoils from them there is always someone ready to put them into action.

The focus of this book is on twenty-five examples of war-related technology and how they came into being, and on the individuals, the scientists who created them. The stories you'll find here will take you to ancient China and ancient Sicily, to medieval Constantinople and Renaissance Italy, from a synthetic fabrics laboratory in Buffalo, New York, to a World War II chamber of horrors in Manchuria, to the rough terrain of Western Australia.

Although all the inventions included here are military related, not all are weapons. Nicolas Appert was a French chef who discovered the process for keeping food fresh in tin cans (actually the first cans he used were cast iron), an invention which proved a tremendous boon to ships' crews on long sea voyages as well as to armies on the move.

Stephanie Kwolek, a chemist and researcher working for DuPont, was working to develop a new synthetic fiber when she stumbled upon a strange substance which, when spun out as a thread, turned out to be five times stronger than steel. Kwolek's discovery is known today as Kevlar, the body armor fabric.

Igor Sikorsky, a refugee from the Russian Revolution, invented the helicopter, which he believed would be useful in transporting fresh troops to battlefields and ferrying back the wounded. By the 1960s, his invention had been armed and converted into a kind of aerial gunship, a turn of events that depressed him. During the final years of his life, he consoled himself by clipping newspaper reports of helicopters that had been used successfully in rescue missions.

Another rueful inventor was Alfred Nobel. In March 1888, when his brother Robert died, a French newspaper confused its Nobels and reported the death of Alfred under the headline, "The Merchant of Death is Dead." Deeply upset that he would be remembered only as the man who unleashed the destructive power of dynamite upon the world, Nobel decided to refurbish his reputation by establishing annual awards to individuals who had made major contributions in the fields of chemistry, physics, medicine, literature and world peace. Those awards are the Nobel Prizes.

Of course, war scientists are not untainted by controversy. Fritz Haber, chemist and ardent German nationalist, never repented the invention and then the deployment of poison gas against Allied troops during World War I. In fact, he regarded it as one of his greatest achievements, and to the end of his life kept a framed photograph of the first cloud of poison gas drifting toward the Allied trenches. His wife Clara, herself an accomplished chemist, did not share his sense of pride. Profoundly ashamed that her husband had perverted the science she loved, Clara Haber killed herself.

Robert Oppenheimer, the father of the atomic bomb, had a weakness for leftist causes. He once admitted that he had been "a member of just about every Communist Front organization on the West Coast" of America. Yet in the 1940s and early 1950s he had testified against colleagues who he said were security risks because they had ties to the Communist Party. Oppenheimer's double standard came back to bite him in 1953 when he lost his security clearance and his position as chairman of the Atomic Energy Commission because of his former membership in Communist organizations.

One of the most controversial war scientists was Wernher von Braun, a member of the Nazi Party, whose experiments to create the V–2 rocket cost the lives of thousands of slave laborers. During the last years of World War II his rockets were used against civilian targets in Britain, France, and Belgium. Yet at the end of the war he was not arrested as a war criminal but was sent to the United States to help develop missiles and eventually rockets for America's space program. American scientists who worked with von Braun admired his genius and found him engaging and personable, but many members of the public were uneasy about having a former Nazi at the head of the U.S. space program. This discomfort often found expression in black humor: in 1960, when von Braun published his memoirs, entitled *I Aim for the Stars*, American satirist Mort Sahl suggested the subtitle should be "But Sometimes I Hit London."

Here then are the stories of twenty-five scientific innovators who represent the paradox of science and technology—their potential for accomplishing great good, and for inflicting great evil.

A heaven-sent weapon
Callinicus' liquid fire

SCIENTIST: Callinicus

AREA OF SCIENCE: Chemistry

MAIN INVENTIONS: Greek fire and flamethrower

IN 861, AFTER TWO LEISURELY YEARS raiding and rampaging along the shores of the Mediterranean, two Vikings from Sweden, Hastein and Bjorn Ironside, were ready to lead their fleet of approximately sixty dragon ships home where they could sell off their captives and show off their loot. It had been a splendid adventure: the cities of the south of France, Italy, and North Africa were richer than those of England and Ireland; the weather was sunny and warm; and there was wine in abundance. While their comrades endured bone-chilling winters in the British Isles and Normandy, Hastein, Bjorn, and their men had wintered along what is now the French Riviera, where for excitement they raided the towns of Nimes, Arles, and Valence, and even sailed over to Italy to sack Pisa.

Hastein was a veteran raider who had long terrorized the inhabitants of England and northern France. The Norman monk and chronicler, Dudo of Saint-Quentin, summoned up every censorious adjective he could recall to describe Hastein's character:

> accursed and headstrong, extremely cruel and harsh, destructive, troublesome, wild, ferocious, infamous, destructive and inconstant, brash, conceited and lawless, death-dealing, rude, everywhere on guard, rebellious traitor and kindler of evil, this double-faced hypocrite and ungodly, arrogant, seductive and foolhardy deceiver, this lewd, unbridled, contentious rascal.

Nineteenth century engraving showing the Roman emperor Nero presiding over the deaths of several of his Christian subjects by burning at the stake.

About a decade before the voyage into the Mediterranean, Ragnar Lodbrok, one of the most fearsome—and successful—Viking raiders of the ninth century, put his 12-year-old son Bjorn in Hastein's custody so the boy could learn how to grow up to be a Viking. By the time Bjorn sailed with Hastein as his co-commander, he had become an accomplished warrior and acquired the nickname "Ironside" because he emerged from every raid and battle unharmed.

As Hastein and Bjorn's fleet approached the Straits of Gibraltar, the outlet into the Atlantic, they found their way blocked by a Moorish fleet. Earlier in the ninth century Vikings had raided Moorish territory in southern Spain, captured and ransacked the city of Seville, and carried off many Moorish captives. Here was the Moors' chance to repay the Vikings.

It is not likely that Hastein and Bjorn were concerned. The Vikings excelled at fighting at sea, and they had sixty ships filled with experienced warriors. The records do not tell us the size of the Moorish fleet, but apparently the Vikings did not feel threatened. As they bore down on the Moors, however, the Vikings saw something odd—bronze and iron tubes mounted on their ships. As they came close enough to board the Moorish vessels, the crewmen standing beside each tube began operating a pump—and from the tubes shot liquid fire. Every ship it touched burst into flames. Every Viking splattered by it roasted alive. The Moors had acquired the secret weapon of the Byzantine Empire—Greek fire.

Hastein and Bjorn led their men in a desperate fight, and some of the Vikings did break through the Moorish blockade and reached the safety of the Atlantic. But not many—of the sixty ships in the fleet, forty had burned and sunk. Since dragon ships carried a minimum of twenty-five men, the lowest estimate is that Hastein and Bjorn lost 1,000 men to a weapon they had never before encountered.

The gift of an angel

The flammable liquid the Moors spewed on the Viking dragon ships was Greek fire, or something close to it. It had been the great secret weapon of the Byzantine Empire, where it was considered so vital to the empire's survival that in a handbook addressed to his son on how to administer an empire, Emperor Constantine VII Porphyrogenitus (905–959) claimed that the formula had been brought down from heaven by an angel who whispered it into the ear of Constantine the Great, Rome's first Christian emperor. Porphyrogenitus insisted that the formula for Greek fire must never be revealed, and told another story

about an imperial government official who blabbed the secret—he was consumed by fire from heaven as he was about to enter Constantinople's greatest church, Hagia Sophia.

More likely Greek fire was concocted by a Syrian architect and alchemist, Callinicus of Heliopolis, in the province of Phoenice (today's Baalbek in Lebanon). Some time before 673, to escape the armies of Islam that were sweeping across Byzantium's provinces in the Middle East, Callinicus fled to Constantinople. To help repulse the Muslim invaders, Callinicus offered the emperor a flammable liquid that could be propelled from a metal tube, what we would regard as a primitive flame thrower. This flammable liquid became known as Greek fire. To this day no one is certain of the ingredients and proportions used to make Greek fire. Even during its heyday, no one outside the Byzantine court knew the secret, although a few educated guesses from the period have come down to us, beginning with that of Marcus Graecus, or Mark the Greek, a chronicler who lived in the tenth century. He believed Greek fire was composed of sulfur, tartar, Persian gum, naphtha (pitch), niter, petroleum and pine resin, all boiled together. The Byzantine princess Anna Comnena (1083–1153) provides a simpler recipe—pine resin and sulfur.

Painting on vellum from a medieval manuscript showing the use of Greek fire against an enemy ship at sea. The Byzantines, in 678 and 717–718 destroyed two Saracen fleets with Greek fire.

13

Whatever the recipe might have been, Greek fire was the perfect weapon, terrifying and destructive. Because it was liquid, it was hard to avoid; a small splatter was enough to ignite a wooden siege engine or a tar-calked ship, or to maim or kill. The pitch component made it so sticky it was almost impossible to get off the skin. And the petroleum ensured that it would burn on the surface of water. There was almost no way to escape it, or to extinguish it. Historian Adrienne Mayor has likened Greek fire to napalm because both substances "adhere to targets and burn at very high temperatures over a prolonged time."

The quest for fire weapons

No one knows the name of the first warrior who fired a flaming arrow into his enemy's camp or village, but he was onto something. In terms of death and destruction, no other weapon available at the time could compare with fire.

We know that in 480 BC the Persians used flaming arrows to destroy the wooden structures and defensive walls atop Athens' Acropolis. In 304 BC the defenders of the island of Rhodes used firepots—clay containers packed with a burning substance such as sulfur or pitch—and other flaming missiles to drive off an invasion led by Demetrius I Poliorcetes of Macedon. The Roman poet Lucan wrote of a sea battle fought in 49 BC between the forces of Julius Caesar and Pompey the Great, in which soldiers on both sides hurled flaming torches dipped in oil and sulfur onto the decks of each other's ships, with tragic results:

> Fire all-consuming ran amongst the ships,
> Whose oily timbers soaked in pitch and wax
> Inflammable, gave welcome to the flames.
> Nor could the waves prevail against the blaze
> Which claimed as for its own the fragments borne
> Upon the waters.

When Alexander the Great attacked the city of Tyre, the Phoenician defenders roasted sand and metal filings over a hot fire, then poured the molten-red particles onto the Macedonians as they stormed the walls. The historian Diodorus Siculus describes the scenes: "The sand sifted down under breastplates and shirts, and scorching the skin with the intense heat inflicted … irremediable disaster. They shrieked supplications like those under torture and there was no one to help them, but from the excruciating agony they fell into madness and died."

Clouds of noxious smoke could also be effective on the battlefield. In 429 BC, during the Battle of Plataea, the Spartans ignited a mixture of resin and sulfur; a favorable wind carried the toxic fumes toward the Plataean troops who scattered as they tried to escape the deadly cloud. The Chinese liked to burn arsenic and wolfsbane and other deadly plants to disperse, sicken, or kill their enemies. In the sixteenth century some Indian tribes in Brazil set fire to giant piles of hot pepper seeds, releasing large clouds of acrid smoke that stung the eyes of the Spanish and Portuguese conquistadors.

The worst of all these early chemical weapons was pitch, a sticky, highly flammable substance derived from petroleum. The Greeks first encountered it after Alexander the Great conquered Babylon. It ignited so quickly and burned at such a heat that initially the Greeks regarded it as a kind of dangerous toy, like fireworks; but very quickly they came to recognize its possibilities as a weapon.

Naphtha is maddeningly sticky—almost impossible to remove. The very high temperature at which it burns causes unbearable pain as it eats through skin, tissue and even bone. And it burns for a very long time. In AD 64, when Nero began his persecution of Rome's Christians (using them as scapegoats for the Great Fire), he ordered that hundreds be bound to crosses set up in his huge pleasure gardens. They were dressed in a naphtha-soaked garment known as the *tunica molesta*, or "torture shirt." As evening fell, Nero's henchmen ignited the Christians' shirts and the gardens were illuminated by human torches.

Breaking the siege

Muawiyah I, founder of the Umayyad dynasty of caliphs in Damascus, is a controversial figure in Islam. Although initially he opposed Muhammed, after his family's fall from power Mecca Muawiyah converted to Islam. Sunni Muslims regard him as a Companion of the Prophet, one of Muhammed's inner circle; Shiite Muslims revile him as a hypocrite who helped to bring down Ali, Muhammed's cousin and son-in-law and the man Shiites regard as the true successor to the Prophet.

Sectarian squabbles notwithstanding, Muawiyah came to power in 661 following the assassination of Ali. While his right to rule as caliph is open to debate, there is no arguing that he was one of early Islam's most successful military commanders. To rival the Muslim armies that had swept through the Middle East, Muawiyah outfitted a Muslim fleet to conquer the islands and coastal towns of the Aegean. He raided the coast of what is now Turkey—the very heart of the

The flamethrower

"Flame has a powerful psychological effect in that humans instinctively withdraw from it, even when their morale is good. In addition, [flame] is a casualty producing and lethal agent." So reads the introduction to the 1944 Australian Army training pamphlet for the flamethrower.

In 1911 Germany became the first nation to develop a modern flamethrower, and it put it to use in World War I to clear Allied troops out of their trenches. Thirty years later, during World War II, both the Allied and the Axis powers had flamethrowers. Nazi Germany tended to use them against civilian populations in reprisal for the actions of the Resistance or other anti-Nazi underground and guerrilla organizations. The Japanese used flamethrowers against Australian troops at the Battle of Milne Bay in Papua New Guinea in 1942, and against Allied forces on Corregidor also in 1942. U.S. troops used flamethrowers against the Japanese when they fought to capture the island of Okinawa in 1945.

During World War II some tanks had flamethrowing capability, but most flamethrowers were backpack units that consisted of two canisters of flammable fuel along with a tank of compressed gas. A tube connected the tanks to the gun. The compressed gas forced the fuel out of the tanks and through the tube; as it flowed past the gun's ignition system the fuel ignited and spewed a deadly stream of fire out of the muzzle.

It was the Vietnam War that made flamethrowers undesirable. The United States used napalm as fuel, a particularly sticky substance that not only clung to whatever it hit, but also burned at a very high heat and was extremely difficult to extinguish. News reports of Viet Cong guerrillas and Vietnamese civilians dying agonizing deaths or suffering horrific wounds from napalm gave flamethrowers a reputation as an especially inhumane weapon. As a result, after 1978 the U.S. military voluntarily gave up using them in combat.

Byzantine Empire—and captured the Greek islands of Cos and Chios, as well as the city of Smyrna. And then he sailed to Constantinople, where he imposed a naval blockade. Of course, the Byzantines still had access to the rest of the world from the landward side of the city, but this naval assault was surprising because it was the first time Constantinople had been attacked from the sea.

Muawiyah positioned his fleet in the Sea of Marmara, thereby blocking Byzantine ships from reaching the Mediterranean, and used Cyzicus, on a peninsula 50 miles from Constantinople, as his naval base. The siege dragged on for five years, from 672 to 677; every spring, summer and fall Muawiyah's ships would blockade the city and pound its walls using catapults, then during winter he would retire to their winter quarters at Cyzicus.

It was Callinicus' liquid fire that finally broke the siege, at the Battle of Syllaeum. The Byzantine emperor, Constantine IV, sent out his fleet with iron and bronze tubes mounted on the railings of every ship. As they drew within range of Muawiyah's fleet, men stationed beside the tubes began operating hand-pumps, and suddenly streams of liquid fire exploded from the mouths of the guns. Every ship it touched erupted in flames. Every man it hit screamed in agony as he was burned alive. Water did not extinguish the fire; in fact, the Greek fire floated on the water's surface, turning the Sea of Marmara into a fiery lake.

The surviving remnants of Muawiyah's fleet retreated from the Sea of Marmara and sailed for home. Along the southern coast of Anatolia a violent storm overtook the fleet, sinking more ships and taking more lives. Muawiyah's five-year siege of Constantinople had been a tremendous waste of men and resources, and it had ended in disaster, but the caliph's troubles were not over. Constantine IV exploited his advantage by forcing Muawiyah to return all the Byzantine islands and cities he had conquered, and compelling him to pay an annual tribute of fifty slaves, fifty horses and 1.343 tons of gold.

Greek fire saved Constantinople more than once. In 717, when a Muslim army of approximately 80,000 men and an armada of 1,800 ships completely encircled the city, it was Greek fire (combined with epidemics in the enemy camp and the unexpected assistance of the Bulgars) that forced the Muslims to give up the siege. Greek fire put down the revolt of the naval commander Thomas the Slav in 821; destroyed almost the entire 1,000-ship fleet of Prince Igor of Kiev in 941; and inflicted a crushing defeat on the Pisan navy in 1099. Strangely, in 1204, when Crusaders from Western Europe stormed Constantinople, the defenders did not use Greek fire. Without their secret weapon, the Byzantines were overwhelmed by the Crusaders, who wrought so much destruction that Constantinople never fully recovered. Over the next 250 years the city slipped more and more deeply into decline until the Turks captured it in 1453, thanks largely to their use of the latest secret weapon—artillery.

What happened to Greek fire? Historians speculate that perhaps the formula had been lost, or that the Byzantine emperor no longer had access to supplies of naphtha as more and more of his territory fell to the armies of Islam. Like its secret formula, the sudden disappearance of Greek fire from the Byzantine arsenal remains a mystery.

Catapult, claw, death ray
Archimedes' strange war machines

SCIENTIST: Archimedes

AREA OF SCIENCE: Mechanical engineering

MAIN INVENTIONS: Giant catapult and death ray

SLOWLY THE MASSIVE WARSHIP APPROACHED the seawall of Syracuse, the point where the battlements rose directly above a narrow strip of the harbor's rock-and-sand beach. In fact, it was not a single vessel that crept across the harbor, but eight warships chained together in pairs in close formation, the decks of each pair covered with heavy wooden planks to create a virtual floating battlefield. Standing on these platforms were *sambucae*, large, towering wooden scaling ladders protected from enemy fire by heavy wicker shields. Once the chained ships reached the city walls all their anchors would be dropped, then the legionnaires would surge up the ladders onto the walls of Syracuse, and begin the conquest of the city. At the same time, from the decks of the other ships in the fleet, the Romans would release upon Syracuse's defenders a deadly rain of arrows, stones and javelins, while on the landward side of the city, more legionnaires would advance carrying scaling ladders to storm the walls. Attacked on two sides, Syracuse was certain to fall. That was the plan.

The paired ships were still inching their way forward when the Romans heard artillery officers on the wall give the order "Fire!," and massive stones came hurtling over the battlements, shattering the ships' planking and splintering the *sambucae*. The Romans had encountered catapults before, but none that could throw such enormous stones and wreak so much damage. As the towers on the

Archimedes, scientist, mathematician, and designer of extraordinary and perhaps even fantastic war machines, portrayed by André Thévet, sixteenth century French Franciscan priest.

chained ships collapsed the Roman fleet pulled back. The Romans knew that Archimedes, a brilliant mathematician and one of the greatest inventors of the ancient world, was inside Syracuse, but they had not expected that he would use his intellect to create new war machines.

A prize in the middle of the Mediterranean

In 214 BC the Romans and the Carthaginians were competing for control of Sicily. Set almost dead center in the Mediterranean, at the tip of the Italian peninsula, the island gave whoever possessed it control of major sea lanes as well as access to an abundance of grain, wine grapes, and olives—for thanks to its fertile soil and long growing season, Sicily was one of the most productive agricultural areas in the Mediterranean. The question in 214 BC was, would Sicily become the breadbasket of Rome, or the breadbasket of Carthage?

Syracuse, on the south-east corner of the island, was founded by Greek colonists from Corinth in 734 or 733 BC. In the eighth and seventh centuries before Christ Greece established settlements from the shores of the Black Sea to what is now Marseille in southern France, with the greatest concentration along the coast of modern-day Turkey and throughout Sicily and southern Italy. The colonies have come to be known as Magna Graecia, Latin for "Greater Greece." The most important colonial city in Italy and Sicily was Syracuse, a military powerhouse and a flourishing center of Greek culture. The Roman senator and orator Cicero (103–43 BC), who saw Syracuse in the first century BC, praised it as "the greatest Greek city and the most beautiful of them all." And it was lovely, set on the Gulf of Syracuse and adorned with glorious examples of Greek art and architecture.

By the third century BC the power of Magna Graecia had declined and two new players were competing for dominance in the Mediterranean—Rome and Carthage. It was this power struggle that in the summer of 212 BC brought the Romans under two commanders to Syracuse. Appius Claudius Pulcher (third century BC) took charge of the land forces, while Marcus Claudius Marcellus (c. 268–208 BC) led into Syracuse's harbor the Roman fleet of sixty galleys known as quinqueremes. The heaviest warship of its day, a quinquereme was manned by a crew of 300 and propelled by 180 slave-rowers. In addition to the crew and the slaves, a quinquereme could carry up to 120 fighting men. Plutarch tells us that Marcellus had equipped his warships "with all sorts of arms and missiles."

Those arms and missiles, however, proved almost useless against the innovative and deadly war machines that Archimedes had constructed. In addition to the boulder-throwing catapult, he had also constructed a huge iron claw that could reach out from the city walls, grab a ship by its prow, lift it out of the water and drop it onto the land, where it smashed to pieces; or, if he preferred, he could use the claw to turn a ship upside down, dumping its crew and soldiers and rowers into the sea before tossing the vessel aside to capsize or sink outright.

On the land side of Syracuse, Archimedes had equipped the defenders with other machines. One was a kind of protomachine-gun that fired multiple rounds of arrows. Another was a crane that dropped massive timber beams and heavy stones on any Roman foolhardy enough to stand below the walls. There were also iron hooks that were used to snag a legionnaire, lift him high, and drop him on top of his comrades. According to the Roman historian Polybius (*c.* 203–120 BC): "Marcellus' operations were thus completely frustrated by these inventions of Archimedes, and when he saw that the garrison not only repulsed his attacks with heavy losses but also laughed at his efforts, he took his defeat hard."

Flustered and frightened by such lethal novelties, Pulcher and Marcellus withdrew their troops. The Greek historian Plutarch (*c.* AD 46–120) tells us that in a rage, Marcellus cursed Archimedes, saying that he "plays pitch-and-toss with our ships, and, with the multitude of darts which he showers at a single moment upon us, really outdoes the hundred-handed giants of mythology." Since direct assaults on Syracuse were pointless, the commanders agreed to lay siege to the city and starve out the citizenry.

A question of technology

Are the ancient historians correct? Did Archimedes create such frightening secret weapons for Syracuse? Given the technology of the time the invention of a bigger, more deadly catapult, the crane that dropped heavy objects, and perhaps even the rapid-fire arrow machine all seem plausible. But it is hard to believe that an iron claw that could lift a quinquereme could have been constructed.

There were two types of artillery in the ancient world, the ballista and the catapult. The ballista was a giant crossbow equipped with a windlass or crank that drew back a heavy bowstring; when the string was released the ballista fired a giant arrow into the ranks of enemy troops, or sometimes bundles of ordinary-sized arrows. The ballista could also be loaded with heavy stones and used as a siege weapon to batter down a city's defensive walls. Philip II of

Macedon and his son, Alexander the Great, were Amongst the first to use the ballista in this manner.

If the ballista was a giant bow, the catapult was a giant slingshot. It had a long wooden arm with a heavy leather sling or wooden bowl at one end. The arm was drawn back tightly by a block and tackle, then a large stone, or lumps of lead, or a hornets' nest, or a clay pot filled with snakes, was loaded into the sling or bowl. When the arm was released, it hurled the contents further and with much more force than anything that could be thrown by even the strongest warrior.

That a new, heavier type of catapult could be developed in Syracuse makes perfect sense, since the catapult was first invented there in 399 BC.

The Eureka moment

Despite the fact that Archimedes (*c.* 287–*c.* 212 BC) is the most famous scientist and mathematician of the ancient world, we possess few hard facts about his life. As is so often the case with the notable men and women of the Greco-Roman world, most of the authentic source material about Archimedes has not survived, but the legends have certainly lived on. For example, the story of Archimedes' "Eureka" moment is first told by the Roman architect Vitruvius, who lived in the first century BC. Hiero II, the ruler of Syracuse, had given a goldsmith a mass of pure gold and ordered him to use all of it to fashion a golden wreath. When the goldsmith delivered the wreath its weight was identical to the lump of gold Hiero had handed over. Still, he wondered if the craftsman had cheated him by mixing in some less-valuable silver and holding back a portion of the gold for himself. But how could he prove it? Naturally, Hiero turned to the greatest mind in the Greek world, Archimedes, but the problem confounded even him.

One day, as he was still contemplating the puzzle, he went to the public baths. The slave had filled the tub to the brim, and as Archimedes sank down the water sloshed over the edges—and that gave him the solution. The volume of the water that spilled out of the tub was equal to the volume of his body. Thrilled by his discovery, Archimedes leaped out of the tub and ran naked through the streets of Syracuse back to his home, shouting all the way, "Eureka! Eureka!"—Greek for "I have found it!"

Vitruvius is our only ancient source for this story, and he wrote it down almost two hundred years after the death of Archimedes. In his treatise on buoyancy entitled *On Floating Bodies*, Archimedes does not tell the story of the wreath and the bathtub, but he does lay down the principle that would have

enabled him to solve such a problem. Silver is less dense than gold. Therefore, if Archimedes submerged the golden wreath in water, then an amount of silver the same weight as the wreath, and finally an amount of pure gold the same weight as the wreath, any differences in the volume of water displaced would reveal whether the goldsmith had swindled Hiero (which, according to Vitruvius, he had).

Sixteenth century wood-carving of Archimedes' legendary Eureka moment in his bathtub..

The death ray

While few if any historians of science believe that Archimedes fashioned an iron claw that could destroy a Roman warship, another of his inventions continues to intrigue the professionals as well as amateurs.

According to the Greek physician Galen (*c.* AD 130–201), Archimedes created several large, highly polished "glasses," probably a term for bronze or copper mirrors (the ancients did not have glass mirrors), which were set up on the city walls. As the Roman fleet came into view, Archimedes' assistants angled the mirrors so that they caught and intensified the rays of the sun, sending out a highly charged reflection at the ships that caused them to burst into flames.

Could such an invention work? In 1973 a Greek historian named Evanghelos Stamatis, an expert on the life and career of Archimedes, teamed up with Ioannis Sakkas, a Greek engineer and expert on solar energy, to put the legend of the "death ray" to the test. Sakkas doubted that the ancient Greeks had the technology to produce huge metal reflectors, but he believed that many smaller reflectors, such as highly polished shields, might have produced the same effect. Speaking to a reporter from *Time* magazine, Sakkas said, "Archimedes could have just lined the men up on the walls and had them focus the sun's rays on the Roman ships, so that the Romans never knew what hit them."

With the co-operation of the Greek navy, Sakkas ordered seventy mirrors coated with a thin sheet of copper, each mirror 5 feet tall by 3 feet wide—about the size of a third century BC shield. The Greek navy took a wooden rowboat, covered it with a coat of tar (which the ancient shipbuilders used to make their vessels waterproof), then mounted on it a plywood cut-out of a Roman galley. The boat was anchored 164 feet out to sea as seventy sailors stood on a pier of the Skaramanga naval base, each armed with a mirror. It took a little time for Sakkas to get the seventy volunteers co-ordinated so that they were all directing the reflections from their mirrors at the ship at the same time. Once the sailors got the hang of it, however, within a matter of seconds the boat began smouldering, then burst into flames.

The experiment did not prove that Archimedes had invented this killer heat ray, but it did suggest that it would have been possible. "Standing on the top of a high wall rather than a sea-level pier," Sakkas said, "Archimedes' men were working at an even better angle than we were."

Jamie Hyneman and Adam Savage, hosts of the popular cable television science program *MythBusters*, have cast doubt on Sakkas' experiment. With a group of students from the Massachusetts Institute of Technology they twice attempted, unsuccessfully, to create Archimedes' heat ray, and came to two conclusions. Firstly, the navy rowboat that burst into flames was stationary and the Roman ships would have been a moving target—it is much harder, virtually impossible, to keep the heat ray focused on a ship that is cruising across the water. Secondly, a cloudless sky is necessary for the mirrors to work, and weather is unpredictable.

The verdict—it's possible that Archimedes could have invented a sun-reflecting death ray, but it's not very probable.

A promising student of the sciences

Science was in Archimedes' blood: his father, Phidias, was an astronomer. But Archimedes would surpass his father, becoming a brilliant mathematician and an inventor so ingenious that long after his death he would be credited with building the most remarkable devices.

We know nothing certain about his education. He may have acquired his belief in a heliocentric universe, in which the planets orbit the sun, from his astronomer father or from reading the works of the astronomer Aristarchus of Samos (*c.* 310–*c.* 230 BC). It's possible that he learned geometry from the disciples of Euclid (*c.* 330–? BC) who operated an academy in Alexandria, Egypt. We know that he corresponded with the astronomer and mathematician Conon of Samos (third century BC), and the mathematician and geographer, Eratosthenes of Cyrene (*c.* 276–*c.* 194 BC), both of whom lived and worked in Alexandria, and it would have made sense for him to travel to Alexandria to study—in the third century BC the city Alexander the Great had founded (and named after himself) was the intellectual center of the Mediterranean world. Syracuse, Archimedes' birthplace, was also an intellectual center, having been home to the poet Pindar and the dramatist Aeschylus, but it could not compete with Alexandria. It makes sense that a promising student of the sciences would have gone to Alexandria to study, but in the absence of any documentary evidence all we can do is surmise.

"Purer speculations"

Amongst the many inventions attributed to Archimedes is the Archimedean screw, also known as the hydraulic or water screw, a tube with a helix, or spiral, inside. The water screw was historically used to irrigate fields. When one end of the tube is immersed in a body of water and the helix is turned, in those days by hand, the water rises to the top. Archimedes' invention may have been an improvement on a form of screw-pump believed by some to have been used to water the Hanging Gardens of Babylon three centuries earlier.

It is said that Archimedes also invented a mini planetarium which showed the movement of the Earth, the Moon and the five known planets at the time (Saturn, Jupiter, Mars, Venus, and Mercury) around the Sun. Cicero saw it when he was in Syracuse.

The quotation "Give me a place to stand on and with a lever I will move the whole world" is attributed to Archimedes. He may have said it, but he did not invent the lever—humans had been using levers for centuries before he was born. But Archimedes may have invented the pulley. There is a story that he demonstrated the strength of his invention by using the pulley to move the largest ship ever constructed in Syracuse.

As far back as Plutarch, readers and historians observed that the facts about Archimedes' career as an inventor were almost impossible to pin down. Plutarch, in fact, believes that this was as Archimedes wished it to be, explaining that the great man repudiated "as sordid and ignoble the whole trade of engineering, and every sort of art that lends itself to mere use and profit." Archimedes prided himself on his contributions to mathematics or, as Plutarch puts it: "He placed his whole affection and ambition in those purer speculations where there can be no reference to the vulgar needs of life." Archimedes' "purer speculations" included the development of integral calculus. He also estimated the value of pi to be between $3\frac{1}{7}$ and $3\frac{10}{71}$. And he proved that the volume of a sphere is two-thirds the volume of the cylinder that encases it.

The fall of Syracuse

For three years Syracuse held out against Marcellus and Pulcher. Meanwhile, leaving some of their force to keep up the siege, the commanders had rampaged across Sicily, capturing other cities and towns from the Carthaginians. One of Marcellus' greatest and bloodiest victories occurred at a place called Acilae (its modern location is unknown). Marcellus attacked as a Carthaginian commander, Hippocrates, was building his camp. The Romans caught the Carthaginians unprepared and massacred 8,000 of them.

Back at Syracuse Marcellus finally spotted a weakness in the city's defenses. Beside a small tower was a wall that was not as tall as the other battlements. Having found the city's one vulnerability, he waited for the best opportunity to attack. Picking his moment during a festival in honor of the goddess Artemis, when the citizens and garrison of Syracuse were drunk, Marcellus sent a detachment of his men with scaling ladders to the low wall. As more and more Romans

Marcellus' triumph

The Greco-Roman historian Plutarch (c. AD 46–120) tells us that after conquering Syracuse, Marcellus returned to Rome where he was awarded a spectacular triumphal parade. His legions marched through the city in full armor, Marcellus rode in a splendid chariot, while behind him the most distinguished of his Syracusan captives walked in chains. (It is an open question whether Marcellus would have subjected Archimedes to this indignity.) This was all standard procedure for a Roman triumph, but what made this occasion especially memorable was the booty.

Before leaving Syracuse, Marcellus had stripped the palaces and temples and public buildings of their finest works of art. The Romans at this time, according to Plutarch, were accustomed to seeing victorious commanders display "barbaric arms and bloody spoils" from the rougher and wilder corners of the Mediterranean world. This was the first time they had seen the exquisite bronze and marble sculptures of the great Greek masters. And they were dazzled.

There were exceptions: many older Romans feared that under the influence of these sensuous Greek masterpieces the younger generation would develop a taste for luxury items and comfortable living, thereby undermining Rome's virile, warlike character. And there was another reason elderly Romans did not like all this Greek booty being displayed in the streets: many of the sculptures were of the Greek gods, and to them it was as scandalous to cart sacred statues through the streets as it would have been if Marcellus had taken Zeus and Apollo captive and marched them through Rome.

climbed over, Marcellus ordered the trumpets to sound. The drunken revelers, thinking the entire city had been captured, panicked. In fact, the Romans were in possession of only a portion of the battlements; if the garrison had been in any condition to fight they probably could have driven them out.

To reward his men for enduring the three-year siege, Marcellus granted them permission to sack the city and take captives who would be sold into slavery, but he insisted that Archimedes should not be harmed.

There are conflicting accounts of what happened next. One story tells how Archimedes had packed up his most valuable scientific instruments and was running through the streets, trying to find a place of safety, when he encountered a Roman soldier. Thinking the chest in the old man's arms was full of valuables, the soldier killed him.

Another version tells us that, as the Romans were raping and slaughtering his neighbors and setting fire to the city, Archimedes remained quietly in his garden working out a mathematical problem. A soldier entered the garden and found Archimedes drawing geometrical figures in the sand. Livy says Archimedes ordered the intruder, "Don't disturb my circles." The Roman author Valerius Maximus (flourished *c.* AD 30) presents Archimedes as more polite, saying, "Please don't disturb this." The version of the story that was current during the Middle Ages presents us with a testy Archimedes telling the trooper, "Fellow, stand away from my diagram." All three versions end the same way—with Archimedes' death at the soldier's hands.

Marcellus greatly regretted that Archimedes had been killed, and tried to make amends by erecting a tomb over the great man's body and carving on the headstone an unusual emblem that Archimedes had requested of his relatives and friends; Plutarch describes it as "a sphere containing a cylinder, inscribing it with the ratio which the containing solid bears to the contained."

A century later the tomb of Archimedes had been forgotten, but about 75 BC Cicero set out to find it. Although many Syracusans told him it had vanished long ago, he persevered, and he found the grave, all overgrown with brambles. He knew it was the grave of Archimedes because the headstone had survived, complete with the sphere and cylinder incised upon it.

Detail from a sixteenth century copy of an ancient Roman mosaic showing the death of Archimedes at the hands of a Roman soldier.

First biological weapons
Hannibal's pots of serpents

SCIENTIST: Hannibal

AREA OF SCIENCE: Biology

MAIN INVENTION: Biological weapons

IT WAS GOING TO BE A GOOD DAY for the men of Pergamon—their fleet outnumbered the Carthaginian ships. If all went as expected, within a few hours Carthage's days as the greatest naval power in the Mediterranean would be over, and their great commander, Hannibal, would be dead or a prisoner of Pergamon's king, Eumenes II. Such an outcome would please Eumenes' strongest ally (and Hannibal's bitterest enemy), Rome.

Hannibal knew the Pergamon fleet had the advantage. He had known it for days but, typical of the general who had terrified the Romans by marching his army and his war elephants across the Alps into Italy, had devised a plan to overcome the enemy's superior numbers. Whenever he was confronted with a difficult situation Hannibal always said the same thing to his anxious officers, "We will either find a way, or make one." And this time he was making his solution.

The general sent his men ashore with orders to collect—carefully—as many venomous serpents as they could find and seal them inside large clay pots. The pots full of snakes were then lined up on the deck of every Carthaginian warship, right beside the catapults.

On the day of battle Hannibal put his navy into formation and waited. The Pergamon fleet, sensing an easy victory, bore down on the Carthaginians. As they came into range, Hannibal gave the order to fire, and his catapult men released a barrage of clay pots. At the sight of the Carthaginians attacking them with crockery, the warriors of Pergamon burst out laughing. But as the pots

Lithographic representation of Hannibal wearing Thracian-style bronze helmet with crest and tail of horsehair.

smashed on the decks of their ships, the laughter turned to cries of alarm, and of pain. Angry serpents tumbled out of the broken pots, writhing, hissing, sinking their fangs into anything that moved.

The terrified soldiers and sailors scrambled into the rigging, climbed atop hatches, leaped over the side into the ocean—anything to escape the tangle of serpents that covered the decks. Taking advantage of the panic, Hannibal's ships attacked, scattered the Pergamon fleet, and captured King Eumenes.

Some historians regard Hannibal's pots of snakes as the first biological weapon. While there is no denying that the use of snakes to terrify and disorient his enemy was spectacular in its ingenuity, it was not the first time in history that an army commander had turned to the animal kingdom for extra reinforcements.

The sting of death

Edward Neufeld, an expert in Mesopotamian history, believes that ancient warriors of the Middle East hurled wasp and hornet nests at their enemies. As the nests smashed open the enraged creatures would attack, causing panic, pain, perhaps even death, Amongst the soldiers. An important issue to bear in mind was blowback—an army that planned to use hornet bombs would need to throw them on a day when there was no wind, or when the wind was at their backs, blowing toward their victims.

Historian Jeffrey Lockwood goes back even further, to the Stone Age, arguing that once our ancestors learned how to hurl rocks and javelins, it would be only natural that some prehistoric warrior with a good throwing arm would heave a hornets' nest into a cave or rock crevice to flush out his enemies. The tricky part was keeping the hornets bottled up—Lockwood suggests that perhaps the ancients plugged the entrances of the nests with mud, or carried them in sacks or baskets.

In the fourth century BC Aeneas the Tactician wrote a book entitled *How to Survive under Siege*, in which he recommended that defenders of a besieged town frustrate sappers tunneling under their walls by digging counter-tunnels into which they could release swarms of wasps and hornets.

In the biblical Book of Joshua, the Lord God reminds the leader of the Israelites how he championed his Chosen People. "I sent the hornet ahead of you," God says, "which drove out before you the two kings of the Amorites" (Joshua 24.12).

The Popol Vuh, one of the sacred texts of the Maya, tells the story of an embattled Mayan town where the citizens placed on their battlements dummy warriors with heads made of gourds. Inside the gourds they had funneled bees and wasps. Thinking the town was poorly defended, the enemy tribe stormed the walls and attacked the dummies, smashing their heads with their war axes:

> *The bumblebees and the wasps came out of the gourds;*
> *like a great cloud of smoke they emerged from the gourds.*
> *And thus the warriors perished because of the insects which stung the*
> *pupils of their eyes and fastened themselves*
> *to their noses, their mouths, their legs, and their arms.*
> *The bees and wasps drove the invaders from the town better than any*
> *Mayan army could have done.*

The Tiv people of what is now Nigeria had large horns in which they trapped bees. When they went into battle, the Tiv aimed these horns, like artillery, at their enemies and sent the little stinging monsters into the enemy ranks. Exactly how they got the bees to go in the right direction remains a mystery.

Typically a sting from a bee, wasp or hornet is painful for only a few minutes or occasionally a few hours; there may be reddening and swelling of the sting site, and the pain may be followed by itching, but within a few days the inflammation and swelling subside and the itching dissipates.

A severe allergic reaction to a sting is another matter entirely. Immediately after the sting the person may feel light-headed and perhaps nauseous. There may be diarrhea or vomiting, trouble breathing, or a sense that the throat is closing, making speech or even swallowing difficult. There can be a severe drop in blood pressure followed by shock or unconsciousness. Death can occur in thirty minutes, although there are cases on record of individuals who died of an allergic reaction to a sting within five minutes.

Multiple bee or wasp or hornet stings can be lethal even for individuals who are not allergic to bee venom, but it calls for a lot of stings—more than one thousand would be necessary to carry off a healthy young adult male, like the warriors who attacked the Mayan town. In ancient times, however, folklore claimed that anyone who was stung twenty-seven times would die. This idea would have raised the casualty rate, but it would have elevated the panic level in any army that was suddenly caught in a swarm of angry hornets.

Following pages:
Detail from the fresco
Hannibal in Italy,
attributed to the sixteenth
century Italian artist Jacopo
Ripanda, in the Palazzo
dei Conservatori, Rome.

Scorpion grenades

In AD 198 the Roman emperor Septimius Severus launched a campaign against Armenia and Mesopotamia. Unwilling to take on the Romans, the king of Armenia sent a message asking for peace, and sweetened his appeal by presenting Severus with gold and other expensive gifts, as well as hostages. Pleased to add a new province to his empire as well as rich tribute to his treasury, Severus withdrew from Armenia and moved on the great fortified city of Hatra near present-day Mosul in Iraq.

The city stood atop a rugged mountain surrounded by desert. It was defended by two rings of city walls and a moat. If an enemy penetrated Hatra's first wall, he would find that he had a moat to cross and another wall to scale. The Roman emperor Trajan had attempted to take Hatra a century earlier and failed.

Enemy of Rome

As the incident of the pots full of venomous serpents suggests, in a fight against Rome Hannibal would stop at nothing. It is said that when he was a child his father, Hamilcar Barca, made the boy lay his hand on the altar of the gods of Carthage and swear a solemn oath to devote his life to the destruction of Rome and the elevation of Carthage as the supreme power in the Mediterranean world.

In 221 BC Hannibal led an army of 38,000 infantry, 8,000 cavalry and a few dozen war elephants from Carthage across North Africa, into Spain and France, then through the Alps and down into Italy, where he crushed every army Rome sent against him, including a force of 80,000 Romans, which he encircled and destroyed at Cannae in the summer of 216 BC. Instead of surrendering, the Roman Senate sent another army, led by Publius

Cornelius Scipio (later known as Scipio Africanus) to Carthage. Hannibal had no choice but to abandon his campaign in Italy and hurry home to defend his country. At the Battle of Zama in 202 BC Scipio inflicted a decisive defeat on Hannibal, killing 20,000 Carthaginians and wounding 11,000 more. But the Carthaginians did not turn on their commander. Instead, they elected him *suffete*, or ruler.

True to the oath he had taken as a child, Hannibal plotted new ways to strike the Romans, but when his plans were discovered he was forced to flee. He sought refuge in Syria, then Bithynia (now northern Turkey), and finally on the shores of the far-off Black Sea. But the Romans were relentless in their pursuit. As they finally closed in on him, Hannibal swallowed poison and died.

The Roman historian Herodian tells us that Severus was determined to succeed. "Severus's soldiers pressed the siege with all the power at their command, endeavouring to capture the city," Herodian wrote. "Engines of every type were brought up to the wall, and all the known tactics were tried." But the Romans were not getting far; the walls were strong and defended by skillful archers. But the Romans were tenacious; they would try again to take the city by storm.

To drive off the Romans, the defenders of Hatra unleashed a new weapon. "Making clay pots, they filled them with winged insects, little poisonous flying creatures," says Herodian. "When these were hurled down on the besiegers, the insects fell into the Romans' eyes and on all the unprotected parts of their bodies; digging in before they were noticed, they bit and stung the soldiers." Historian Adrienne Mayor has pointed out that there are no poisonous flying insects in the desert around Hatra, but there are many, many scorpions.

People of the ancient world were more afraid of scorpions than of snakes. The Roman naturalist, Pliny, called scorpions, "a dangerous scourge [with] venom like that of a serpent, with the exception that its effects are far more painful, as the person who is stung will linger for three days before death ensues."

Aristotle reported that there were so many scorpions in the desert, which stretched between Susa and Media in the kingdom of the Persians, that before the king of Persia would travel in that region he sent out an advance guard with instructions to kill as many scorpions as they could find. Whoever exterminated the most would receive a gift from the king.

While not all scorpions are deadly, those that are—such as the ones found in the Middle East—cause a gruesome death. Symptoms include profuse sweating, incontinence, vomiting blood, difficulty breathing, and convulsions. If the person stung does not fall unconscious, he or she suffers extreme pain. No wonder the people of the ancient world lived in dread of scorpions, and that the Roman emperor's bodyguards, the Praetorians, adopted the scorpion as their emblem.

The terrifying scorpion grenades, combined with the heat and an epidemic that, according to Herodian, caused "more casualties … than from enemy action," demoralized the legions and convinced Severus, at last, to retreat.

Bee bombs

Using insects as enemy repellent was not limited to the ancient world. In 908, when Vikings were weakening the walls of Chester in England, the locals collected their beehives and threw them into the mouths of the Vikings' tunnels.

During the Thirty Years' War an ordinary citizen of the town of Kissingen in Germany suggested to his neighbors that they pelt the attacking Swedish army with beehives. Their armor protected the Swedish fighting men from bee stings, but not their horses. The scene before the town walls degenerated into pandemonium, with hundreds of bucking, screaming warhorses trying desperately to escape from the swarm of bees.

Time and again we find examples of the effective use of the beehive method of defense. The garrison of a castle on the Greek island of Astipalaia drove off pirates by dropping beehives on them. When Turkish artillery breached the walls of the Hungarian town of Stuhlwiessenburg, the defenders threw all the town's beehives into the gap and thereby kept the Turks out. In the 1600s marauders attacked a convent at Wuppertal in northern Germany. The nuns overturned their beehives and ran inside to safety as the bees attacked the raiders. Wuppertal was renamed Beyenburg, "Bee Town", in honor of the victorious stingers.

But there are limits to how far even the brawniest man can throw a hornets' nest. To achieve any real distance required machinery, and the catapult did the job nicely. The Greeks invented the catapult originally to hurl heavy stones at defensive walls, but the machine was also an excellent way to fire hives at the enemy. Beginning at least in the fourth century BC, when Philip of Macedon, father of Alexander the Great, lobbed beehives and wasp nests at his enemies, military commanders used catapults to fling wasps, hornets, and bees into the ranks of their enemies. The Romans were so fond of this missile that by the fifth century there was a shortage of beehives in the empire. In the twelfth century, during the Third Crusade, Richard the Lionheart used catapults to pitch hives into Saracen strongholds. And in Spain throughout the thirteenth century Christians and Moors fired beehives at each other.

The bug pit

If serpents, scorpions, and stinging insects could be used to cause terror, pain and death, they could also be used to punish and execute prisoners. That Apache Indians staked out their white captives on anthills is one of the most persistent stories of the American West; it is also one of the most difficult to prove. But there is a documented instance of insects being used as a method of torture.

In the 1830s, when Russia and England were jockeying for influence in Central Asia, in what are now the countries of Kazakhstan, Kyrgyzstan, Tajikistan, Turkmenistan and Uzbekistan, there ruled in Bukhara an emir named

A Roman war machine: The Catapult. Wood engraving after a painting by Sir Edward Poynter, nineteenth century British artist.

Nasrullah Bahadur-Khan. In 1838 Lieutenant-Colonel Charles Stoddart was sent to Bukhara to win the friendship and good will of the emir, but Stoddart had no knowledge of local customs or protocol. He rode into the palace square, which was forbidden. As the emir approached him on horseback, Stoddart saluted, but did not dismount and bow to the self-styled "Shadow of God on Earth." And finally, the letter of introduction from Queen Victoria to the emir had not been signed by the queen herself, which Nasrullah took as a personal affront.

The emir vented his displeasure by having Stoddart lowered into a shaft 21½ feet deep, known locally as "the Black Well." Once the prisoner reached the bottom the rope was hauled up and the iron grate clanged shut. Stoddart was alone in the dark with countless assassin bugs. According to biologist and historian Jeffrey Lockwood, "The bite of these insects has been compared to being pierced with a hot needle, and the digestive enzymes that they inject [into their victim] cause suppurating sores."

Over the next three years Nasrullah amused himself by releasing Stoddart from the Black Well for a time, then returning him to the bug pit. In 1841 Captain Arthur Conolly came to Bukhara to make another attempt to ally the emir with England, but his superiors repeated a mistake made by the men who had sent Stoddart to Bukhara: they sent Conolly to the emir with a communiqué that was not signed by Queen Victoria. Nasrullah confined them in an ordinary prison cell for four months, then threw them into the Black Well where for two months the assassin bugs ate the Englishmen alive. Finally, in an act of mercy, Nasrullah had the prisoners brought out of the well and beheaded.

The plague in China

Since the 1920s Ishii Shiro, a Japanese medical researcher and microbiologist, had been interested in the military uses of disease—in other words, how to use disease as a weapon. Initially he had experimented with spraying disease microbes over a target area, but he found that heat, cold, and ultraviolet radiation destroyed the bulk of the bacteria before they reached the human population. Furthermore, bacteria could not move about; where they landed was where they stayed. Ishii realized that the solution was to let disease spread in the way nature had intended—via infected fleas, flies, and mosquitoes.

In 1939, during the Second Sino-Japanese War, Ishii released a horde of rats infested with the fleas that carry the bubonic plague bacteria near the Chinese village of Nomonhan near the Mongolian border. The rats scattered through the village and the surrounding area, infecting some of the Chinese troops and civilian population, but not enough to set off an epidemic. Ishii gave up on the rat-based delivery system, and developed a new method by which plague-infected fleas could be released in enormous numbers over a desired area. Initially he thought to pack the fleas inside a bombshell, but tests proved that the explosion of the shell killed almost all the fleas. So Ishii hired porcelain manufacturers to fashion fragile ceramic bulbs that could hold up to 6,000 fleas and would shatter on impact, releasing their deadly cargo.

Before dropping his flea bombs, Ishii tested the potency of the bacteria on human beings: Chinese, Mongolian, and Korean peasants, anti-Communist Russian refugees, and American, British, Australian, New Zealand, and Dutch prisoners of war. To learn what was the lethal level of infection, he experimented on hundreds, perhaps thousands, of these human guinea pigs behind the walls of a grotesque medical "research" facility known as Unit 731, located at Pingfan in China, 15½ miles from the city of Harbin. No one knows how many men, as well as women, children, and even infants, were killed at Unit 731 to advance Ishii's research.

In 1940 the first of Ishii's flea bombs was released over Chuhsien, where hundreds fell ill with bubonic plague and twenty-one died. A much heavier bombing mission was flown over the city of Quzhou where the epidemic would last for six years, taking the lives of 50,000 people. In 1941 and 1942, more bombing runs over dozens of Chinese villages, towns, and cities filled the air with deadly fleas; at least 100,000 men, women, and children died.

—⁂—

Perhaps as far back as the prehistoric era, warriors have used serpents, scorpions and swarms of bees and wasps to terrorize and drive off their enemies. In most cases the stings were painful, but not deadly—a fact that inspired the sadistic emir of Bukhara to use assassin bugs to torture his prisoners. It took the advances in medical science of the late nineteenth and early twentieth centuries to find a new way to use mammals and insects as a weapon. A swarm of angry wasps could inflict pain and panic, and send an army running off the battlefield, but a swarm of disease-infected fleas could set off an epidemic that could weaken, and even wipe out, an army, a city, or a whole district of the countryside. In the hands of commanders like Hannibal, reptiles and insects were frightening but imprecise weapons; it took men like Ishii Shiro to turn such weapons into a science.

Flying, dancing powder
Wei Boyang's heaven-shaking thundercrash bomb

SCIENTIST: Wei Boyang

AREA OF SCIENCE: Chemistry

MAIN INVENTION: Gunpowder

Ironically, it was the quest for immortality that led to the invention of gunpowder. Alchemists—part chemist, part magician, part theologian, part quack—were common ... [in the] East and the West. In Europe they sought the formula that would change base metals into gold. In Asia they sought the elixir that would ensure eternal life. Taoists were especially keen to find this life-prolonging potion, although some of the ingredients they used, such as mercury and lead, hastened death rather than postponing it ... At least one emperor of China went mad and died from consuming a daily dose of a tonic that included mercury.

TAOIST ALCHEMISTS STUMBLED UPON the partial ingredients for gunpowder when they began mixing saltpeter (potassium nitrate) with sulfur. In AD 142, Wei Boyang recorded in his treatise on alchemy, *The Kinship of the Three*, that mixing saltpeter, sulfur and charcoal caused the three powders to "fly and dance". Although he was not precise about the proportions, this is the earliest record of a formula for gunpowder; it is also the earliest reference to its volatility. Not all historians recognize this as the first description of gunpowder—they point to Wei's propensity for obscuring his discoveries by writing in code. Yet many other historians believe they have deciphered Wei's meaning accurately, that he was the first man we know of to have stumbled upon the recipe for gunpowder.

A seventeenth century illustration of the Siege of Constantinople. Under Constantine XI's leadership the city held out against forty-seven days of heavy artillery fire. On May 29, 1453 the walls were breached and the Turkish forces broke in.

43

In the decades after Wei there is no doubt that other Chinese alchemists were experimenting with gunpowder: texts that date back to the third century AD tell of unexpected explosions in the laboratories of alchemists, which were probably the result of gunpowder trials that went wrong. *Zhenyuan Miaodao Yaolüe* (*Classified Essentials of the Mysterious Dao of the True Origin of Things*), a Taoist book from the mid-ninth century, warns of what can occur when experimenting with the black powder: "smoke and flames result, so that their [the alchemists'] hands and faces have been burnt, and even the whole house where they were working burned down." There is no surviving documentation, however, to tell us exactly when the Chinese, through painful trial and error, stumbled upon the correct formula for gunpowder—75 percent saltpeter, 15 percent charcoal, 10 percent sulfur.

These three ingredients were not difficult to find. Sulfur occurs naturally and is often found underground near salt deposits. Charcoal is made by burning wood under conditions where it receives very little oxygen, such as inside a kiln. And saltpeter can be found crystallizing atop rotting vegetation, or can be made by mixing manure with wood ash spread out in a thin layer. The moisture in the manure bed rises to the surface where it crystallizes, and those crystals are saltpeter.

The first grenades

The Chinese had a fondness for things that blew up with a loud bang. In ancient times, on the morning of Chinese New Year, people tossed lengths of green bamboo onto open fires. When the air and sap trapped between the joints in the stems expanded in the heat and the pieces of bamboo burst, they created a terrible noise that was believed to frighten away evil spirits. The Venetian merchant and traveler, Marco Polo, claimed that the sound of bamboo exploding could be heard 9½ miles away. Even when gunpowder first became available, people in China were still marking the New Year by tossing green bamboo into the fire. But from early in the eighth century they were also celebrating New Year by igniting firecrackers (gunpowder-filled tubes of paper) and setting off other gunpowder-powered fireworks. In other words, the Chinese had discovered the entertainment factor of gunpowder.

Exactly when the Chinese began using gunpowder in warfare is also a mystery. Since it was their secret weapon, it should come as no surprise that they did not record its manufacture and use in battle. We do know that by AD 969 a combustible paste made of gunpowder mixed with honey was smeared on arrowheads that were used to set enemy siege engines and camps on fire. By 1200, the Chinese were using a type of firecracker known as a "ground rat" in battle. The paper tube was open at one end; when the firecracker was lit, the burning gas burst out of the opening, propelling the tube along the ground in an erratic manner that resembled the skittering of rats. Ground rats did no physical harm in battle, but they did panic enemy troops, and especially enemy cavalry.

Sometimes a bamboo tube packed with gunpowder was tied to a lance, the fuse was lit, and the lance hurled into the enemy's ranks where the explosion caused terror as well as many casualties. The Chinese also created metal bombs packed with iron shrapnel and equipped with a fuse. They launched these bombs from catapults, which was a tricky business: the fuse had to be long enough that the bomb would not explode in mid-flight, but short enough that the enemy could not extinguish it once it landed in their midst. And there was always the chance that the bomb might explode as the catapult crew was preparing to fire it.

In 1231 Ögödei Khan, the son and successor of Genghis Khan, sent an army into northern China to extend the Mongols' control in the region. Outside the city of Kaifeng, the Mongols forced an army of prisoners to dig a trench that would undermine part of the city walls. As protection against the arrows, spears and other missiles the Chinese would rain down upon the diggers (sappers), the Mongols stretched thick ox-hides over the tunnel. But the defenders of Kaifeng had something that would do more than pierce the tough hide. They attached metal balls packed with gunpowder to chains, lit the fuse, then lowered them to the point where they were suspended just above the ox-hide. When these grenades exploded, they tore the hides and the sappers to bits.

The fire drug

About 1288 the Chinese had success with an early model of what we would call a rocket launcher. They forged bronze vase-shaped containers, poured gunpowder into the bottom and stuffed the mouth of the vessel with a bundle of arrows. At the base of the container was a small hole through which a fuse protruded. The fuse ignited the gunpowder, which shot the arrows out, killing or wounding several of the enemy with a single blast.

Gunpowder historian Jack Kelley has found that the Chinese liked to give their bombs descriptive names: "Match for Ten Thousand Enemies Bomb," "Bone-Burning and Bruising Fire-oil Magic Bomb" and "Bandit-Burning

Vision-Confusing Magic Fireball." According to Kelley, these bombs not only wrought carnage Amongst enemy troops, but the concussion was powerful enough to "knock birds out of the sky."

Building a powerful bomb was relatively simple, but learning to harness and direct their power proved more complicated. Centuries would pass in China between the invention of gunpowder and the invention of the cannon. The earliest Chinese cannon dates from 1332 and is so short—not quite 14 inches long—that it would not have done much damage against an advancing enemy army. Nonetheless, it was a start, and within approximately twenty years the Chinese developed larger cannon that could fire iron or stone balls.

Interestingly, in spite of its obvious military uses, gunpowder at this time was known in China as the "fire drug," a reference to the days when Taoist alchemists hoped the black powder held the key to immortality. Of course, gunpowder had the exact opposite effect.

The gunners' patron saint

Some time between 1240 and 1280 gunpowder arrived in the Islamic world. Exactly when, or how, or precisely who brought the secret out of China is unknown. It is possible that the formula was derived from the Mongols who ruled China in the thirteenth century and were, during this time, at war with the Mamluks in Egypt. The only thing certain is that by 1280 the formula was known Amongst Muslim engineers: it is recorded in Hassan al-Rammah's *The Book of Military Horsemanship and Ingenious War Devices*, completed in 1280.

At about the same time gunpowder arrived in Europe. A weapons manual entitled *The Book of Fires for the Burning of Enemies*, written at the time as Al-Rammah's text by a mysterious figure known only as Marcus Graecus, records the formula. We do not know whether the secret came to Europe via the Muslims, or was brought home by merchants who traveled the Silk Road to the court of the Great Khan. By the 1260s it was known in England where Roger Bacon (1214–1292), a Franciscan friar who taught philosophy and the natural sciences at Oxford University, described the properties of gunpowder and warned that it could be used in weapons so fearsome "that a man can hardly protect himself or endure it."

But gunpowder as the Chinese used it—in small grenades and arrow-launchers—did not much interest the Europeans. They wanted a weapon that could blow away masses of infantry, pierce the heavy steel armor of knights and pulverize stone battlements. That weapon was eventually created in 1324 by metallurgists in the German city of Metz. Inspired by barrel construction (of all things), the Metz metallurgists forged several iron tubes and bound them together with steel hoops. They called their weapon a "culverin" or a "bombard", and it fired stone balls known as "wall-crackers."

The early culverin had many problems. In the first place, it was inaccurate. Because the inside of the tube was smooth, as the ball exploded out of the tube it bounced along the inside; when it blasted out of the culverin's mouth, it could fly off in almost any direction. All a gunnery crew could do was point the culverin at a target and hope for the best.

As the name "wall-cracker" suggests, the stone missile wasn't large enough to do more than crack defensive walls. Fired into the advancing ranks of infantry or cavalry, the stone ball could kill or maim every man and horse in its erratic path, but because the ball remained solid it did limited damage. In terms of psychological warfare, however, the roar and flash of a culverin when it was fired was terrifying, not least for the artillery crews who, if they mismeasured the gunpowder, would be wiped out should the culverin itself explode. Given the risks of their profession, artillerymen chose a patron saint to protect them: St. Barbara, a Christian virgin whose pagan father beheaded her for joining the outlawed religion. According to the legend, as Barbara's head dropped to the ground, her heartless father was instantly destroyed by fire from heaven.

Twentieth century drawing showing a brass culverin, recovered from the wreck of the Mary Rose *warship, which sank off Spithead, near Portsmouth, in 1545.*

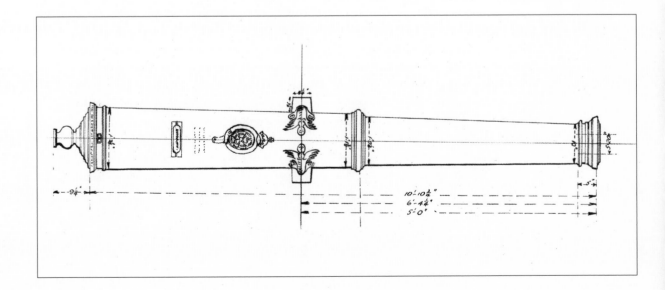

A famous victory

One of the earliest instances in which artillery was used in battle was at Crécy in northern France on August 26, 1346. The English king, Edward III, accompanied

The Petersburg crater

It was one of the greatest wartime mining disasters in military history. In 1864 Union troops under General Ulysses S. Grant were closing in on Richmond, Virginia, where the Confederacy's brilliant General Robert E. Lee had erected a massive and elaborate series of trenches and bunkers around the capital, including fortifying the city of Petersburg, just south of Richmond. Union General Ambrose Burnside had assaulted the Petersburg trenches and made it to within 459½ feet of a main fortress, but was driven back by the Confederates. An infantryman from the coal-mining district in Pennsylvania told the general, "We could blow that damn fort out of existence if we could run a mine shaft under it."

Mining an enemy's defenses was an old art that dated back to the ancient world, long before gunpowder was discovered. The besiegers dug a tunnel under the enemy's defensive wall, shoring up the walls and ceiling with heavy logs and timber beams. Once the tunnel reached under the wall, the miners set fire to the supports and ran out to safety. The wood burned, the tunnel collapsed, and the undermined city wall fell in a heap of rubble. Adding gunpowder intensified the level of carnage and destruction.

Grant signed off on the plan and the Pennsylvania troops began digging a 5085 foot tunnel beneath the Petersburg trenches. When they reached the point where they believed they were under the Confederate bastion, they dug a number of perpendicular tunnels. These they filled with 2.23 tons of gunpowder. Before 5:00 in the morning on July 30, 1864, the miners lit the fuses, ran outside and waited.

With a deafening roar the gunpowder exploded, creating an enormous crater and reducing a Confederate artillery battery and an entire Confederate infantry regiment, between 250 and 350 men, to dust and ashes. The Union troops were supposed to charge around the perimeter of the crater and into the Confederate fort. Instead, they surged down into the 29½ foot deep hole—and found that the walls were too steep to allow them to climb out. And more Union men kept running into the pit behind them.

Meanwhile, the Confederates regrouped along the edge of the crater where they rained down a deadly fire on the helpless Union troops. The Union lost 504 killed, 1,881 wounded, 1,413 missing or captured. General Grant wrote, "It was the saddest affair ... in the war."

by his 16-year-old son Edward the Black Prince, squared off against the King of France, Philip VI. The French force may have been as large as 80,000; the English had 16,000 men. But King Edward had also brought along five small cannon made of bronze or iron. The Battle of Crécy has gone down in history as a famous English victory, won thanks to the skill of the 7,000 English and Welsh archers whose longbows rained down deadly volley after deadly volley upon the French, killing thousands. The effect of the five cannon was probably more psychological than anything else: the noise they made frightened the French knights' warhorses and unnerved many of the fighting men. We know the English gunners fired stone balls at Crécy—several were uncovered on the site of the battle in 1850; these would have caused only limited casualties, but certainly would have added to the chaos and panic in the French ranks.

After his victory at Crécy, Edward III moved on to the great French port city of Calais. Here his little cannon proved completely ineffectual: the stone balls were too small to even crack the city's walls—they simply bounced off. Eventually Edward captured the city, but through the old-fashioned method of a prolonged siege.

Yet it was obvious to military engineers in the West that cannon had potential. Armorers began to improve their effectiveness by making them bigger so they could fire larger stones, but still the stones only dented the walls without bringing them down. Furthermore, these bigger guns were difficult to move, could take days to assemble, and still had a propensity to blow up, killing everyone in the vicinity.

In order to use cannon more effectively against infantry and cavalry, gunners loaded them with gravel that would spew out of the cannon's mouth in a wide arc, cutting down everything in its path. Attacking armies learned very quickly, however, that they could render a cannon powerless by going around it. Since the machine was so heavy, the only way to adjust its position was to dismantle and reassemble it—something simply impossible to accomplish in the midst of battle.

Sultan Mehmet's monster

Over the next century, the masters of the new technology of artillery worked to improve their product so that it could overcome the old technology—stone defensive walls that encircled every city and castle in Europe. One of the masters of cannon manufacture was a Hungarian known only as Orban. In 1452 he offered to build bronze cannon for the Byzantine emperor, Constantine XI, whose empire had shrunk to the capital city and a few tiny outlying territories. Constantine knew the Turks, under the ambitious, warmongering sultan Mehmet II, were preparing to attack Constantinople, and artillery might be the weaponry that would save his city. But Constantine's treasury was nearly empty; he could not afford to pay Orban's salary, let alone buy batteries of bronze cannon. Destitute, and at heart a mercenary, Orban left Constantinople and offered his services to Sultan Mehmet, promising to build a cannon that would reduce the city's massive walls to dust. Mehmet hired him on the spot.

The cannon Orban made was a monster: 27 feet long, its barrel 26½ inches in diameter with walls 7 inches thick. It fired a stone ball that weighed over 992 pounds. In January 1453 Mehmet watched as Orban's crew of gunners tested the new weapon. They lit the fuse and a moment later the huge ball shot out of the cannon; it traveled over 1¼ miles, and when it hit the earth the force of the impact drove it 6½ feet into the ground. Mehmet was impressed, and ordered Orban to keep working—although on smaller guns. The monster was too big, too costly and took too long to fire.

When Mehmet marched on Constantinople in April 1453, he had with him about seventy cannon that he arranged in batteries around the city. On April 12 all was in readiness, and what historian Roger Crowley has called "the world's first concerted artillery barrage" began pounding the 1,100-year-old walls of Constantinople. To the horror of the city's defenders, wherever a cannonball struck, the wall crumbled. Fortunately for the defenders, the monster cannon itself, which the Greeks inside the city called "the Basilica" or "the Royal Gun", was so unwieldy and difficult to operate that it could be fired only seven times a day.

On 29 May, after forty-seven days of shelling which had reduced large portions of the walls of Constantinople to piles of rubble, the Turks surged into the city. Constantinople fell, the first major victim of gunpowder-powered artillery. From that day, warfare would never be the same.

Guns from the West

Although these early cannon were unwieldy, inaccurate and dangerously unpredictable, the Europeans did not give up on them. The fall of Constantinople convinced armorers and military commanders across the Continent that gunpowder weapons would revolutionize warfare.

And while they worked on creating forms of artillery that were lighter, more mobile and more accurate, they also produced small, hand-held versions. The 1400s saw the introduction of the first pistols and muskets in Europe, and the discovery that a bullet could pierce steel armor—certainly unhappy news for mounted knights who for centuries had relied upon their armor to protect them in battle. Armor, at least over the torso, would continue to be worn into the 1600s, but it was little more than decorative, a nod to tradition; firearms had made it obsolete.

Every few years brought new advances in firearm technology—at least in Europe. Strangely, in China where gunpowder and explosive weapons were first invented, the development of firearms stalled. By the early 1500s the best gunpowder-based weapons were manufactured in Europe and were being exported to China, Japan and the Islamic lands. The Chinese, in quest of eternal life, discovered gunpowder, and the Europeans, recognizing its possibilities, went on to invent dozens of ingenious ways to make it ever more deadly.

Hateful to God
Zhuge Liang's new, improved, repeating crossbow

SCIENTIST: Zhuge Liang

AREA OF SCIENCE: Mechanical engineering

MAIN INVENTION: Repeating crossbow

THE IMAGE IS INSTANTLY RECOGNIZABLE across China: a man seated in a four-wheeled carriage, dressed in the robes of a Taoist monk, and holding a fan of white feathers. The figure is Zhuge Liang (181–234), one of the most learned men of his time, a brilliant military strategist and inspired inventor.

Zhuge was born in what is now Shandong Province, located on the Yellow Sea. The late second and early third centuries in China were years of civil wars, famines and epidemics, and Zhuge's family was not spared: his mother died when he was nine, his father died when he was twelve, and two years later the uncle who had taken in Zhuge, his two brothers and his two sisters also died.

The death of Zhuge's uncle was a direct result of an invasion of Shandong by Cao Cao, a cruel, tyrannical warlord determined to become emperor and unite China under his rule. It was while fleeing the invasion that Zhuge's uncle became fatally ill. The five children survived to settle in what is now Hubei Province, where the girls married and the brothers started a farm.

After laboring all day in the fields, Zhuge spent several hours each night studying. A few chance encounters with Taoist monks and scholars in the neighborhood helped him to advance quickly. While still a young man he acquired the nickname "Sleeping Dragon." The dragon in this case represented wisdom, while "sleeping" referred to Zhuge himself, whose intellectual gifts were underutilized on his farm and waiting for an opportunity to display themselves.

Zhuge Liang, one of the greatest strategists of the Three Kingdoms period in China, is traditionally depicted in the robes of a Taoist monk and bearing a fan made of white crane feathers.

That opportunity came in 207 when Liu Bei, another warlord and Cao Cao's rival, visited the farm and invited Zhuge to join his inner circle of advisers.

The Three Kingdoms

China as we know it today did not exist in Zhuge's day. In fact, China would remain fragmented until the thirteenth century when the Mongol leader Kublai Khan completed the conquest begun by his grandfather Genghis Khan, proclaimed himself emperor of a newly united China, and established a new ruling dynasty, the Yuan.

Zhuge Liang was born just as the Han dynasty, which had ruled for almost four hundred years, was dying out. The death blow came in 184, when Zhuge was three years old: a widespread peasant uprising led by a rebel movement known as the Yellow Turbans, which destabilized the Han government. As the Han dynasty hovered on the verge of collapse, three warlords seized the initiative and carved up the realm into what became known as the Three Kingdoms. Each of these warlord-kings wanted to reunite the old Han realm under his own rule, however, and so the country was plunged into civil war.

Of the three warlords, the two strongest were Cao Cao and Sun Quan—they had the largest armies and held sway over the largest territories. But the third, Liu Bei, was perhaps the most determined. He came to prominence in 184 when he raised an army and won several victories over the Yellow Turban rebels. With a successful army behind him, Liu was now in as good a position to seize power over the old Han kingdom as Cao Cao and Sun Quan. In addition, he claimed descent from Emperor Jing (188–141 BC), which made him appear to be less of a grasping warlord and more of a legitimate successor. Nonetheless, before he could become emperor he still had his two rivals to defeat.

Fire ships

Shortly after he joined Liu's staff, Zhuge presented what has come to be known as the Longzhong Plan. Liu ruled the kingdom of Shu (a region around the city of Chengdu), the smallest of the Three Kingdoms. Since Cao Cao, who ruled the northern kingdom of Wei, was the greatest threat, Zhuge urged Liu to form an alliance with Sun Quan, ruler of the Wu kingdom to the east. The two warlords would launch a two-pronged attack against Cao Cao; once he had been defeated, Liu would turn on Sun Quan and conquer his kingdom.

Zhuge's plan got off to an excellent start; Sun Quan leaped at the opportunity to unite with Liu against Cao Cao. During the winter of 208–209, the three warlords and their armies and ships met on the Yangtze River at a place called the Red Cliffs. Liu and Sun were badly outnumbered, with 50,000 men to Cao Cao's 220,000, but Liu had brought Zhuge Liang along. As he walked along the Yangtze where Liu and Sun's armies were camped and their ships anchored, Zhuge noticed that Cao Cao had lashed all his ships together, stern to stern, making them, essentially, one giant vessel. It looked impressive, but Zhuge realized that Cao Cao had immobilized his fleet—no one ship would be able to move until it had disengaged from two others. And that gave Zhuge an idea.

Kublai Khan (1215–1294), the Mongol leader who unified the Three Kingdoms and founded the Yuan dynasty of 1271–1368.

A day or two later, Cao Cao received a message from one of Liu and Sun's commanders, offering to desert and bring a handful of ships with him. Cao Cao replied that both the deserter and his ships would be welcome. A few hours afterwards, Cao Cao watched with pleasure as several ships broke away from Liu and Sun's fleet and sailed across the Yangtze toward him. Suddenly, when they were very close to Cao Cao's own fleet, fire erupted on each of the ships—and their crews scrambled over the side into small boats, which they rowed back to the opposite shore. Before Cao Cao could react, the traitor's fire ships were Amongst his fleet. Tied together as they were, the flames spread quickly from ship to ship until the entire fleet was engulfed in flames. Tens of thousands of men and countless horses burned to death or drowned. Cao Cao collected the survivors and headed back north, but Liu and Sun's troops followed, harassing them all along the way, and inflicting even more casualties.

According to legend, it was not Zhuge's powers of observation that were responsible for this stunning victory, but his command of Taoist magic: he had summoned a strong wind that propelled the fire boats directly into Cao Cao's fleet.

It's said that before a battle, Zhuge would examine the field, then select high ground where he could sit in his carriage, his white feather fan in his hand, observe the fighting, and send fresh orders to the commanders to adjust the deployment of their troops. It is possible that this is how he watched his first victory, the Battle of the Red Cliffs.

Repeated, massive volleys

Zhuge devoted the rest of his life to serving Liu Bei, and then Liu Bei's son Liu Shan. It was during this time that he invented the repeating crossbow or, rather, developed an improved version of the weapon. (The earliest repeating crossbow dates from the fourth century BC and was found in Tomb 47 in Qinjiazui, Hubei Province.)

Zhuge's crossbow featured a mounted magazine or clip which could hold ten steel-tipped arrows, also known as bolts (the earlier model held only four bolts). Each bolt measured 7 inches.

Zhuge equipped his crossbow with a simple but ingenious lever: push it forward and it drops a bolt into the grooved chamber; pull it back and it draws the bowstring taut; press down a bit harder on the lever and it releases the bolt. The operation was so simple that a skilled crossbowman could fire two bolts per second. The world would not see such an extraordinary rate of fire in any other weapon until the invention of the machine-gun in the nineteenth century.

There was one disadvantage to Zhuge's crossbow—for reasons not entirely understood, the crossbowmen did not bring the weapon up to their shoulder to fire it like a musket, but braced it against their hip. For this reason the weapon's accuracy was diminished. But what the crossbow lost in accuracy it compensated for in volume: because the crossbowmen were massed together, precision firing was not necessary—repeated, massive volleys of crossbow bolts more than made up for the lack of precision. If a practiced crossbowman could fire 120 bolts in one or two minutes (allowing time for him to reload the magazine), one hundred or more crossbowmen could fire 12,000 bolts in the same period. Chinese commanders found that such a rate of fire was equally effective on the battlefield, from the battlements of a besieged, walled town or from the deck of a warship. In fact, the Zhuge repeating crossbow was such an effective weapon that Chinese troops were using it as late as the First Sino-Japanese War of 1894–1895.

Modern-day experiments have shown that a Zhuge crossbow can fire a bolt 1201 feet, but it was probably most effective—especially as an armor-piercing weapon—at a range of no more than 180½ feet.

"Hateful to God"

In Greece the first crossbow appeared in the fifth century BC—the same time as it was invented in China. Over the next century it evolved from a personal weapon into a huge siege engine. Greek engineers built giant crossbows, known as *ballistas*, that could fire treetrunk-sized arrows into an enemy army or into a fortified town. The small crossbow would not return until about AD 950, when it was introduced as an alternative to the standard bow. With a standard bow, the muscle power and stamina of the archer determines the power and accuracy of each shot. After a certain point, however, the archer's muscles will tire and his arms begin to tremble from the constant exertion, with the result that his shots will no longer be very effective.

A crossbow, on the other hand, is mechanized. The first crossbows in Europe did require some effort: the archer rested the device, point downward, on the ground while bracing it against one leg as he pulled back the bowstring. Then he dropped the bolt into the notch, lifted the crossbow to his shoulder, took aim and fired. The improved crossbow which appeared on the weapons market in the fourteenth century was entirely mechanized—the archer drew back the

bowstring by turning a small hand-crank. With such a weapon an archer could shoot all day without ever becoming physically exhausted.

The improved crossbow's one drawback, however, was the time it took to load the bolt and draw back the bowstring—usually a full minute. An archer using a longbow could fire four or five arrows in the same time. But a crossbow bolt tended to be deadlier than a standard arrow—it was heavier, was propelled with much greater force and at distance of up to 180½ feet could penetrate steel armor.

Historian Robert L. O'Connell points out that the crossbow played havoc Amongst the knights, and with the principles of chivalric warfare. Knights were professional fighting men, equipped with the best weapons and armor, and always hailing from the upper classes. In battle against men of their own noble rank, they were reluctant to kill their opponents, preferring to take them prisoner and demand from their families a high ransom. Crossbowmen had no such scruples. In the article "The Life and Hard Times of the Crossbow", O'Connell notes, "In seconds an amateur with a crossbow could wipe out years of costly training, to say nothing of generations of noble (even royal) breeding. When commoners on foot could so easily kill their social betters, the fabric not only of warfare but of European society began to fray."

When the Byzantine princess Anna Comnena first saw a crossbow in action, about 1097, she wrote, "This crossbow is a bow of the barbarians quite unknown to the Greeks … and verily a devilish invention."

And she was not alone in this opinion. Amongst the upper classes especially, the crossbow came to be regarded as an unfair weapon, so much so that the Church weighed in: at the Second Lateran Council called in Rome by Pope Innocent II in 1139, the Holy Father and the bishops declared, "We prohibit under anathema that murderous art of crossbowmen and archers, which is hateful to God, to be employed against Christians and Catholics from now on."

The emergence of the longbow

In spite of the scorn of the ruling class and the threat of excommunication from the Church, kings and commanders continued to use crossbowmen—they were simply too effective to ignore. In the fourteenth century, however, a new weapon was developed in England which undermined the crossbow's pre-eminence on the battlefield. English bow-makers began to use the wood of the yew tree to fashion bows up to 6½ feet in length—the famous English longbow, light, strong

Copperplate engraving (1588) of a ballista, the giant Greek-designed form of crossbow used for projecting heavy missiles.

and supple. An arrow fired from a longbow traveled a much greater distance than those from previous bows: with a longbow a skilled archer could hit a target 754½ feet away. Furthermore, he could fire an arrow every five seconds, or twelve per minute. Since crossbows were only effective against targets no further than 180½ feet away, and were slow to load as well, the advantage on the battlefield passed to archers armed with longbows.

At Crécy in France in 1346, English longbowmen showed what they could do by firing upon a corps of crossbowmen—Genoese mercenaries fighting for the French. Although the crossbowmen had more powerful weapons, they were limited by range and rate of fire. The English longbowmen mowed down 2,300 of the enemy in record time and from a safe distance.

Zhuge Liang's legacy

Zhuge Liang's reputation as an inventor looms large in Chinese folklore. He is credited with introducing the landmine. While it is often difficult to sort fact from fiction in the stories about Zhuge, in this case we can say that it is unlikely that he developed a landmine—gunpowder-based weapons were not in use in China until the fourth century, more than sixty years after Zhuge's death.

Another military invention credited to Zhuge is the signal lantern, an early form of the hot-air balloon. Oiled ricepaper is stretched over a light bamboo frame to form a rough bell shape. A small lit candle is suspended inside; the candle flame heats the air within the bell, causing it to rise. Legend says Zhuge used these lanterns to send military signals at night, but the renowned historian of science, Joseph Needham, has proven that the Chinese were using such lanterns as early as the third century BC—600 years before Zhuge.

According to another legend, Zhuge is also the inventor of that staple of Chinese cuisine, the steamed bun. Having just scored a victory over a barbarian king, Zhuge was leading his army home when he encountered a flooded, swift-flowing river. With no fording place to be found, Zhuge was not sure what to do. A barbarian captive told him that Amongst his people they would behead fifty men and throw the heads into the river as a sacrifice to the river god. Zhuge had more than fifty captives, but he refused to kill them. Instead, he slaughtered fifty cows, placed some of their meat inside balls of dough shaped like human heads, steamed the buns and tossed them into the river. This gift pleased the river god, and the army was able to cross in safety. Back at home, the troops made these buns for themselves, and called them *mantou*, which means "barbarian heads."

The most famous victim of a crossbow

Richard the Lionheart (1157–1199), the most famous of the medieval kings of England, fell victim to a crossbow while besieging Châlus-Chabrol, an insignificant little castle in Haute-Vienne in central France. Late in the afternoon of March, 25 1199, Richard walked from his pavilion to the castle to see how the siege works were coming along. A bolt from a crossbow suddenly whizzed past his head. Looking up, Richard saw the archer who had fired the arrow, and in a light-hearted moment applauded him for his daring. But the man took aim again, and this time his bolt struck Richard in the shoulder near the base of his neck (the king had neglected to don his armor).

Back in his tent Richard tried to pull out the arrow, but it was too deeply embedded. He called a surgeon, who had to cut the king's flesh, making the wound bigger, to remove the arrow. Within a matter of days the wound became infected and gangrene set in.

Meanwhile, the English had taken the castle and captured the crossbowman who had hit the king: a teenage boy. He was brought to the tent where the king lay dying; as a final gesture of mercy, Richard pardoned him. It is said that once the king was dead, one of his officers seized the boy, flayed him alive, then hanged his corpse.

Arguably Zhuge's most enduring legacy is a book attributed to him, *The Thirty-Six Stratagems*. For 1,700 years it has been a handbook in China on how to succeed in war, politics or business. Most of the tactics Zhuge recommends are based on deception; for example, he recommends hiding your true goal; employing a third party to do your dirty work for you; ingratiating yourself with your rival so he will not suspect that you are working against him. From *The Thirty-Six Stratagems* the reader gets the impression that Zhuge Liang was a master of cunning, yet in China he is revered as a man of tremendous intellectual gifts, a sage, even a kind of saint—in Chengdu there is a temple dedicated to his memory. He is also a hero in one of the most popular of ancient Chinese novels, *Romance of the Three Kingdoms*. In recent times he has made the transition to a new kind of immortality—he is one of the heroes in the "Dynasty Warriors" video game.

Renaissance tinkerer
Leonardo da Vinci's machine-guns

SCIENTIST: Leonardo da Vinci

AREA OF SCIENCE: Mechanical engineering

MAIN INVENTIONS: Machine-gun, submarine, flying machine, giant ballista

IN 1482 LEONARDO DA VINCI WROTE to Ludovico Sforza, Duke of Milan, requesting a post as a military engineer and creator of new weapons:

> I can make armored wagons carrying artillery, which shall break through the most serried ranks of the enemy, and so open a safe passage for [the] infantry. I can construct cannon and mortars and light ordnance … When it is impossible to use cannon I can supply in their stead catapults, mangonels, trabocchi, and other instruments of admirable efficiency not in general use—in short, as the occasion requires I can supply infinite means of attack and defense.

Of the thirty-four lines of the letter in which Leonardo lists his talents, twenty-eight describe his aptitude for designing and building devices for the military; only six referenced his gifts as an artist. "I can further execute sculpture in marble, bronze or clay, also in painting I can do as much as anyone else." Then he added, "Whoever he may be."

Michelangelo, Raphael, Leonardo da Vinci—the three greatest artists of the Renaissance. Yet art was only one of Leonardo's interests. The flight of birds, the circulation of the blood, the science of hydraulics, even the unpredictability of the weather fascinated him. His body of work includes not only sublime works

Leonardo da Vinci: a nineteenth century engraving by Rafaello Morghen after an undated self-portrait by the inventor.

of art such as the *Mona Lisa*, the *Virgin of the Rocks* and *The Last Supper*, but also page after page of sketches of the anatomy of humans, animals and plants; detailed drawings of strange apparatus, including flying machines and diving suits; and detailed notes on how to construct canals, build portable bridges, and employ deadly new weapons.

Early successes

Leonardo was born on April, 15 1452 in the village of Anchiano, near the town of Vinci about 22 miles west of Florence. His father Piero was a prominent notary in Florence; his mother, Caterina, was a peasant who for a time had been Piero's mistress. Piero made it his responsibility to raise the boy and arranged for Caterina to marry a man from the Vinci neighborhood. Leonardo must have shown talent in drawing early because at the age of fifteen his father apprenticed him to Andrea del Verrocchio, one of the most successful artists in Florence, a man who excelled as a painter, a sculptor, and a goldsmith.

The earliest known work by Leonardo is the figure of a kneeling angel in a painting entitled *The Baptism of Christ* (1475). It was customary at the time for a skillful assistant to paint a few of the lesser figures in a scene while the master painted the most important ones. Usually the viewer can spot the difference in talent, but in this case Leonardo's angel is equal in quality to Verrocchio's figures of Christ and St. John the Baptist. It was Leonardo's first great success, and he was only twenty-three at the time.

Three years later the young artist struck out on his own, opening a studio in Florence, where he painted his lovely *Annunciation* and his portrait of Ginevra de Benci. In 1481 he received an important commission from the monks at the Monastery of San Donato in Scopeto—they wanted a large-scale altarpiece of the Adoration of the Magi. Leonardo made a good start, but never completed the painting—a pattern he would repeat throughout his life. In fact, it was while he was working for the monks of San Donato that he wrote to Duke Ludovico asking for a different kind of job.

Italy in the fifteenth and sixteenth centuries was in almost constant upheaval, with both the King of France and the Holy Roman Emperor invading the country, and wars breaking out Amongst the Papal States, Milan, Florence, Naples and Venice. Possessing the latest weaponry and the most powerful artillery, and building the strongest fortifications, became paramount for princes and popes alike. Architects who had designed fine palaces and beautiful churches were pressed into service—Filippo Brunelleschi and Michelangelo were just two such masters who accepted commissions to design fortifications.

The letter Leonardo wrote to the Duke of Milan emphasizes his skill as a mechanical engineer. How long Leonardo harbored a passion for engineering is unknown but, as his sketchbooks and notebooks show us very clearly, anything mechanical fascinated him. That he should be interested in weapons is no surprise—the archer, the crossbowman and the armored knight were all giving way to their high-tech counterparts, the fusilier and cannoneer. Military technology was the cutting-edge technology of fifteenth century Europe—quite naturally, anyone who possessed even a hint of the imagination and curiosity of Leonardo would be drawn to it.

From the peasantry to the nobility

The duchy of Milan occupied the far northern region of Italy, where the Alps spill out onto the plains of Lombardy. Just across the mountains are France, Germany and Austria—and in the Middle Ages and the Renaissance era, all three were desirous of extending their rule into Italy. The duke of Milan, therefore, was not only obliged to protect his own lands from being overrun but also served as the guardian of Italy's northern gate, the man who stood between invaders and the rest of Italy.

The Sforzas were new to this responsibility. Early in the 1400s Francesco Sforza, the son of peasants, joined the army of Filippo Visconti, Duke of Milan. Through a combination of natural talent, sheer determination and good luck, Francesco rose to the rank of general. He married Filippo's illegitimate daughter, Bianca, a step that elevated him from the peasantry to the nobility. Even more incredible, Duke Filippo—who had no other child than Bianca—promised that at his death, he would bequeath the duchy of Milan to Francesco. In 1447 Filippo Visconti died and the former peasant inherited one of the wealthiest duchies in Italy.

Duke Francesco proved to be a shrewd politician. He formed alliances with the powerful Medici clan in Florence and King Louis XI of France (the French had often tried to annex Milan, so this alliance neutralized the threat). For the defense of his city he rebuilt the great fortress of Porta Giovio. To encourage commerce he constructed a canal that linked Milan to the River Adda. And as an expression of compassion for his subjects he founded the Great Hospital.

The Italian Renaissance was in full flower in the 1450s, and Francesco participated in it, inviting to his court artists and scholars, including many Greek exiles who had fled the old Byzantine Empire after the fall of Constantinople to the Turks in 1453.

Francesco died in 1466 and was succeeded by his eldest son, Galeazzo Maria, a cruel, dissolute young man who so antagonized his people that on the day after Christmas 1476, as he stood in the porch of the cathedral of Milan, three young noblemen attacked and killed him.

Galeazzo was succeeded by his brother Ludovico who, in 1482, invited Leonardo to join his court in Milan.

The biggest business

Milan at this time in history was one of the largest cities in Europe, home to 300,000 people. The surrounding plains were lush and fertile, famous for their rice fields. During the Middle Ages, the city had become a center of the wool industry, and wool was still a money-making proposition. But more recently Milanese entrepreneurs had decided to tap into the market for luxury goods: outside the city they planted orchards of mulberry trees, grown specifically to feed the silkworms that were the heart of Milan's new booming silk industry.

But the biggest business in Milan was munitions. More than a hundred workshops fashioned weapons as well as armor, which not only boosted the local economy but also gave the city a distinctively martial character. Naturally the weapons-makers always had an eye out for the next enhancement or innovation in their field, something that would better defend Milan from her enemies while also boosting their own businesses.

Leonardo's letter to Duke Ludovico was not some Renaissance version of cold-calling; he knew that Milan had become the premier manufacturer of weapons in Italy. And he hoped that by offering the duke new weapons he would win a post in the duke's court, along with a handsome salary.

Ballistas and bombards

From Leonardo's drawings and notes we know that he had at least three types of weapons in mind for Milan: the ballista, the bombard and the repeating arquebus or musket. The ballista was an old weapon—first used in ancient Greece, it resembled a large crossbow and could fire giant arrows or large stones. Leonardo's

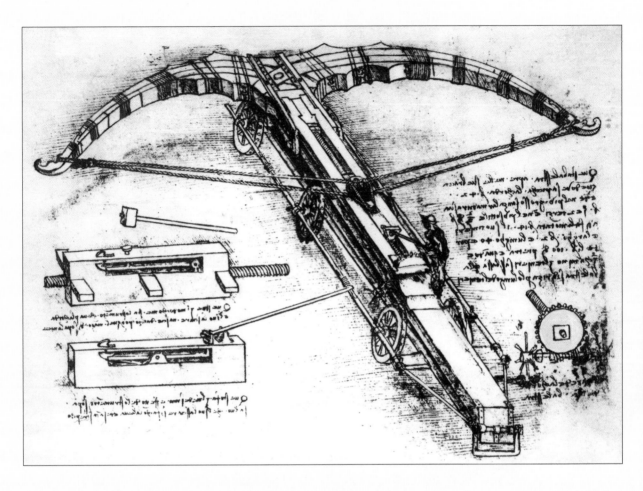

Leonardo's design for a giant ballista, c. 1499, annotated in his trademark mirror handwriting.

ballista was unlike anything seen previously: it was enormous, approximately 19½ feet long, with a bow about the same size, mounted on a carriage so large it took three pairs of wheels to support and move it.

Leonardo's ballista was not just big; it was also an improvement on existing designs. For example, he called for the huge bow to be laminated to improve its flexibility. The bowstring could be drawn taut by turning a gear, or by using a lever—Leonardo had not decided which device he preferred. And the bowstring could be released either by striking the trip with a mallet, or by releasing the lever. Again, Leonardo had not decided which method worked best (there is no evidence that he ever created working models of these weapons). To compensate for the size of the ballista, Leonardo canted the wheels, mounting them at a slight angle to stabilize the carriage.

The Last Supper

Duke Ludovico never did commission Leonardo to build any of his marvelous weapons; instead, in 1495, he commissioned Leonardo to decorate a wall of the refectory, or dining room, of Santa Maria della Grazie, the Dominican friars' monastery in Milan. The wall was large—29½ feet long—but this was no challenge to a man at the height of his powers and recognized as Italy's greatest living artist.

Leonardo's approach to painting this mural was as unconventional and controversial as some of his designs for weapons. Ludovico and the Dominicans must have assumed that he would follow the tried and true method of *buon fresco*, a process that called for the artist's assistants to apply a fresh coat of wet plaster to the wall, no larger than the artist could paint in a single day. The artist would set to work immediately, applying wet paint to wet plaster. When the paint and the plaster dried, the painting literally had soaked into the wall.

But Leonardo did not want to be rushed; he wanted to linger over this work, which meant he could not use the *buon fresco* method. Instead, he prepared his own pigments and invented resin-based sealants that he believed would bind the painting to the dry wall. He welcomed visitors to the refectory, permitting them to stay as long as they wished and watch him work. It was common for him to engage his visitors in conversation, often explaining to them his ground-breaking technique for mural painting. One frequent visitor recalled that sometimes Leonardo "stayed there from dawn to sundown, never putting down his brush, forgetting to eat and drink, painting without pause." Other times he would walk over to the monastery from his house, "clamber up onto the scaffolding, pick up his brush, put in one or two strokes, then go away again."

The finished painting was an undisputed masterpiece, but if Leonardo believed that his new pigments and sealants had made *buon fresco* obsolete, he was mistaken. *The Last Supper* began to deteriorate during his own lifetime. By 1587 an observer described the painting as "half ruined."

Over the centuries other artists have tried to "restore" *The Last Supper* by repainting it, typically with unhappy results. Between 1977 and 1999, art restorer Pinin Brambilla Barcilon removed layers of dirt and mould, and the wretched attempts to "touch up" the work. Underneath she found Leonardo's original brilliant colors, as well as the original postures and facial expressions of the Apostles. No restoration can bring back *The Last Supper* Leonardo completed in 1498, but what we have now is better than no *Last Supper* at all.

Leonardo also proposed a new type of missile to be fired from his massive ballista. Shaped like a giant dart, the missile was packed with gunpowder and shrapnel; it would explode on impact, although we do not know what type of triggering device he intended for it.

Leonardo did not invent the bombard, but he did imagine a new type of missile for it. Bombards were large-caliber cannons with a thicker and shorter barrel than other artillery pieces, which made them capable of hurling heavier stones or cannonballs. One of the largest fifteenth century bombards was commissioned as a gift for James II of Scotland by Phillip III, Duke of Burgundy, and cast in the foundry at Mons, Belgium about 1449; the Scots named this super-gun Mons Meg. It weighed 15,366 pounds, was 15 feet in length, and had a calibre of 20 inches. And it could fire cannonballs that weighed 397 pounds.

Leonardo's bombard cannonball had a light outer shell. Upon firing, the shell split open, releasing dozens of smaller projectiles. The purpose of such a missile, of course, was to increase the amount of damage inflicted upon the enemy in a single shot.

The quest for firepower

During the late Middle Ages the great achievement of the crossbow and the longbow had been their ability to allow masses of archers to send an enormous volley of arrows or bolts into the ranks of the enemy from a safe distance. As artillery and firearms entered the military picture, kings and their commanders wanted to apply the same principle to the new weapons. Leonardo's multi-balled bombard shell was a step in the right direction but it was better suited as a siege weapon; what military men wanted was an anti-personnel gun.

The earliest reference to such a weapon dates from 1339; sometimes known as a ribauldequin or volley gun, it is more often referred to as an "organ gun", because the gun barrels were laid side by side like the pipes of an organ. We know that organ guns were used by the armies of Ghent in 1382, of Burgundy in 1411 and of Venice in 1457. By 1500 the French had an organ gun comprised of fifty barrels.

But the early organ guns had serious flaws. Firstly, given the primitive state of gun manufacturing at this period, there was a very good chance that at least one of the barrels would misfire and explode, with disastrous results for the gunner and anyone else in the general vicinity. Secondly, it took a long time to reload fifty barrels; after the initial blast, an hour might pass before the gun was ready to fire again. And then there was the maneuverability factor: trying to move a weapon composed of fifty bronze or copper gunbarrels across the uneven ground of a battlefield, or rutted unpaved roads, would be difficult at the very least. Nonetheless, the quest for increased firepower continued.

Centuries ahead of his time

Leonardo's first response to the military's desire for a rapid-fire anti-personnel weapon looked back to the crossbow. He imagined a crossbow machine-gun that can only be described as weird. Leonardo's sketch calls for a giant treadmill, large enough for a man to stand inside. Mounted within the wheel are four crossbows. The exterior of the wheel is covered with steps; a team of men propel the wheel by climbing the steps continuously. As the treadmill turns, the crossbows come within reach of the crossbowman inside the wheel who fires them in succession through a slit in the wheel.

While the crossbowman is relatively well protected inside the wheel, the team of men walking the tread are exposed, so Leonardo did a rough sketch of a large wooden shield or screen set at an angle over them to ward off arrows, bullets, and other missiles. The treadmill crossbow machine was too big, too unwieldy, and too unpredictable since the rapid-fire feature depended entirely on the stamina of the men driving the wheel. As a field weapon it was hopeless.

But Leonardo did not stop there. His sketchbooks show drawings of three weapons that are real forerunners of the machine-gun. The first design calls for mounting several musket barrels on a wooden carriage which is itself mounted on a wooden frame that resembles a wheelbarrow—for easy maneuverability. The second design keeps the treadmill idea, but on a much smaller scale. Leonardo's drawing shows eight musket barrels mounted in eight ranks upon a metal drum. As the gunner turns a crank the drum revolves and the guns fire as they reach the top. With this second design Leonardo was more than three hundred years ahead of his time—a similar device with several revolving gun barrels, the Gatling gun, would be developed in 1862 during the American Civil War.

The third type of repeating gun was smaller. It featured twelve barrels mounted in three ranks on the metal drum. As one gunner fired the first tier of guns, a second gunner reloaded the guns on the second tier; meanwhile, the third tier was cooling down.

Letting a gun or cannon barrel cool before firing it again was a well-understood principle by Leonardo's day. Repeated rapid firing made the muzzles literally too hot to handle, and in some cases caused them to explode. Leonardo tackled this problem too, designing a copper musket with a water-chamber to cool the barrel.

Dying in the king's arms

None of Leonardo's designs for weapons was ever constructed. Ludovico certainly never asked him to produce his giant ballista or his peculiar treadmill-crossbow machine-gun, both of which struck the duke as too impractical, too unwieldy ,and too difficult to get to and from a battlefield.

For the rest of his life, Leonardo's ideas and inspirations for new machines did not extend any further than his sketchpads and his notebooks. In 1513 he retired in Rome, still painting and sketching from time to time, rarely receiving any visitors, mostly keeping to himself.

Then in 1516, Francis I, King of France, invited Leonardo to join his court at Fontainebleau. Leonardo accepted, and the king treated him as a revered and much loved teacher, or even father. Francis, realizing that the crowds and protocol of the royal court made Leonardo uncomfortable, gave him a manor house where he could enjoy his privacy. There Leonardo spent the last three years of his life. When he was dying, Francis hurried to his bedside, and held the old genius in his arms until the last breath left him.

Massed firepower
Marin le Bourgeoys' flintlock

SCIENTIST: Marin le Bourgeoys

AREAS OF SCIENCE: Metallurgy and mechanical engineering

MAIN INVENTION: Flintlock rifle

ONE OF THE PRIZES in the Arms and Armor collection of the Metropolitan Museum of Art in New York is a flintlock hunting rifle. It is 4½ feet long, and weighs 6 pounds. Its steel barrel and wooden stock are both exquisitely embellished. Engraved upon the musket are the crowned monogram of Louis XIII, King of France, and a crossbow flanked by the letters PB—the initials of Pierre le Bourgeoys. The le Bourgeoys brothers—Marin, Pierre and Jean—ranked Amongst the finest musket-makers in Europe. It was in their workshop in their hometown, Lisieux in Normandy, that Marin le Bourgeoys invented the flintlock mechanism that revolutionized the musket. And it was in that same workshop in 1630 that Pierre le Bourgeoys fashioned the superb flintlock for King Louis, displayed today in New York.

Matches, wheels and snaps

The "lock" in the terms matchlock, wheel-lock, snaplock and flintlock is a synonym for "mechanism". The earliest muskets in Europe required the user to lower a burning splinter of wood onto the flashpan to ignite a small dab of gunpowder. The flash produced in the pan traveled through the touch-hole in the gun barrel, igniting the larger charge of gunpowder there and causing the musketball to shoot out of the barrel. Unfortunately, this early fifteenth century musket was cumbersome to use, requiring the soldier to balance the gun with one hand while he lit the gunpowder with the other.

A musketeer fitting a bayonet to his weapon; illustration from a French book of military art dated 1696.

The matchlock developed by the Ottoman Turks in the 1440s was an improvement because it mechanized, in a simple way, the process of setting off the powder in the flashpan. The "match" was a piece of slow-burning cord, similar to a fuse, held by a clamp mounted on the gun's stock either in front of or behind the flashpan. By pulling a trigger, the user dropped the burning end of the match into the flashpan.

The matchlock had two main advantages: the user steadied the weapon with both hands and could aim at his target without having to manipulate the match himself. But there were disadvantages, too; having a burning match in close proximity to gunpowder increased the risk of accidental explosions; and in wet weather it was impossible to light the match.

The next advance in firearms technology, the wheel-lock, eliminated the need for any type of burning match. The wheel-lock operated like the modern-day cigarette lighter, using friction to create a flame, but the mechanism was much more complicated. To put it simply, a tiny vice held a little piece of a stone known as iron pyrite; when the musket's trigger was pulled, a grooved steel wheel turned, grinding against the iron pyrite, producing sparks which fell on the powder in the flashpan and created the necessary charge to fire the weapon. The wheel-lock was invented about 1500, but because it was so difficult to manufacture, which made it expensive to purchase, an alternative was sought almost from the moment it appeared on the market.

The next stage was the snaplock. It had a spring-powered bent lever known as the cock with a clamp that held a small piece of flint. To fire the musket, the user "cocked" the lever by pulling it back with his thumb. A catch kept the lever in place. When the user was ready to fire, he pulled the trigger; this released the catch, the cock fell forward, striking a steel plate, which sent a shower of sparks on the powder in the flashpan.

The snaplock was invented by an unknown gunsmith, probably in Germany, about 1540. It was inexpensive, and easy to manufacture and to use. And it had another advantage—because it could be fired at a moment's notice, a soldier could march into battle or a hunter could walk into the forest with their musket loaded.

The king's favorite toy

We know very little about the man credited with inventing the flintlock. Marin le Bourgeoys (*c.* 1550–1634) was born in Lisieux in Normandy. It was a small, quiet town in le Bourgeoys' day; today it is an international pilgrimage destination, with tens of thousands, sometimes hundreds of thousands, coming annually to venerate the relics of another famous native, St. Thérèse of Lisieux, fondly known as the "Little Flower."

Like so many accomplished men of the Renaissance era, le Bourgeoys had more than just one talent. He was a painter and a maker of astronomical instruments as well as a gunsmith. In 1598 King Henri IV invited le Bourgeoys to court, appointing him *Valet de Chambre*. He was kept on by Henri's son, Louis XIII.

From childhood Louis XIII (1601–1643), son of Henri IV and Marie de' Medici, had a passion for hunting with falcons and with muskets. He shot his first bird from his bedroom window when he was about five years old. Understandably, the sound of the firearm frightened him at the time, but as he grew older he became fascinated by anything that would explode, as well as all things military. As a child he had a miniature musket, sword and knife, and was permitted to call out the royal guard to drill with him and fire their weapons. He proclaimed that he was a musketeer. One of little Louis' favorite activities was ordering the guard to fire salvo after salvo as his parents watched. In effect, guns became his favorite toys. Once, when he was late for Mass and found the chapel door locked, he threatened to fetch his *arquebuse* and blast the door open.

It was some time between 1610 and 1615—when Louis was between nine and fourteen years old—that le Bourgeoys invented the flintlock. His invention marked a significant improvement on musket technology: firstly, it had a half-cocked position—the forerunner of the safety lock; secondly, the firing mechanism was more reliable—there were fewer misfires with the flintlock than there had been with the matchlock and wheel-lock; thirdly, the flintlock came equipped with an automated flashpan cover which kept the gunpowder dry.

Le Bourgeoys' lock mechanism differed from earlier models. A sharp piece of flint was clamped tightly in the jaws of the cock. Mounted just in front of the cock was a small upright finger of roughened steel known as the frizzen. The frizzen was tilted forward a bit toward the cock so that when the user pulled the trigger the flint would strike it at an oblique angle. As the flint struck the frizzen, the frizzen popped forward, uncovering the flashpan so the gunpowder could be ignited. Unlike the snaplock, which showered sparks in every direction, the flint-and-steel of the flintlock directed the sparks precisely into the flashpan.

We do not know what young Louis thought the first time he saw le Bourgeoys' flintlock, but we do know that as an adult he appreciated it tremendously. Louis kept the le Bourgeoys brothers busy fashioning elaborate flintlocks for himself (such as the one in the Metropolitan Museum of Art), and as gifts which the king presented to his favorites at court or to distinguished visitors.

Ideal for hunters, but too expensive for the troops

In spite of the superiority of the flintlock over the matchlock, for most of the 1600s most royal armies—even the army of France—did not replace their old firearms with le Bourgeoys' new weapon. It was simply too great an expense to discard thousands of matchlocks and purchase a flintlock for every musketeer. There was one exception: musketeers assigned to protect artillery were armed with flintlocks. Matchlocks with their ever-smouldering fuses had caused too many accidental explosions at gunnery positions. The flintlock eliminated that risk.

One of the first monarchs to adopt the flintlock was King James II of England and Scotland—but that did not occur until 1685, about seventy years after le Bourgeoys invented it. The armies of the Netherlands made the shift to flintlocks five years later. In France the flintlock remained the hunting gun of choice Amongst the upper classes, but still had not displaced the matchlock from the royal armories.

In the 1690s, when French commanders began reporting that their men were picking up the flintlocks of fallen English and Dutch troops and using them in place of their matchlocks, Louis XIV ordered that the matchlocks were to be replaced—but gradually, regiment by regiment, so as not to overburden the treasury.

Soldiers who had used matchlocks and flintlocks preferred the latter because they found them easier to use and more dependable—clearly an improvement over all previous muskets. Nonetheless, the gun was far from perfect. There were twenty-five steps to follow to load and fire it (much better than the matchlock, which involved forty-three steps). The "flash in the pan" syndrome, in which the powder burned but the musket did not fire, did not occur as often with flintlocks as with matchlocks, but it still happened often enough to irritate the troops and their officers. The greatest problem with a flintlock was the flint. It broke, fell out of its clamp or wore down. Musketeers rapidly learned to carry extra flints. When the Lewis and Clark expedition set out in 1804 to explore America's newly acquired Louisiana Territory, the party was armed with flintlocks, and took the precaution of adding 500 spare flints to the supplies.

"You may as well fire at the moon"

Of course, the flintlocks issued to the army looked nothing like the flintlocks the le Bourgeoys brothers crafted for King Louis XIII. These were practical, stripped down, military weapons. No gold inlay, no silver-plated mechanisms, no mother-of-pearl embellishments.

Flintlocks issued to the military were available in two forms—the French *fusil* and the English Brown Bess. The fusil was 58 inches long, weighed 10 pounds, and fired a lead ball that weighed 1 ounce. The Brown Bess was 70 inches long, weighed 11 pounds, and fired a 1 ounce lead ball. English gunsmiths had discovered that by making a longer barrel they gave the gunpowder more time to burn, thereby increasing muzzle velocity, or the speed with which the musket ball shot out of the barrel, which improved the gun's accuracy. As a

The flintlock's contributions to the English language

Flash in the pan This expression refers to something or someone who in spite of an impressive appearance at first proves to be disappointing. The saying is derived from a flintlock that misfires: the flint strikes the frizzen, the spark falls on the powder, but the musket does not fire.

Go off half-cocked The half-cocked position was the safety position on a flintlock; if it was half-cocked, the musket would not fire. Of course, accidents happened, and if the spring catch mechanism were worn out or faulty, the cock could disengage and fire before the rifleman was ready. To go off half-cocked means for some action to occur prematurely.

Lock, stock and barrel This colloquialism refers to the three parts that make up a flintlock: the firing mechanism, or lock; the gunstock; and the barrel or muzzle. The expression means "everything" or "the whole thing."

result, the Brown Bess became the preferred weapon in Europe and in the New World. Between the early 1700s and the early 1800s, 7 million Brown Bess flintlock muskets were manufactured.

There was one important feature the flintlock, and all other muskets, lacked—they did not have a sight for aiming at a target. This did not overly concern military commanders. They believed that precision aiming wasted time; it was more important for a large number of troops to fire a deadly volley of lead into the massed ranks of the enemy. And to accomplish that, all that was necessary was for the musketeer to point his flintlock in the proper direction.

When troops drilled in the peace of their camp or on the parade ground, they could fire five shots per minute, but that rate of fire was impossible amidst the chaos of battle. The situation improved slightly with the introduction of the cartridge, a small packet of greased paper that held a musketball and the correct charge of gunpowder. The musketeer tore open the cartridge, poured the contents down the barrel, then, using his ramrod, tamped down the greased paper. An experienced soldier could accomplish this action in about twenty seconds.

To compensate for the time lost reloading, the English developed the tactic of firing by platoons. The first rank knelt on the ground, the second stooped over their shoulders, the third stood upright. The kneeling rank fired first. As the second rank fired, the first rank reloaded. As the third rank fired, the second reloaded. At this point the first rank was ready to fire again. In this way infantrymen could keep up a steady stream of non-stop firing.

This mass of fire compensated for one of the major failings of the flintlock (in fact, of all muskets): beyond 328 feet, it was difficult to hit let alone kill anyone. Muskets fired their lead balls at a low muzzle velocity—in other words, the bullets did not move very fast. The firearms historian W.W. Greener has observed that over a distance of only 394 feet, a ball fired from a musket drops 5 vertical feet. An expert marksman could probably hit his target at a range of 246 feet, and perhaps even 311½ feet. Massed troops firing in ranks could do some damage at up to 607 feet, but beyond that point troops were perfectly safe from harm. Britain's Colonel George Hanger, writing in 1814, observed:

> *As to firing at a man 200 yards away with a common musket you may*
> *as well fire at the moon and have the same hope of hitting your object.*
> *I do maintain and will prove whenever called upon that no man was*
> *ever killed at 200 yards by a common musket ...*

Of necessity at that time, battles occurred at very close range. This also explains the order given to the American troops at the Battle of Bunker Hill in 1775: "Don't fire until you see the whites of their eyes."

By the 1750s, European armies were no longer firing in small platoons of a few dozen men but in whole battalions of 500 men or more. Theoretically, these platoons of 500 men could fire between 1,000 and 1,500 bullets per minute. Under such devastating fire one side or another would eventually break ranks and run off the field. The winner, of course, was whichever army held its ground.

Enter the Pennsylvania rifle

The first settlers in the French and English colonies in North America carried matchlocks and wheel-locks. They tended to be so heavy that the musketeers carried with them tall metal forks which they planted upright in the ground, resting the barrel in the fork before firing. Colonial gunsmiths forged their own barrels and fashioned their own stocks, but imported the locks, or firing mechanisms, from England, France or what is now Belgium. It was only after 1725 that skilled gunsmiths in Lancaster, Pennsylvania began manufacturing a musket that became known as the Pennsylvania flintlock. Later, gunsmiths in Kentucky adopted the Lancaster method and, out of a sense of regional chauvinism, called these guns the Kentucky rifle (also known as the long rifle).

This American flintlock was modeled on the Jaeger, the German hunting rifle (eighteenth century Pennsylvania had a large population of German immigrants). The great technological advantage of the Pennsylvania was the rifled bore of its barrel. The interior of the traditional musket barrel was smooth. After the musket was fired, the lead ball was propelled down the barrel, ricocheting off the smooth sides as it went. By the time it shot out of the mouth of the barrel, the trajectory of the bullet was entirely unpredictable. The interior of a rifled barrel was engraved with a shallow spiral groove that spun the lead ball and kept it moving in a straight line. The rifling combined with the length of the barrel—45 inches on average—ensured that the Pennsylvania flintlock was much more accurate than standard flintlocks such as the Brown Bess. For example, while a British soldier firing a Brown Bess could hit a man 246 to 311½ feet away, an American firing a Pennsylvania flintlock could kill a man at a distance of 902 feet.

Following pages: An early twentieth century postcard based on the painting The Death of General Warren at the Battle of Bunker Hill, June, 17 1775, *by American Revolutionary War artist John Trumbull.*

By the time of the French and Indian War of the 1750s and 1760s, Pennsylvania rifles were in use throughout the American colonies. These "home-made" flintlocks gave the American militia and the Continental Army an advantage in the colonies' war for independence from Great Britain—and considering that the British had the greatest army and navy on Earth, the colonists needed every advantage they could get.

The Pennsylvania gunsmiths added another feature which hunters and militiamen found useful: a compartment in the butt-stock to hold extra flints and tiny squares of linen for tamping down the ball and charge.

The terror of hand-to-hand combat

Soon after the numerous armies of Europe adopted the flintlock, the bayonet was developed, supposedly in the French city of Bayonne. The first bayonet was a long sharp knife that was jammed into the muzzle or barrel of the flintlock—it was known as a plug bayonet. Of course, this prevented the musketeer from reloading and firing his weapon, but there were other problems as well—it was common for a musketeer to slice open his hand when trying to fix the bayonet, and it was just as common for the bayonet to fall out.

The socket bayonet was developed in 1687; it slipped over the end of the muzzle and was held in place with a simple lug nut. Now the musketeer could reload and fire, but warily—as with the plug bayonet, one careless move and he would cut himself.

Most bayonets were about 18 inches long. Added to a musket nearly 6½ feet long, it became a formidable weapon, especially against cavalry. But it was also terrifying in hand-to-hand combat, inflicting appalling wounds; it was not unheard of for opposing armies to keep their distance rather than make a bayonet charge. In his book *Military History*, J.W. Fortescue observed, "All nations boast of their prowess with the bayonet, but few men really enjoy a hand-to-hand fight with the bayonet. English and French both talk much of the bayonet but in Egypt in 1801 they threw stones at each other when their ammunition was exhausted."

The bayonet remained exclusively an accoutrement of the military. Hunters, settlers, mountain men, Indian fighters and other civilians who carried a flintlock never adopted the use of the bayonet.

A long run

Marin le Bourgeoys' flintlock is a phenomenon in the history of firearms. While other muskets became obsolete within decades after they were first invented, the flintlock endured for almost two hundred years. It armed British, French, Dutch, and Spanish troops at home and in their empires around the globe. It was the gun that colonists and settlers carried to the Americas and Australia. It was the preferred hunting rifle of royalty and of backwoodsmen. And the flintlock remained popular until the introduction of the percussion cap made the flint, the frizzen, and the flashpan obsolete.

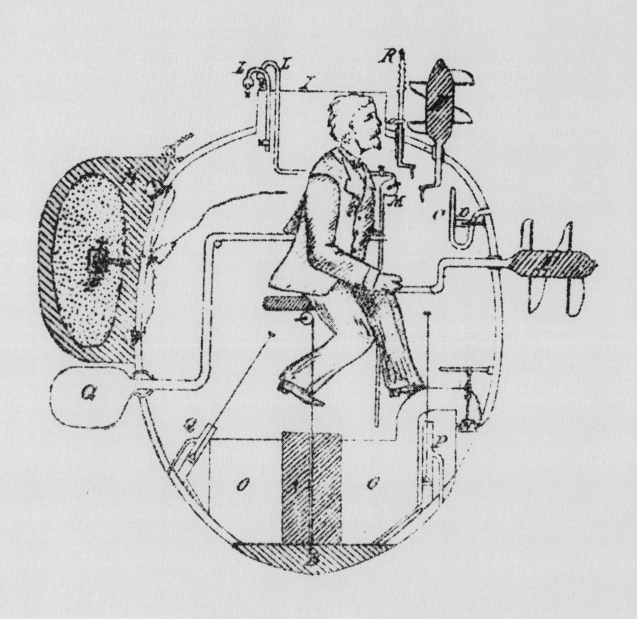

An effort of genius
David Bushnell's submarine

SCIENTIST: David Bushnell

AREA OF SCIENCE: Submersion technology

MAIN INVENTION: Submarine

A FEW PROFESSORS AND STUDENTS from Yale College, along with a handful of curious passers-by, stood by the shore of a pond in New Haven, Connecticut, where one of the college's most promising students of mathematics and chemistry was conducting an outdoor experiment. At the age of thirty-two, David Bushnell (1740–1824) was an old man Amongst the students, most of whom were teenage boys. But Bushnell hadn't been able to get to college any sooner—his parents had needed his help to coax a living from their hardscrabble farm near the Connecticut town of Saybrook. When his father died in 1767, leaving him a small sum of money as an inheritance, Bushnell used it to enroll at Yale and begin his education.

On this day in 1772 Bushnell was about to demonstrate an underwater bomb. A few months earlier he had succeeded in igniting 2 ounces of gunpowder underwater. Now he was ready to showcase the possibilities of a new type of weapon that he believed could blow out the hull of a warship. At the bottom of the pond he had sunk a wooden jug packed with 32 ounces of gunpowder. On top of the jug rested an oak plank 2 inches thick. On top of the plank stood a large barrel called a hogshead, filled with stones. Running through the hogshead and the plank down into the jug of gunpowder was a long fuse. Bushnell lit a match, ignited the fuse, and urged everyone to stand a good distance away. A moment later a terrible explosion erupted from the pond, "rending the plank … demolishing the hogshead, and casting the stones and the ruins … with a body of water, many feet into the air,

Historic engraving of the cross-section of the first military submarine, designed by David Bushnell.

to the astonishment of the spectators", as a delighted Bushnell described the scene.

Bushnell had proven that he could detonate a powerful bomb underwater; the next question was how to affix the bomb to the underside of a warship. Over the next two years Bushnell experiment with a variety of designs for what he called his "Sub-Marine Vessel."

A national priority

At sunrise on April, 19 1775, more than a dozen years of antagonism and animosity between Great Britain and its thirteen colonies in North America came to a head on the village green in Lexington, Massachusetts, when seventy-seven American militiamen stood their ground against 250 British regulars who had come to confiscate the town's stockpile of weapons and gunpowder. Someone opened fire—although no one has ever been able to determine which side shot first. In the hail of gunfire that followed, eight militiamen were killed and ten wounded; only one British soldier was wounded. America's war for independence had begun, and with the British Navy ready to blockade the colonies' ports and harbors, Bushnell's Sub-Marine Vessel was no longer an intellectual exercise, it was a national priority, the construction of which must be kept secret.

Bushnell moved into a shed on Poverty Island in the Connecticut River, not far from the family farm. He let it slip that he had decided to go into the fishing business, and planned to operate a small boatyard on the island. Since Poverty Island has access to both the Connecticut River and the Long Island Sound, the story made perfect sense.

Inside the shed Bushnell was building his submarine. He constructed it of oak reinforced with iron bands, like a barrel. A coating of tar made it waterproof. To enter the submarine he affixed to the top a raised brass hatch, with six small windows, which meant that he could see where he was going before he submerged. Modern submarines still have this raised entry—it is known as a conning tower. In a compartment at the bottom of the vessel he placed 198½ pounds of lead as ballast to keep the submarine stable and upright in the water. He installed a second compartment at the bottom that he could open by stepping on a brass valve to take in water when he wanted the submarine to dive; a brass hand-pump expelled the water when he wanted to surface. Fresh air entered through pipes that ran up the hatch cover; when the submarine dived, valves inside the air pipes closed automatically. There was enough air inside for Bushnell to stay underwater for thirty minutes.

Bushnell designed his submarine to accommodate only one man, and that man would be very busy. There was no technology in the 1770s to harness electricity or steam or fuel oil to make the submarine go—all of its movements required human muscle power. Sitting on a wooden bench inside the submarine, the pilot operated a hand-crank with his left hand which turned the propeller on the front of the vessel: if he was very strong and turned the crank very fast—and assuming he was not going against heavy tides or currents—the pilot could make the submarine move at nearly 3 miles per hour. To steer, he used his right hand to operate a lever attached to the rudder attached to the rear of the submarine. Another propeller was mounted on the top of the submarine—the pilot turned this crank to raise or lower the vessel. And since the submarine stood only 6½ feet tall and was only a metre wide, the pilot had little room inside to maneuver; every movement had to be precise.

Bushnell nicknamed his vessel the *Turtle* because its shape reminded him of two large turtle shells bolted together. Most people thought it looked more like an egg.

A detour to Saybrook

The wind blowing in from the Connecticut River chilled 69-year-old Benjamin Franklin, but what he was watching off Ayers Point held his interest. David Bushnell's submarine appealed to Franklin on every level—as a man of science, as an inventor, and as an ardent advocate for American independence. On that October day in 1775 Great Britain possessed the greatest navy in the world; the thirteen colonies had no navy at all. Yet Franklin could see that Bushnell's vessel might be the "secret weapon" America needed against the mighty British fleet.

Bushnell had always been a reticent young man: he did not have the audacity to write to the great Dr. Franklin with an invitation to inspect his invention. But Dr. Benjamin Gale, one of his friends in Saybrook, had no such qualms. Gale described the *Turtle* to Franklin as an underwater vessel that could attach to the hull of a British warship a mine, or bomb, so powerful as to sink it. That was an invention Dr. Franklin wanted to see. On his way to Cambridge, Massachusetts, to meet with George Washington, newly appointed commander-in-chief of the American army, Franklin made a detour to Saybrook.

Bushnell had never thought of his submarine as a nautical oddity, he had designed it as a weapon of war. Amongst its other cranks and levers, the *Turtle* had a long, sharp screw attached to its exterior. Once the submarine was beneath an enemy vessel, the pilot turned a crank attached to the screw, which bored its way into the timbers on the bottom of the ship. Once the screw penetrated the wood deeply enough, the pilot released it, and released the bomb which was attached to the back of the *Turtle* and connected to the

What became of David Bushnell?

In 1783, after the American victory over the British, David Bushnell asked the Connecticut General Assembly to make good on the promise of the Council of Safety to reimburse his expenses for constructing the *Turtle* and its bombs; along with his petition he submitted a bill for £489. He had no documentation for this agreement, and the Council of Safety had been disbanded, but the assemblymen agreed they ought to give Bushnell something: they voted him a payment of £150. Being cheated by his own government only added to the bitterness of Bushnell's disappointment over the failure of the submarine project.

When Bushnell left home in 1787 he headed south, to Georgia, on the invitation of an old Yale classmate, Abraham Baldwin, and settled in Warrenton, where he introduced himself to his neighbors as Dr. David Bush. He started a private academy where he taught classes in science and religion, and he opened a medical practice (when or where he studied medicine is another mystery in the David Bushnell story). No one in Georgia had the

least idea that he was an inventor, a man who had known George Washington, Benjamin Franklin, Thomas Jefferson and Israel Putnam. They knew him only as a dedicated teacher and a kindly country doctor. He never married, and he never mentioned any family.

In 1824 Dr. Bush died—he was eighty-four years old. When the executors of his estate read the will they discovered that Dr. Bush's true name was David Bushnell; the will instructed them to find the children of his brother Ezra Bushnell of Saybrook, Connecticut, to whom he bequeathed all his assets and property. The executors found Ezra's children—two grown sons, Ezra Jr. and Nehemiah—both living in Saybrook. The two men could not have been more surprised to learn that their long-lost uncle had died only recently, and had left them everything he owned.

The submarine is David Bushnell's legacy to the world. As George Washington wrote of the *Turtle* in a letter to Thomas Jefferson, "I then thought, and still think, that it was an effort of genius."

screw by a rope. Then the pilot turned the *Turtle* around and returned to the place from where he had embarked.

Bushnell's bomb held 154½ pounds of gunpowder and was equipped with a mechanical timer which was set before the mission began (it could be set up to twelve hours in advance). When the timer ran out, a small hammer inside the bomb struck a piece of steel—just like on a flintlock rifle—which produced sparks that ignited the gunpowder.

Benjamin Franklin was impressed. He told Dr. Gale that by his calculations Bushnell's 154½ pound bomb had three times the amount of gunpowder necessary to sink the largest ship in the British Navy.

A successful experiment

Only rarely did David Bushnell pilot the *Turtle*—he lacked the strength to turn all the cranks and pump the pumps and pedal the gauges, and he couldn't tolerate the stale air and the stink of tar inside the submarine. But his younger brother Ezra was a robust young man who didn't mind the smells and close quarters of the *Turtle*; Ezra became the pilot of the first submarine.

For months Ezra practiced operating the *Turtle*, learning all its idiosyncrasies, and working with his brother on improvements. David had installed a compass, and a gauge that measured how far the *Turtle* was traveling below the surface of the water, but once the submarine was submerged it was pitch black inside—Ezra could not see where he was going, nor did he have any idea at what depth he was traveling. Initially David tried using a single candle inside the vessel, but the flame burned up the oxygen too quickly. The problem seemed insoluble until David remembered foxfire, a phosphorescent fungus that sometimes occurs on rotting tree trunks. He dismantled the glass tube depth-gauge, adding a cork and wires smeared with foxfire: the cork would rise or sink as the *Turtle* rose or sank, a quick glance at the wires and the glowing cork would tell Ezra his depth. David also applied foxfire to the compass. It gave a blurry reading of direction, but it was better than cruising blind.

In the fall of 1775, after Franklin's visit, the brothers decided to make a trial run. In the Connecticut River lay the decaying hulk of an abandoned ship—that would be the target. Beneath the surface of the river, Ezra used the foxfire gauges to chart his course. He found the hulk, drove the screw into the rotting timbers, released the bomb, then turned back to shore where David was waiting. They watched as the bomb exploded, reducing the ruined ship to splinters.

Dr. Gale was as delighted by the *Turtle*'s success as were the Bushnell brothers. In letters to friends he extolled the wartime possibilities of the "famous Connecticut Water Machine." Gale had no idea that the postmaster of Killingworth, Connecticut, was an ardent Tory, a supporter of the British Crown's authority in the colonies. The postmaster, who knew Gale supported American independence, opened all the doctor's letters, copied them out, and sent the copies to William Tryon, the former royal governor of New York. The letters that described the *Turtle* and its smashing "raid" on the hulk dismayed Tryon; he forwarded the letter to Vice-Admiral Molyneux Shuldham, commander of the British fleet that was blockading Boston Harbor. Tryon warned Shuldham that this new Yankee invention could blow his ships out of the water, but Shuldham dismissed the warning as the product of an overactive imagination. The vice-admiral made no effort to arrest the Bushnells, or to find and destroy the *Turtle*. Meanwhile, David and Ezra were planning to bring their submarine to Boston where they would lift the blockade by blowing up as many British ships as possible.

The *Turtle*'s second chance

During the night of March, 3–4 1776, American troops under the command of General George Washington and General Henry Knox dragged fifty-nine cannon to the crest of Dorchester Heights above Boston Harbor. Knox had taken the cannon from Fort Ticonderoga, a major British bastion on the shores of Lake Champlain, which had been captured the previous year by Ethan Allen and his band of guerrilla fighters who called themselves the Green Mountain Boys. Using ox-drawn sleds, Knox and his men had hauled the cannon through deep winter snows to Cambridge, Massachusetts; the journey took fifty-six days, but at the end of it Washington had the artillery he needed to drive the British fleet away from Boston.

On the morning of March, 4 Vice-Admiral Shuldham and his officers awoke to find the Americans in possession of Dorchester Heights and more than four dozen cannon trained on their ships. For thirteen days the British debated their options—engage the Americans, or withdraw. Ultimately, Shuldham decided to preserve his magnificent fleet intact. On St Patrick's Day, March, 17 1776, the British fleet sailed out of Boston Harbor.

Rebels up and down the Atlantic coast rejoiced at the news—all except David Bushnell. He had planned to demonstrate the effectiveness of the *Turtle* by unleashing it on the British warships. General Washington himself would be a witness as the *Turtle* blew the finest ships in the British Navy to smithereens. Congress would order more submarines to be built, and Bushnell would become a wealthy man. Already his invention was causing excitement in government—the Connecticut Council of Safety had agreed to reimburse him for the expense of constructing the *Turtle* (unfortunately he failed to get that promise in writing).

Bushnell's disappointment was short lived. In the summer of 1776 Vice-Admiral Shuldham sailed into New York Harbor, followed by a second British fleet under the command of Admiral Richard Lord Howe. Five hundred

Sergeant Ezra Lee, in David Bushnell's Turtle, *launched an attack on the British warship HMS* Eagle *on September, 7 1776.*

British ships filled the harbor, blocking the Hudson and East Rivers; more than 32,000 British troops were encamped on Staten Island. New York City, Long Island, New Jersey and the Hudson Valley were in danger of falling into British hands. Merchant ships could not enter or leave New York; ships bearing supplies and reinforcements for the American Army in New York were also kept out. The British enforced the blockade so that even fishing boats were forbidden to pass.

The blockade gave David Bushnell a second chance to prove the effectiveness of the *Turtle*; with Ezra's help, he transported the submarine to New York City, where General Israel Putnam welcomed the brothers and identified for them their first target—the man-o'-war *Asia*, armed with sixty-four cannon.

David and Ezra arrived in New York in August; within days Ezra was stricken with typhoid fever. Rather than endure another disappointment, David called for volunteers to learn how to pilot his submarine. The men of Connecticut came to his rescue—General Samuel Parsons offered three likely young men, including a 27-year-old sergeant, Ezra Lee. David packed up the *Turtle* and took it back to Saybrook where there was virtually no risk of being followed by the British; there he gave the three volunteers a crash course in how to operate his submarine. They had been training for only a few days when news reached Bushnell that the British had defeated George Washington in Brooklyn and driven the American troops across the East River to Manhattan. The citizens of New York expected a British invasion at any moment. Unwilling to waste any time, David packed the *Turtle* and his trainees onto a ship and sailed down the Long Island Sound into the East River, to South Ferry, the southernmost tip of Manhattan Island.

The Americans were eager to strike a major blow against the British, so in consultation with General Putnam, David named as his target the HMS *Eagle*, the ship commanded by Admiral Lord Howe. To make the assault David chose Ezra Lee because, as he put it, "he appeared more expert than the rest."

The Turtle *and the* Eagle

Just after midnight Ezra Lee lowered himself into the *Turtle* and closed the hatch. Men in two whaleboats manned their oars and pulled away from South Ferry, towing the submarine between them. They headed for the British armada, strung out across the harbor at Staten Island, 5 miles from Manhattan. When they were close to the *Eagle* but still far enough away to escape detection, the oarsmen stopped; Lee opened the hatch to express his thanks and receive their wishes of good luck, and the whaleboats turned back.

David Bushnell

Lee and Bushnell believed the water was sufficiently still that he could power the *Turtle* up to the *Eagle* with no trouble; instead, the ebb tide pushed the submarine toward the Narrows, the channel that leads from New York Harbor out to the Atlantic Ocean. For hours Lee struggled with the rudder and propellers, trying to correct his course. Finally, around 4:00 in the morning, he was near the *Eagle*—he could even hear a few sailors talking on deck. Opening the lower compartment to take on water, he watched the depth gauge as he took the *Turtle* beneath the waves. It was black as night inside the compartment as Lee steered by the dim glow of the foxfire compass points. Then he heard the hatch bump against the hull of the *Eagle*. He was in position!

Lee began to drill the screw into the bottom of the warship, but the screw would not penetrate. He tried several times to pierce the underside of the *Eagle*, even moving the *Turtle* about, thinking that he had by chance struck an iron brace or bolt, but no matter where he tried, he could not drive in the screw.

Frustrated, he pumped out the water and rose to the surface. It was sunrise. Later Lee recalled:

> I hove about to try again but on further thought I gave out, knowing that as soon as it was light the ships' boats would be rowing in all directions, and I thought the best generalship was to retreat as fast as I could as I had four miles to go before passing Governors Island.

As he moved toward the tip of Manhattan, the sun struck the brass hatch. British troops on Governors Island saw the flash of light on the water; several piled into a rowboat and took off after the strange object. Eager to outrun them, Lee cut loose the 154½ pound bomb. The British troops saw it, assumed it was a floating mine, and turned back for shore; Lee reached South Ferry unharmed. As he stood at the ferry landing explaining the reason for his failure to Bushnell and General Putnam, the timer in the bomb "went off with a tremendous explosion," Lee said, "throwing up large bodies of water to an immense height."

Lee suggested that he could not pierce the hull of the *Eagle* because it was plated with copper. Bushnell rejected that explanation—copper is a soft metal, the screw could have penetrated it he argued. He attributed the failure to inexperience—Lee was "not well-skilled in the management of the vessel."

Bushnell and Putnam sent the *Turtle* out two more times, once again with Lee, then with another of the trainees. Both missions also ended in failure. By now the British were swarming over Manhattan Island. As Washington and his

93

troops were making a last stand at Fort Washington at the northern end of the island, Bushnell was loading the *Turtle* onto a sloop in preparation to escape upriver. But as he sailed north, British artillery on the shore fired on the sloop, sinking it.

The inventor survived, swam ashore, and even recovered his *Turtle*, but he never sent it on another mission, and what became of the world's first submarine remains a mystery. Nonetheless, the American government did not lose interest in submarine warfare—as late as 1787 Bushnell and Thomas Jefferson were corresponding on how to build more vessels like the *Turtle*.

In December of 1787, David Bushnell left Saybrook without telling anyone where he was going—not even his brother Ezra. No one in his hometown ever saw or heard from him again.

In 2002, Rick Brown and Laura Brown, directors of Handshouse Studio and faculty members at the Massachusetts College of Art, in collaboration with the U.S. Naval Academy, built a replica of the *Turtle*. For the sake of authenticity, the Browns and their team of builders used the same materials and processes as David Bushnell would have done, including bronze casting, blacksmithing and glass blowing. The *Turtle* itself they carved out of a single log. Early in 2003 they conducted an unmanned test in Snug Harbor, Duxbury, Massachusetts, to make certain the *Turtle* was watertight. In April 2003, they transported the *Turtle* to the U.S. Naval Academy in Annapolis, Maryland, where a member of the faculty, Professor Lew Nuchols, volunteered to operate the machine. It operated perfectly at a depth of 16½ feet.

The British fleet at anchor in Staten Island Narrows, 1776. The Turtle *would have had little chance of success against these odds.*

A very immoral act
William Congreve's rockets

SCIENTIST: William Congreve

AREAS OF SCIENCE: Chemistry and missile technology

MAIN INVENTION: Submarine

SIR WILLIAM CONGREVE (1772–1828) inherited his interest in technology from his father, Lieutenant-General Sir William Congreve. The senior Congreve focused his talents on things military, at one stage developing a method for using windmills to send military signals. While fighting against the rebels in America's war for independence, he invented a brass cannon that weighed only 3 pounds—small enough to be packed on a horse and rushed to wherever it was needed on the battlefield. He also discovered a cheaper way to make gunpowder, and it was this discovery that earned him his epitaph. "He saved his country a million of money," it reads, "but he died unenriched himself."

By the age of thirteen the younger Congreve had developed a passion for the latest invention, the hot-air balloon. In a letter to his father, young William declared himself "fully bent on going to the Moon in an aerial balloon".

In 1804, when Napoleon had swept across Europe and was threatening to invade England, William Congreve the younger, now thirty-two years old, began to think how he could contribute to the defense of his country. He began to explore the capabilities of rockets.

"Hindoo" rockets

The earliest rockets were developed in China in the thirteenth century, where they were known as "fire arrows." The Chinese used them as weapons as well as in fireworks displays. Perhaps as early as the fifteenth century

Sir William Congreve viewing the bombardment of Copenhagen in September 1807.

rockets were being used as weapons in India, where they were known as *ban* or *bana*, derived from the Sanskrit word for "arrow." The Indians discovered that rockets were especially useful for setting fire to fortresses, towns, and military supply trains.

One of the earliest descriptions of the type of rocket used by the "Hindoos" was written in 1790 by an Englishman named Quintin Crawford:

> *The rocket consists of a tube of iron, about eight inches in length, closed at one end. It is filled in the same manner as an ordinary sky-rocket, and fastened toward the end of a piece of bamboo, scarcely as thick as a walking cane, and about four feet long, which is pointed with iron. At the opposite end of the tube from the iron point ... by setting fire to the match, it goes off with great velocity. By the irregularity of its motion, it is difficult to be avoided, and sometimes acts with considerable effect, especially Amongst cavalry.*

Although some European sources make the doubtful claim that Indian rockets could travel 1½ miles, in truth they rarely reached targets 2,953 feet away. Nonetheless, Indian sultans took great pride in their rocketeers: in religious processions and parades on state occasions, the rocketeers marched closest to their sovereign.

The Indians had discovered that in battle rockets could be as effective as cannon, but were cheaper to manufacture and easier to move—the heaviest rocket weighed only 12 pounds, little more than a flintlock rifle. At the attack on the city of Seringapatam in 1799, the army of Tipu Sahib of Mysore used rockets to defend the city against the army of the British East India Company. The British captured Seringapatam and killed Tipu Sahib, but they came away impressed by the Indians' rockets. The commanders wrote to the Board of Ordnance requesting that they explore the possibility of manufacturing rockets—a request the Board passed along to the Royal Laboratory. But the gentlemen of the Royal Laboratory had no idea how to manufacture rockets that troops could carry into battle.

It was at this point that William Congreve stepped in. He began by examining the Indian rockets that had been brought home as prizes of war; these became the basis for the rockets he would design and which would bear his name.

The prince's favorite

Congreve's first attempts to build a rocket fell short of his Indian prototypes—Congreve's prototypes rarely traveled 2,132½ feet, 820 feet less than the Indian models. But by experimenting with different strengths of gunpowder as well as rocket launchers that could be adjusted to fire at different elevations, he increased the firing range of his rockets. He found that a 3 pound rocket fired at an elevation of 25 degrees would travel 5,249 feet; a 6 pound rocket did even better—just over 6,561½ feet when fired at 35 degrees of elevation. Further, Congreve added something new to his rockets—a sharp point like an arrowhead so the rocket would embed itself into whatever it hit.

As luck would have it, the Prince of Wales (the future George IV) also had an interest in science in general and rocketry in particular. Congreve wrote to the prince about his work with rockets. When they met, the prince was so impressed that he had a rocket workshop built at Woolwich, and ordered various government departments, including the Arsenal and the Royal Brass Foundry, to exert themselves to assist Congreve. The Woolwich workshop became the Western world's first rocket factory.

Congreve demonstrated his rockets in the marshes near the factory before a small, select audience that included Prime Minister William Pitt, and Minister of War Robert Stewart, Viscount Castlereagh. In addition to rockets, he also developed flat-bottomed boats that could slip quietly into harbors and serve as launching platforms for the rockets. All the demonstrations went so well that in the fall of 1805 the British government was ready to see Congreve's work in action. They ordered 3,000 rockets in two sizes, 6 and 8 pounds, as well as a dozen launchers, from the Woolwich workshop for an attack on the French city of Boulogne. But the weather did not co-operate—rough seas and high winds made it impossible to fire the rockets. Although there was nothing Congreve or anyone else could have done about the wind and the waves, he was savaged in the press. Had not the Prince Regent and the Prime Minister stood by him, his career in rocketry might have come to an inglorious end.

A second shot at Boulogne

In April 1806 Congreve had a second chance to prove the effectiveness of his rockets. With a large supply of rockets he traveled to Naples, Britain's ally against Napoleon, where he used them successfully against the French at Gaeta. These rockets were better than those he had brought to attack Boulogne—Congreve had developed a heavier model that weighed 31 pounds, was encased in iron, and had a range of an unprecedented 1986½ feet.

In October of that year Congreve had a second shot at Boulogne. Eighteen cutters, each propelled by six oarsmen, had been equipped with frames for firing his rockets. On a night blessed with calm seas, the cutters entered the harbor and began firing. Within ten minutes fires broke out around the city, within thirty minutes 200 rockets had rained down on the city itself. Reports of the battle are contradictory: the British claimed to have burned several ships as well as buildings in the town; the French claimed that there had been no fires, that the rockets were easy to extinguish. Congreve's account only further muddies the waters: he insisted that the cutters had fired 400 of his rockets. One thing is certain—after the second assault on Boulogne, the British government considered the Congreve rockets had proven themselves effective in battle.

"A very immoral act"

Napoleon's successful campaign in northern Germany and Poland had put the Danish government in an unenviable position. All of Denmark's allies were gone: Prussia had been defeated, Russia had pulled out of the war, Sweden had allied itself with Great Britain and there were rumours that the Swedes planned to seize Norway (at the time, part of the kingdom of Denmark). And of course, the French were at Denmark's southern border. Anxious that Napoleon might overrun Denmark and capture the Danish fleet, the British demanded that the Danes place their fleet in British custody for "safe-keeping."

Understandably, the Danish government hesitated. Which was worse, inviting an attack by the British or an invasion by Napoleon? As Denmark dithered, the British government sent a fleet armed with artillery and Congreve's rockets to Copenhagen. Simultaneously, Britain sent an envoy, Francis Jackson, to the Danish court—but Jackson's peremptory manner and thinly veiled threats so outraged the Danes that they resolved to fight the British rather than hand over their navy.

On September, 2 1807, without any declaration of war, the British fleet bombarded the city of Copenhagen. Amongst its weapons were Congreve rockets, fired by sixteen civilian employees of the Ordnance Department and supervised by Congreve himself. They lobbed 300 rockets into the city, setting off a terrible fire. Charles Chambers, one of the British naval officers, wrote in his journal, "[T]he night proved unusually dark and shewed off this dreadful fire to the utmost advantage … The light arising from it was so great as to enable me to read or write on the Quarterdeck of the *Prometheus* with much facility."

It was the Congreve rockets that had set off the blaze, creating an inferno in the old city that took 2,000 lives and sent such monuments as the 387 foot steeple of Our Lady's Church toppling into the devouring flames.

The use of the rockets against a civilian population horrified the Western world. Czar Alexander I declared that it was "an act of violence, the like of which history, so fertile in examples, cannot show." In America, Thomas Jefferson declared the British bombardment of Copenhagen "signalized … the total extinction of national morality." And even England's King George III condemned the bombardment as "a very immoral act." As for Congreve, the day after the fire burned out, he slipped into the city in disguise to inspect the destruction wrought by his rockets. He was satisfied with their effectiveness, while regretting the loss of life and the destruction of property.

In spite of the international expressions of horror over the destruction of Copenhagen, both sides used rockets throughout the Napoleonic Wars. Amongst the English, the use of Congreve's rockets became ubiquitous. They were used against French ships at the Battle of the Basque Roads in 1809. The Spanish and the Portuguese used them against the French in the Peninsular War of 1808–14. The British used Congreve rockets to shell Flushing in Holland in 1809, Danzig (modern-day Gdansk) in 1813 and Toulouse in 1814. On October, 16 1813, at the Battle of Liepzig, also known as the Battle of Nations, Captain Richard Bogue and the 150 men of the Royal Artillery Rocket Brigade so terrified 2,500 French infantrymen that they surrendered. Tragically, at the moment the French gave up, Bogue was killed. After the battle Czar Alexander I of Russia and King Charles XIII of Sweden conferred military orders on Bogue posthumously. The Congreve rockets were acquiring a reputation, and Congreve was awarded the honorary rank of lieutenant-colonel in 1811. He succeeded to his father's baronetcy in 1814, becoming Sir William.

The world's first weapons system

William Congreve had developed the first of what is called today a weapons system (his own terminology was very close to ours—he called it the Congreve Rocket System). Congreve's system covered everything: the different calibers of rocket and the range of each; the equipment necessary to transport and launch

Following pages: Bombardment of Copenhagen, 2nd–5th September 1807, a colored aquatint by Johann Lorenz Rugendas, showing the terrible fires caused by Congreve's rockets and the many rocket launchers.

Congreve's other inventions

Although he will always be most famous for his rocket, Sir William Congreve was an ingenious man, an inveterate tinkerer, who in his lifetime had perhaps dozens of ideas for inventions, including ...

- a rocket-powered harpoon for whalers
- unforgeable banknote paper
- a perpetual motion machine

- a clock that employed a rolling steel ball to keep time
- a timed fuse for explosives
- a hydro-pneumatic device to open and close canal locks and
- improvements in manufacturing steam engines, gunpowder, gas meters and fireworks.

the rockets; tools for repairing them; instructions for the rocket troops; and standards for mass production.

By 1814 Congreve was offering rockets in ten different calibers that could strike targets as close as 2460½ feet and as far off as 9186 feet. He offered incendiary rockets, scatter-shot rockets and explosive rockets to suit various targets—towns, ships, massed troops in the field.

The payload differed from rocket to rocket. A 6 pound rocket carried a 3 pound ball known as a shot; a 9 pound rocket carried a grenade; a 24 pound specimen carried a hollow warhead packed with 200 lead balls which, upon impact, scattered Amongst troops; and the 32 pound rocket carried an incendiary device.

Military men found that rockets had several advantages over artillery: they were lightweight; they were easy to use; and they did not recoil when fired, which made them safer than cannon and also made them suitable for anything from a battlefield, to the battlements of a town, to the deck of a warship.

Unfortunately, accuracy was an issue. Congreve observed that a rocket's trajectory dipped soon after it was fired. To compensate for this he suggested raising the firing elevation by a few degrees. This improved the rocket's performance, but because the gunpowder and firing mechanism at this time were not very powerful, a strong wind was all it took to push a rocket off course.

An inexact science

A Congreve rocket looked like a skyrocket used in fireworks. It was mounted on a light wooden guide stick about 15 feet long—an appendage which, it was hoped, would stabilize the rocket's trajectory and make it more accurate. Congreve had designed a portable A-shaped firing frame, but the rockets could also be fired simply by leaning them against a wall, a fence, the railing of ship—as long as the wall, fence or railing was high enough to achieve the proper angle.

Congreve found that increasing the amount of gunpowder in the propellant chamber made the rockets travel further. For example, 14 ounces of gunpowder propelled the rocket 2,953 feet. The rockets were ignited with a fuse, although rockets equipped with an explosive warhead had two fuses: one at the base of the rocket tube to launch it, with a second fuse lying along the exterior of the rocket, attached to the warhead. The ignition of the rocket ignited the warhead's fuse while the rocket was in flight. If all went well, the fuse would reach the warhead just before it struck its target. Unfortunately, this was not an exact science—often a rocket exploded before reaching its target.

In 1813 new rocket detachments, numbering in total 194 officers and men, were assigned to the Royal Artillery. In 1814 most British warships included Congreve rockets Amongst their weapons. That same year the Royal Navy dedicated two sloops, *Erebus* and *Galguo*, as rocket ships; Congreve supervised their refitting. During the War of 1812, which pitted Great Britain against the United States once again, *Erebus* saw action along the Atlantic coast, most famously in the harbor of Baltimore, Maryland.

The rockets' red glare

On September, 12 1814, fifteen British frigates sailed into Baltimore Harbor intent upon capturing one of America's greatest port cities. Baltimore in 1814 was the third largest city in America with a population of 50,000. It had a thriving shipbuilding industry, and was a prosperous center of international trade. By capturing Baltimore the British would strike a blow against the U.S. economy—but before they could reach the city, they must get by Fort McHenry, the island fortress that guarded the harbor.

This was a modern fort, completed in 1802; it was built of red brick in the then popular five-pointed star design which enabled defenders to rain down crossfire on attackers that approached the walls from any direction.

Fort McHenry was garrisoned with 1,000 troops led by Major George Armistead. At 6:30 in the morning of September, 13 the British warships opened fire with Congreve rockets, and mortars that fired 9 and 11½ inch bombs. The Americans, armed with artillery, returned fire, but their cannonballs fell short of the British ships. In a daring move, Vice-Admiral Sir Alexander Cochrane sailed closer to the fort, but once the ships were within range the American gunners peppered them with artillery fire until Cochrane ordered his fleet to retreat. For twenty-five hours the British kept up their bombardment, but the garrison gave no sign that it was ready to surrender.

Imprisoned aboard one of the British warships was a Maryland physician, Dr. William Beanes, who had been falsely accused of helping American troops round up British stragglers after the burning of Washington. John S. Skinner, assigned to act as an intermediary between the U.S. government and the British in the Chesapeake region, set out for Baltimore Harbor under a flag of truce to persuade the British commander that he had arrested an innocent man. Skinner had asked a Georgetown lawyer, Francis Scott Key, to accompany him and help make his case to Vice-Admiral Cochrane.

Their mission was a success, but as the battle was about to commence, Skinner, Key and Beanes were informed that they must remain aboard their truce ship, safely out of the range of fire, until the battle was over. Thus they became eyewitnesses to the bombardment of Fort McHenry.

After a night filled with the roar of artillery, the explosions of bombs and shrieking of rockets, Key feared that the fort had fallen—and that Baltimore would be taken. But as the sun rose, he saw the American flag was still flying over the fort—Major Armistead had not surrendered. Vice-Admiral Cochrane called off the attack, allowed his three American guests to depart safely, and sailed his fifteen warships out of the harbor.

That day, Key wrote a poem about the bombardment of Fort McHenry, in which he recalled "the rockets' red glare, the bombs bursting in air." The rockets that gave off the red glare were Congreve rockets. And the poem became the national anthem of the United States.

—∭—

William Congreve worked on his rockets off and on for the remainder of his life, eventually developing a rocket with a range of 2 miles. But he never succeeded in improving their accuracy. Military commanders came to use the rockets in tandem with artillery. The psychological effect of the explosive rockets was undeniable, but it was the artillery that could be relied upon to do the most damage. The Congreve rocket was replaced in the 1850s by a new rocket also designed by an Englishman, William Hale, who discovered that the trajectory could be stabilized and a rocket's accuracy improved by drilling exhaust holes in the shell casing; these caused the rocket to spiral, thereby keeping it in a straight line. The method was based on the same technology as the spiral etched into the interior of a rifle barrel.

From 1814 until his death, Congreve served as Comptroller of the Royal Laboratory of Woolwich Arsenal, as had his father before him. For the last ten years of his life he also served as a Member of Parliament. In 1821, when his first patron, the Prince Regent, was crowned George IV, Congreve paid tribute to the new king with a magnificent display of fireworks in London's Hyde Park.

Safe and nutritious
Nicolas Appert's canned goods

SCIENTIST: Nicolas Appert

AREA OF SCIENCE: Food preservation

MAIN INVENTION: Preserved food

IN 1545 THE ENGLISH GARRISON occupying the French port of Calais was called out to attack a French force that was in the area. The English men–at–arms made a very poor show: they were weak, sullen, sickly, bad-tempered. No plague had swept through the barracks; what afflicted the men was poor nutrition and intestinal disorders. After weeks of receiving no pay, the troops could no longer purchase their own fresh provisions in the Calais market and had been forced to fall back on eating the supplies in the army's storehouse.

Elis Gruffydd, a Welshman who was serving with the English, complained that "the salt beef stank when it was lifted out of the brine, the butter was of many colors and the cheese dry and hard." Complaining about spoiled food had been a full-time occupation Amongst soldiers and sailors for centuries, but when they described what was served to them at mealtimes the men did not exaggerate. Army food was disgusting, and navy food was worse.

For most of human history the methods used to preserve food were drying, salting and pickling in vinegar or brine. Under optimum conditions these methods worked reasonably well, but the armed forces, particularly the navy, rarely operated under optimum conditions. For example, barrels of hard-baked biscuits and dried peas were stored in the ship's hold where the dampness caused the dried foods to rot. Yet according to the regulations of the British Admiralty, if food went bad it must still be served to the men—cheese being the single exception, because the stench from a rotten wheel of cheese could permeate an entire ship.

Nicolas Appert (1750–1841), the French chef who invented the technique of preserving food by canning.

The trick, then, amongst sailors was to find methods to make food gone bad safe and, if possible, palatable once again. Once weevils had infested the hard tack (biscuits), the seamen would tap their share on the tabletop to dislodge the bugs. Another method was to lay the infested biscuits on a tarpaulin in the sun to drive out or kill the weevils. The biscuits could also be re-baked; in this instance the weevils would become part of the biscuit, but at least they would be dead.

To get maggots out of spoiled meat, the sailors placed a dead fish on or beside it—experience had taught them that maggots preferred fish to beef or pork.

It was the boast of the Admiralty that every seaman got a pound of meat, a pound of biscuit, and 1 gallon of ale daily—more than most poor farm families consumed in a day. Less well advertised was the condition of the food once the men were at sea.

Chef to the aristocracy

It's said that either Frederick the Great or Napoleon coined the aphorism, "An army marches on its stomach." Whoever said it, he was correct. Soldiers who suffer from poor nutrition and spoiled food do not fight well. Yet in the late eighteenth century commissary officers still could not keep the military supplied with fresh, nutritious provisions. So in 1795 the Directory, the five-man executive committee that governed France at the time, offered a prize of 12,000 francs to anyone who invented a new, effective method to keep food fresh. The man who rose to the challenge was a 45-year-old professional chef named Nicolas Appert.

Appert was born in 1750 in Châlons-sur-Marne, a small town in France's famous Champagne region. Since his father operated an inn and a brewery, Nicolas spent his childhood, as he described it, "in the pantries, the breweries, store-houses and cellars of Champagne, as well as in the shops, manufactories, and warehouses of confectioners, distilleries, and grocers." He spent his adolescence training as a cook, and at the age of twenty-two received his first important post—as chef to the Prince Palatine Christian IV. He would move on to cook for the Duke des Deux Ponts and then the Princess of Forbach.

After this successful career as chef to the aristocracy, Appert moved to Paris where he opened a confectionery store. It was while he prepared candy for his customers that he became interested in food preservation.

As a chef he knew from firsthand experience that the age-old methods of preserving food turned eating into an ordeal rather than a pleasure. Drying,

Scurvy

During their two-year circumnavigation of the globe (1519–1521), the men of Ferdinand Magellan's fleet fell ill with a strange disease. Somewhere in the Pacific Ocean they had run out of fresh food and were reduced to chewing on leather and eating the ship's rats. "As a result of this bad nourishment," one of the crew wrote, "a strange disease fell upon us. The upper and lower gums swelled so greatly as to cover the teeth."

Magellan's men were suffering from scurvy, caused by a deficiency of vitamin C. No one in the sixteenth century had the least idea that there was such a thing as vitamin C, but through trial, error and dumb luck, centuries earlier the Vikings, the Chinese, and the Dutch had discovered that scurvy could be avoided if cranberries, horseradish, sorrel, or even sauerkraut were part of the shipboard diet.

One such example of dietary serendipity occurred in 1600 when James Lancaster led the first English ships to the East Indies. In his private store of provisions—a privilege granted to ships' officers—he had bottles of lemon juice. Every day he dosed his entire crew with three spoonfuls. While the crews of the other four ships in his little fleet fell ill with scurvy, Lancaster's own crew passed the voyage virtually unscathed. The directors of the East India Company had no idea why the lemon juice had prevented scurvy, but they were impressed with the results. They ordered that all ships sailing under the company flag must carry lemon juice.

In 1747 an English surgeon, Dr. James Lind, began experimenting with possible treatments for scurvy. Working with twelve scurvy-afflicted sailors, he tried various remedies, everything from cider to diluted sulfuric acid. The men who recovered fastest were those who drank lemon and orange juice. Dr. Lind published his findings, but the Admiralty refused to implement them, arguing that it was too expensive to provision ships with fruit juice. As a result, during the French and Indian War in North America, 130,000 British sailors died of scurvy. Not until the early nineteenth century did the Admiralty finally come around and begin to include limes in the seamen's diet, which led American sailors to nickname their English colleagues "limeys."

salting and pickling stripped foods of their natural flavors, made them hard to chew and even harder to digest, and in many cases robbed them of their nutrients. Appert, for whom freshness, flavor, fragrance, and texture were essential, began a series of experiments that would result in a new method of preservation that kept food fresh and tasty.

Appert's experiments coincided with the French Revolution. From the day in 1789 when a mob attacked the Bastille, Paris became the epicenter of the uprising that all but massacred France's royal family, sent countless aristocrats to the guillotine and murdered an untold number of priests, nuns and ordinary French citizens who dared to criticize the revolution. And as if Paris were not chaotic enough, the city was beset time and again by food shortages that sent angry mobs rampaging through the streets. In 1795, to escape the turmoil and at the same time save his life—as a former servant of aristocrats, Appert could have come under suspicion as a counter-revolutionary—he gave up his store in the capital and moved to Ivry-sur-Seine, a small quiet village about 6 miles outside Paris.

"Very edible"

It was in this bucolic setting that Appert found a safe, flavorful, nutritious method of preserving food. He filled glass bottles with meat, fruits and vegetables, sealed them, then stood the bottles in a tub of hot water. The hot water bath was not unique to Appert—the English had been preserving fruit in this manner for years, and English cookbooks available in the late eighteenth century described the process. Being a chef, it is highly probable that Appert was acquainted with this process.

By plunging the jars into hot water, English cooks (and Appert, too) partially cooked the food inside, killing all the bacteria. Because the jars were sealed, no new bacteria could enter and the food remained sterile. Neither Appert nor the English cooks knew that this is what happened when they preserved food in jars and bottles, because no one at the time had any idea that bacteria existed. But having grown up Amongst the vineyards of Champagne, Appert knew that when wine was exposed to air, it spoiled; the same was true of food. The secret, then, to keeping food fresh was to seal it. And like vintners all across France, Appert would eventually use cork to seal his bottles and jars of preserved foods.

Appert had tasted everything he bottled himself, of course, and was pleased with the results. He had shared the foods with some of the villagers of Ivry-sur-Seine, who also found them an improvement over conventionally preserved foods.

In 1803 Appert sent samples to the French Navy at Brest. The bottles sat in a storeroom for three months before they were opened. Afterwards an officer sent a report of the meal to the Minister of the Navy in Paris:

The broth in the bottles was good, the broth with boiled beef in another bottle was very good as well but a little weak; the beef itself was very edible. The beans and green peas, both with and without meat, have all the freshness and flavor of freshly picked vegetables.

A second test was made during a four-month sea voyage. Appert supplied a bottled menu of eighteen different items, including partridges. When the jars were opened and the food heated and served, the officers and crew discovered that everything was as fresh as the day it had been sealed.

In the first years of the nineteenth century, with England and France at war, the French government was eager to find new ways to supply the tens of thousands of French soldiers and sailors with healthy food. Encouraged by the report from Brest, members of a government commission invited Appert to demonstrate his method. Appert raised the stakes by issuing an invitation of his own: having sealed the foods in their jars, he asked the gentlemen to return a month later to taste them. On the appointed day the commission members sat down to sample Appert's specialities. They were delighted, and filed a report urging the purchase of Appert's bottled foods, especially for the navy. They also recommended his foods for hospitals.

An overnight success

While the support of the government—and the 12,000 franc prize—pleased Appert, he was ambitious for something more. He sought the patronage of Grimod de La Reynière, a gourmand with a genius for self-promotion. His annual *Almanach des Gourmands* has been characterized by food historian Sue Shephard as "a kind of forerunner to the *Guide Michelin*." A favorable write-up in the *Almanach* could make a chef or a food supplier a wealthy man, while a bad review—and de La Reynière could be vicious—meant ruin.

In a daring move, Appert sent samples of his bottled food to de La Reynière. To his relief, the gourmand approved. "In each bottle and at little cost is a glorious sweetness," rhapsodized the gourmand, "that recalls the month of May in the heart of winter." Not only did de La Reynière approve, but he offered to become Appert's patron and help him distribute his revolutionary product to institutions and grocers' stores throughout France.

Thanks to de La Reynière's endorsement, Appert's food preservation business boomed overnight. He built a processing plant in the middle of a large fruit and

vegetable garden. Forty women tended and harvested the crops, then processed them. Meanwhile, Appert wrote a book, *The Book of All Households: or The Art of Preserving Animal and Vegetable Substances for Many Years*, in which he described how to process and preserve fifty different types of food. The book became a culinary bestseller that went through four editions.

The pirates

While Nicolas Appert was being lionized in France, across the English Channel King George III granted a patent to Peter Durand to preserve food in "vessels of glass, pottery, tin or other metals or fit materials." Durand was descended from French Huguenots who had found refuge from religious persecution in Protestant England. He was a purveyor of food and wine with clients in France as well as in England. Durand admitted that preserving food in glass vessels was an "invention communicated to me by a certain foreigner." It's uncertain whether or not Appert was that "certain foreigner."

Pirating inventions was commonplace at this time and would continue to be throughout the nineteenth century. But Durand was careful enough to alter the method so that his act of technological piracy appeared somewhat less blatant. In his patent there is mention of using steam and ovens to heat the food, but Durand introduced a serious improvement: in place of fragile glass bottles and jars, he would seal his food inside metal cans. Durand is often credited with inventing the tin can, although he did not. His cans were made of cast iron plated with tin, and instead of Appert's cork stopper, Durand soldered his cans shut with a tin-plated lid.

To get his idea into production Durand collaborated with two engineers, John Gamble and Bryan Donkin, and the owner of an ironworks, John Hall. In 1812 they opened their Preservatory, as they called it, in Bermondsey. Their biggest client was the Royal Navy, which ordered approximately twenty-four thousand cans of food annually. The Preservatory's canned vegetables virtually eradicated scurvy aboard English ships.

The American market

In 1824 Englishmen Thomas Kensett and Charles Underwood brought canned food to the United States. Kensett and his father-in-law, Ezra Daggett, opened a factory on the New York City waterfront where they canned lobster, oysters and

These Union veterans of the American Civil War (1861–1865), in the dining hall of a National Home for Disabled Volunteer Soldiers in Marion, Indiana, were largely sustained by canned foods during the hostilities.

salmon, as well as meat, fruits and vegetables. Underwood opened a factory in Boston, where he specialized in canned pickles and condiments.

Kensett, Daggett and Underwood's timing could not have been better. Since 1804, when the United States had purchased from Napoleon the vast Louisiana Territory west of the Mississippi River, wagon trains of American settlers had been moving into the new country in ever-increasing numbers. They needed food for a journey that often took months, and canned foods were ideal.

There was one problem that the inventors of canned food had not addressed—how to open the can. Initially they were broken open with a hammer and chisel. In 1850 Ezra Warner of Waterbury, Connecticut, introduced what he called a can-opener. It had a distinctly military appearance—in fact, Warner's can-opener reminded most people of a bayonet. To open the can one hammered the sharp blade into the lid; then, using a sawing motion, moved the blade around the rim of the can. The sharp knife and the sharp lid resulted in so many household accidents that it became common for shoppers to ask grocery store clerks to open the cans for them. A safe can-opener that clipped on to the rim of the can was not invented until 1870.

In 1861, when civil war broke out in the United States, the heavily industrialized North already had canned food factories in operation, and the Union Army became their biggest customer—during the four years of war American troops consumed 120 million cans of food. At the outset of the war the annual production of canned food stood at about 5 million cans; by 1865, when the Civil War ended, canning factories were churning out 30 million cans a year to meet the demand.

While Durand and his partners and Kensett, Daggett and Underwood were prospering, Nicolas Appert had fallen on hard times. His factory outside Paris had been requisitioned as an army hospital, with the result that most of his equipment was broken, stolen or lost. He had gone to England to assert his rights as the inventor of the food bottling process and demand compensation from Durand, but the English government rejected his claim.

After the restoration of the Bourbon monarchy in 1814, Appert's fortunes improved. The government of Louis XVIII formally recognized his contributions to humanity and presented him with a generous grant so he could equip a new food preservation factory. He received a new contract from the French Navy, and one of the first things he did was adopt tin-plated iron canisters for the food, although he still sold food in glass jars to grocers.

Appert continued to search for improved methods of preserving food. By the 1830s, when he was in his eighties, he had all but completely mechanized his canning factory. Before his death in 1841 at the grand old age of ninety-one, he finally handed over operation of his factory to his nephew, Raymond Chevallier-Appert.

Appert was all but forgotten after his death. The first serious revival of interest occurred not in his native France but in America, when in 1942 the Institute of Food Technologists in Chicago inaugurated the Nicolas Appert Award to recognize individuals whose work had advanced food technology. France dragged its feet until 1955, when the postal service issued a stamp in Appert's honor. In the years that followed a few busts were erected. But something as simple as marking his birthplace at Châlons-sur-Marne did not take place until 1986.

The equalizer

Samuel Colt and the revolver that won the West

SCIENTIST: Samuel Colt

AREA OF SCIENCE: Mechanical engineering

MAIN INVENTION: Repeating revolver

THE HANDBILL HAD BEEN CIRCULATING through the village of Ware, Massachusetts for a couple of days, and what it promised was irresistible. It read, "Sam'l Colt will blow a raft sky high on Ware Pond." The day the 15-year-old had chosen for the demolition was America's Independence Day, July, 4 1829, a day when fireworks of all kinds were a holiday tradition.

At the appointed hour, the villagers, many in their Sunday best in honor of the Fourth of July, walked down to the pond. There was young Colt, making some last-minute adjustments to what he described to the small crowd as an underwater mine. He had packed a box with gunpowder, attached it to the underside of the raft and pushed it out toward the center of the pond. From the box a wire wrapped inside tarred rope ran to the shore. When everything was ready, Colt sent an electrical charge down the wire. Protected by the rope, the current shot straight to the mine, detonating it with a tremendous roar. As promised, the raft blew sky high. And accompanying it was a huge geyser of pondwater and muck that soaked and befouled the spectators on shore.

Furious at having their clothes ruined, some of the men in the crowd turned on Colt. Samuel didn't try to talk his way out of trouble—he ran. As he dashed through the village he met Elisha Root, a 21-year-old mechanic; Root stood between the boy and the angry, dripping crowd until he had persuaded them to go home, put on dry clothes, and leave the boy unharmed.

Samuel Colt (1814–1862), designer and manufacturer of Colt revolvers.

That Fourth of July Samuel Colt learned the importance of precision when working with explosives. And he acquired a new friend—in later years Elisha Root would collaborate with him, supervising the construction of Colt's Patent Fire-Arms Manufacturing Company and the day-to-day operations of producing the most famous revolver in the world.

From inventor to huckster

How Samuel Colt (1814–1862) came upon the idea of a pistol with a revolving cylinder that held six bullets is open to debate. One story, immortalized in bronze at the Samuel Colt Memorial in Hartford, Connecticut, tells how Sam at the age of sixteen went to sea where, inspired by the ship's wheel or perhaps a windlass, he whittled from a block of wood the model for the revolving cylinder. Another story recounts that he got his idea from primitive repeating weapons on display at the Tower of London (his ship, the *Corvo*, had stopped in London en route to its primary destination, Calcutta). Then again, he may have heard accounts of an American inventor, Elisha Collier, who in 1813 had designed a repeating flintlock (Collier's creation failed to find a market largely because his cylinder had to be turned by hand—a feature Colt would never adopt).

When Sam, now seventeen years old, returned home to America, he borrowed money from his father to have two prototypes made of his revolver. Both were duds—one would not fire, and the other blew up. Frustrated by what he considered to be a time-wasting harebrained idea, Mr. Colt refused to squander any more money on his son's schemes. In fact, he would not even help Samuel with basic living expenses. To keep body and soul together, Sam put aside his dream of being an inventor and entrepreneur, and became a huckster.

While studying chemistry at school in Ware Sam had been introduced to nitrous oxide, popularly known as laughing gas. He acquired a supply of the gas and traveled through the United States and Canada, billing himself as the "celebrated Dr. Coult of New York, London, and Calcutta." In front of paying audiences he gave demonstrations of the wondrous properties of nitrous oxide—specifically its ability to make anyone who inhaled it act in ways that were very silly and extremely entertaining. For three years "Dr. Coult" toured with his laughing gas, but in all that time his mind remained fixed on how to produce a revolver.

Belly up

The year 1836 was a busy one for Samuel Colt. He hired a Baltimore mechanic named John Pearson to make a new model. Somehow he persuaded his father to lend him $1,000 so he could travel to England and France to acquire patents for his revolver, then he hurried back to the United States to patent his invention there. Immediately afterward he convinced a group of wealthy New York investors to put up $300,000 so he could open a factory, the Patent Fire-Arms Manufacturing Company, in Paterson, New Jersey. To attract business, he used part of the venture capital to open a sales office and showroom on Broadway in Lower Manhattan.

Colt's first revolver was a five-shooter (initially it proved too difficult to manufacture a cylinder for six bullets). Hoping for an army contract, he demonstrated his pistol at the U.S. Military Academy at West Point. Inexplicably, the representatives of the Army Ordnance Department rejected the revolver, preferring to continue arming the troops with single-shot flintlock rifles and pistols that had barely changed since the French and Indian War eighty years earlier.

The rejection was a major disappointment for Colt, but it especially irritated his New York investors, who began to ask hard questions about when they could expect a return on their $300,000. In December 1837 Colt received a letter from Colonel William S. Harney, placing an order for 100 of his guns. Harney was bogged down in the vast swamps of the Florida Everglades, trying to defeat the Seminole Indians while contending with swarms of mosquitoes, poisonous snakes and alligators. "I am … confident," the colonel wrote to Colt, "that [your guns] are the only things that will finish the *infernal war*." Even so, it took eighteen months before the Army Ordnance Department approved Harney's order. By then it was too late for the Patent Fire-Arms Manufacturing Company; unable to capture a share of the market and drowning in debt, Colt was forced to close his factory.

Orders, but no factory

On June, 8 1844, a typically blistering summer day in south-central Texas, a war party of about eighty Comanche Indians had fourteen Texas Rangers and their 27-year-old captain, John C. Hays, pinned down beside a creek near the Pedernales River. Badly outnumbered and with no hope of reinforcements—the nearest settlement, Seguin, was 50 miles away—the Rangers couldn't expect to come out of this fight alive. When the Comanches emerged from their hiding places and dared the Rangers to come out and fight in the open, the Rangers, unwilling to let such an insult pass, stood, fired their rifles, then drew their Colt five-shooters and charged. "My five-shooting pistols ... did good execution," Hays recalled later. "Had it not been for them, I doubt what the consequences would have been. I cannot recommend these arms too highly."

While the Patent Fire-Arms Manufacturing Company was still in business, one of Colt's few customers had been the Navy of the Republic of Texas (from 1836 to 1846, Texas was a sovereign nation). Colt sold approximately two thousand seven hundred pistols to the Texas Navy, and some of these had found their way to the Texas Rangers. After Hays and his Rangers had routed the Comanches with their Colt revolvers, another Texas Ranger, Captain Samuel H. Walker, wrote to Colt with an idea that would make the revolver better. "With improvements," Walker said, "I think [the Colt revolver] can be rendered the most perfect weapon in the World for light mounted troops ... The people throughout Texas are anxious to procure your pistols." What Walker had in mind was a pistol that fired .44 caliber bullets (the Colts that had been manufactured in Paterson were .34 or .36 caliber), and he wanted the cylinder to fire six shots, just as Colt had fashioned years earlier in his hand-carved wooden prototype.

Walker's letter was followed by one from General Zachary Taylor, also in Texas. He wanted 1,000 revolvers, could Mr. Colt deliver them within three months? General Taylor's request amounted to a $25,000 order, something no entrepreneur would permit to pass by. But there was a problem—Colt no longer had a factory. And so he turned to a man who did—Eli Whitney Jr., the son of the man who invented the cotton gin. Whitney manufactured army rifles in his factory in Whitneyville, Connecticut; together, he and Colt retooled some of the equipment to produce 1,000 revolvers that incorporated Walker's suggestions.

A sole proprietor

It was the automated revolving ammunition cylinder that set Colt's pistols apart from all other firearms of his day. Both rifles and pistols were still being loaded as they had been since they first appeared in fourteenth century Europe: the powder and ball were dropped down the muzzle, then tamped into place with the ramrod. An agile, experienced rifleman could load and fire perhaps three or four shots per minute. But Colt imagined a firearm that could fire six shots within seconds.

"The equalizer"

"Abe Lincoln may have freed all men," went a popular post-Civil War saying, "but Sam Colt made them equal."

After the Civil War, particularly after the completion of the transcontinental railroad in 1869, countless thousands of Americans, as well as immigrants from Mexico, Europe and Asia, poured into the American West. It was wild country, populated not only by hostile Indians, but also by all manner of outlaws and desperadoes. Firearms were essential for self-defense, and by far the favorite sidearm was the Colt revolver. Powerful and easy to use, it became known as "the Equalizer" and, perhaps ironically, "the Peacemaker." The model most Westerners considered indispensable was the SAA, or Single Action Army revolver, a .45 caliber pistol with a 7½ inch barrel. In 1873 it became standard issue for U.S. troops stationed in the West. Captain John R. Edie, who tested the SAA for the U.S. Ordnance Board, concluded, "This pistol, for efficiency, safety, simplicity, and lightness, is far in advance of any military pistol that has yet appeared." In addition to being the preferred sidearm for the troopers, the SAA was also popular with civilians. Although somewhat smaller than the version favored by the Texas Rangers thirty years earlier, mechanically the SAA was the same pistol that Colt had developed based on Captain Walker's suggestions.

General George Armstrong Custer carried his Colt pistols into the Battle of the Little Bighorn. Theodore Roosevelt, who for a couple of years tried his hand at ranching in North Dakota, ordered a special pair of Colt revolvers with ivory grips engraved with his initials. Legendary gunslingers such as Bat Masterson, Wyatt Earp and Wild Bill Hickok all carried Colts. So did Jesse James, the Dalton Gang, Billy the Kid and the man who shot the Kid, Pat Garrett. Indian police who patrolled the tribal reservations were also armed with Colts. And of course all the cowboys in Buffalo Bill's Wild West Show carried Colts (in this case, firing blanks). In the 1870s and 1880s, Colt sold approximately forty thousand revolvers—average price, $14. It became known as "the gun that won the West".

For dudes, Colt's made fancy versions with ebony, horn or mother-of-pearl grips. They embellished the revolvers with images of grizzly bears, bighorn sheep, the Goddess of Liberty, even bar-room nudes—whatever the customer wanted. The company also branched out into other types of firearms, from easy-to-conceal derringers to shotguns to Gatling guns—the first successful machine-gun.

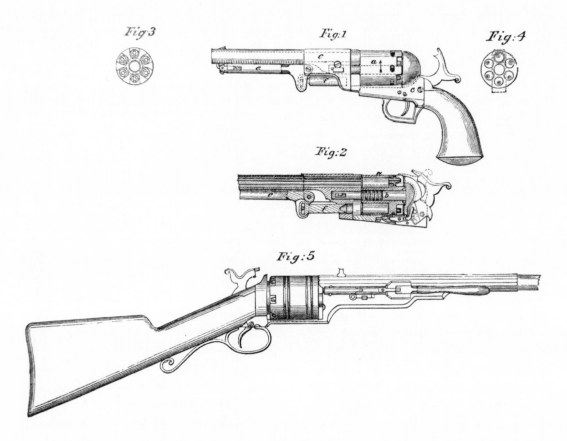

*Cutaway illustrations
of handguns designed
by Samuel Colt.*

The essential mechanism in the Colt revolver was a ratchet that ran through the center of the cylinder; each time the pistol was fired, the ratchet turned the cylinder counter-clockwise, lining up the next chamber. Whoever was armed with a Colt could fire five shots (and very soon, six) in succession before having to reload. Furthermore, Colt's pistols were compact. The revolvers the Texas Rangers carried in the 1840s had 9 inch rifled barrels and weighed about 4½ pounds.

It took six months instead of three to fill the order from General Taylor, and by the time the guns arrived a war had broken out between the United States and Mexico. As a token of his appreciation, Colt made a point of sending a pair of what he called the "Walker revolver" to Captain Walker; tragically, four days after he received the guns, Captain Walker was killed leading a charge at Huamantla in Mexico.

Like the Texas Rangers, the officers and fighting men in Mexico recognized the superiority of the Colt weapons immediately. More orders followed, enough to convince a group of businessmen in Hartford, Connecticut, to lend Colt $5000 so he could open a small factory in their hometown. Colt set himself up as the sole proprietor of this new factory; after his experience in New York, he was through with meddling investors. Writing to a friend he declared:

> [I] have sole control and management of my business and intend to keep
> it as long as I live without being subject to the whims of a pack of dam
> [sic] fools and knaves styling themselves [as] a board of directors …
> My arms sustain a high reputation Amongst men of brains in Mexico
> and now … is the time to make money out of them.

The man he placed in charge of overseeing the construction of the Colt factory and of the machinery within it was his old protector from his boyhood days in Ware, Elisha Root. Colt paid Root $5000 per year—an astronomical sum for the time. But Root was worth it. He had a genius for mechanics and a gift for managing employees. While Root ran the factory, Colt drummed up sales.

Since his business had been jump-started thanks to the good opinion of the Texas Rangers Hays and Walker, and the order from General Taylor, Colt again cultivated the U.S. military. He hired influential officers to promote his pistols amongst military men as well as in Congress, himself targeting state governors, persuading them to arm their militias with Colt revolvers. In spite of the effort expended by Colt and his agents to acquire government contracts, throughout the late 1840s the greatest demand for Colt revolvers came from private individuals. The California Gold Rush of 1849 saw a steep increase in sales as the would-be gold miners purchased Colts before heading west.

In 1849, ready to capitalize on his European patents, Colt traveled to England where he ingratiated himself with influential members of the British government by presenting them with beautifully embellished Colt pistols. In 1851, at the Crystal Palace Exposition, Colt acquired exhibition space where he displayed 500 of his revolvers; as he expounded on the advantages of his revolver, servants served brandy to Colt's visitors.

In 1853 Colt opened a factory in London, thus becoming the first American manufacturer to open a European office. He secured a government contract; between 1853 and 1857 his factory turned out 200,000 revolvers that were used by British troops in the Crimean War. Meanwhile, back in Hartford, Elisha Root had built a new factory, the Colt Armory, where 150 guns were produced every day. Selling price: $24.

New England in the 1850s was the heart of the new precision machine-tool industry. Colt and Root took advantage of this innovation, insisting that the revolvers be comprised of interchangeable parts. Previously, guns had been made by hand, a slow process that left a wide margin for error and required a broken or damaged firearm to be left for a long period with a gunsmith whose repair work had to be handcrafted.

Colt's machine-made revolvers not only were produced more quickly, but also were of very high quality and identical (assuming the manufacturing machinery was properly calibrated). If anything on a Colt pistol broke down, the owner simply went to a Colt dealer who would replace the defective part with a component he had in stock from the Armory.

Arming both sides

Samuel Colt was an ardent Democrat. During the election of 1860, even with the United States teetering on the brink of civil war, he stuck to his party and voted against the Republican candidate, Abraham Lincoln. At polls set up inside the Armory, Colt stood over the ballot boxes to make sure his employees voted Democratic, too.

As the Southern states seceded from the Union, their representatives placed orders for Colt revolvers—and Colt filled them without a qualm of conscience. He continued shipping his revolvers—hundreds of them—to the Confederacy into the summer of 1861. Only after the Battle of Bull Run in July 1861 did he finally suspend his contracts with the South: after such a major battle it became too risky for a Northern armaments firm to supply the rebels.

But Colt also had contracts from the Union. "Run the Armory night and day with double sets of hands," he instructed his foremen. "I had rather have an accumulation of arms than to have money lying idle." Employing nearly 1,000 men, Colt manufactured and sold almost one hundred and fifty thousand revolvers for the U.S. military before a disastrous fire in 1864 destroyed the Armory, putting the company out of business during the last year of the war. Colt did not live to see the disaster—he had died suddenly in 1862 at the age of only forty-seven. He left his wife, Elizabeth, and their three-year-old son, Caldwell, a fortune of $15 million (roughly the equivalent of $300 million today).

An American legend

In the twentieth century the renamed Colt's Manufacturing Company continued to receive large government contracts: during World War I and World War II the Colt pistol was again the military's standard sidearm. The company delivered approximately 2.5 million .45 caliber pistols to the U.S. military and, following the tradition set by Samuel Colt in the 1840s, offered comparable weapons for sale on the civilian market. The company was so successful that even during the Great Depression of the 1930s, Colt's paid dividends to its investors.

In 1986, to celebrate its 150th anniversary, Colt's produced reproductions of its most popular revolver of the nineteenth century, the SAA.

Colt's survives today, manufacturing M-4, M-16, M-16A1 and other weapons for the U.S. military. But the greatest achievement of the company and its founder was to create a firearm that is so closely intertwined with American history, so identified with the settlement of the West, that it has become more than a well-made firearm. It has become an American legend.

The merchant of death
Alfred Nobel and dynamite

SCIENTIST: Alfred Nobel

AREA OF SCIENCE: Chemistry

MAIN INVENTION: Dynamite

SATURDAY SEPTEMBER, 3 1864 was a warm, sunny fall day. At Heleneborg, the estate outside Stockholm that the Nobel family was using as a laboratory and factory, 21-year-old Emil, the youngest of the Nobel children, was working in the yard with his friend Carl Hertzman mixing up a batch of nitroglycerin to fill an order from the Ammeberg and Northern Railways. Nitroglycerin was a mixture of gunpowder and glycerin that created an explosive more powerful than anything else available in the mid-nineteenth century. There was already a substantial supply on hand in the old coach house that the Nobels used as a storage facility—251½ pounds of it, in fact.

The Nobels' neighbors worried about having an explosives factory in the vicinity, but Emil's older brother Alfred and his father, Immanuel, assured everyone that there was nothing dangerous about the experiments they conducted.

Suddenly the inhabitants of Stockholm heard a tremendous roar, and saw a huge yellow flame erupt into the sky over Heleneborg. House and shop windows on Kungsholm Island in the harbor shattered and peddlers' carts in Munkbron Square toppled over from the force of the explosion.

The first witnesses to reach the estate were horrified by what they saw. A Stockholm newspaper reported:

> There was nothing left of the [Nobel] factory … Most ghastly was the sight of the mutilated corpses strewn on the ground. Not only had the clothes been torn off but on some the head was missing and the flesh

Studio portrait, c. 1893, of Alfred Nobel, the inventor of dynamite, a few years before his sudden death at the age of sixty-three.

ripped off the bones … Mr [Immanuel] Nobel was not himself present, but one of his sons is said to be Amongst the victims, and another son sustained major head injuries.

Amongst the dead were Emil Nobel and his friend Hertzman; Herman Nord, a 13-year-old boy who worked at the lab; Maria Nordqvist, the family's 19-year-old housekeeper; and a carpenter named Nyman, who happened to be walking past when Heleneborg blew up. Alfred Nobel had been working in one of the labs; the impact of the blast threw him to the floor, and flying shards of glass and splinters of wood lacerated his face and head.

Physically, Alfred Nobel recovered from his wounds. Emotionally, he was permanently scarred by the memory of that day. One of his inventions had taken the lives of five innocents, including that of his much-loved youngest brother. For the rest of his life he refused to speak of the tragedy. But he was not about to abandon his experiments with high explosives, either.

The frightened inventor

The Nobels' father, Immanuel, came from a family so poor they could not afford to send him to school. His father had taught the boy to read and write, and whatever else he knew Immanuel learned on his own. He was an extremely intelligent child, and as he grew his thirst for knowledge only increased. Science and engineering fascinated him, and he was also an avid reader of French and English literature.

Just as keen as Immanuel's desire for an education was his determination to escape poverty. He started up a construction company in Stockholm, but it failed. In 1837, when no one in Sweden would lend him money to start a new business, Immanuel moved to Russia, where in St. Petersburg he established a firm that manufactured military equipment for the army. His second son Alfred was three years old when his father went away. It took five years of endless work and struggle before Immanuel felt convinced that his business was sufficiently well established that he could send for his wife Andriette and their children Robert, Ludvig, Alfred and Emil to join him.

Amongst other things, Immanuel's company manufactured floating mines, also known as torpedoes, which the Russian high command bought in large numbers during the Crimean War (1853–1856). Robert Nobel laid the mines throughout the Gulf of Finland in a manner so ingenious—not to mention potentially deadly—that no British warship would risk entering.

In Russia, Immanuel became a success. He paid off his debts in Sweden, and even had cash to spare so he could help his poor relatives. Most important to him, he had the money to give his sons a formal education. It was at the Technical Institute of St. Petersburg that young Alfred Nobel learned about a yellowish oil called nitroglycerin, discovered in 1846 when the Italian chemist Ascanio Sobrero mixed nitric acid, sulfuric acid and glycerol. Later, when he moved to Paris to study chemistry under Théophile-Jules Pelouze, Alfred Nobel and Ascanio Sobrero worked together in the same laboratory.

Sobrero's discovery had frightened him. The explosive power of nitroglycerin seemed to him devastating and uncontrollable. "One drop [of nitroglycerin] heated on platinoid metal ignites and burns violently," he wrote. "Under certain circumstances, it may detonate with enormous violence." He was experimenting with a tiny quantity in a test tube when it exploded; the injuries he suffered left his face badly scarred.

Sobrero was not the only chemist studying nitroglycerin—his teacher Pelouze had worked with it; so had Nobel's teacher in St. Petersburg, Nikolai Zinin; and years earlier a Swedish chemist, Carl Wilhelm Scheele, had laid the groundwork for its development. One problem that perplexed all these chemists, including Sobrero, was developing a method that would ignite nitroglycerin consistently. Alfred Nobel solved that riddle with a small charge of gunpowder and a fuse. The burning fuse lit the gunpowder, which caused the nitroglycerin to explode. It was a simple, elegant solution that irritated many of his colleagues. Even more irritating, especially to Ascanio Sobrero, was Nobel's grasp of nitroglycerin's potential in the marketplace.

In later years Nobel tried to remain on friendly terms with Sobrero, who became increasing embittered that Nobel had found a practical use for his discovery. On several occasions Sobrero complained publicly that Nobel was acting as if he had been the discoverer. In fact, Nobel was inconsistent on this matter: if a single individual or even an entire audience believed he invented nitroglycerin, he rarely corrected them.

"Terrible havoc"

Atmospheric pressure is an easy way to understand the power of nitroglycerin. The normal atmospheric pressure we experience at sea level is measured at 1 atmosphere. An explosion of gunpowder is measured at 6,000 atmospheres. And a detonation of nitroglycerin is measured at 275,000 atmospheres.

No previous man-made substance ever had such explosive power—no wonder it scared Ascanio Sobrero. And to make matters worse, nitroglycerin seemed impossible to control.

Gunpowder is useful in cannon and firearms because its thrust is linear. The force of nitroglycerin, on the other hand, explodes in every direction. Nitroglycerin could never be used in a weapon because, as the chemist and historian G.I. Brown has observed, the "intensity of the blast would shatter the gun barrel instead of ejecting the cannonball or shell."

Even without Nobel's gunpowder charge, nitroglycerin was a volatile, unpredictable explosive that caused terrible accidents. In 1865 a German salesman forgot a sample case full of nitroglycerin in a New York hotel. When a guest noticed that the case was giving off smoke, an obliging hotel porter hauled it outside where it exploded, injuring nineteen people, blowing out all the windows of the hotel and the neighboring houses, and creating a 5 foot deep crater in the street.

In 1866 in Sydney, Australia, two cases of nitroglycerin leveled an entire complex of warehouses and killed a dozen men. A steamship carrying a cargo of nitroglycerin exploded as it sat at a dock in Panama: forty-seven people were killed. In San Francisco, nitroglycerin reduced the granite Wells Fargo building to rubble, killing ten people. The *San Francisco Chronicle* reported, "The explosion was so powerful as to shake the earth like an earthquake for a circuit of a quarter of a mile." Remains of the victims were found two blocks away. And in Kruemmel, Germany, Nobel's own factory was destroyed in an explosion.

The disasters frightened people across the globe. In 1869, with the passage of the *Nitroglycerin Act*, the explosive was banned from England. France and Belgium followed suit. So did the state of California. Sweden, Nobel's homeland, did not ban the substance, but did outlaw transporting it through the country. Railroad and shipping companies refused to carry it, and longshoremen refused to load or unload it.

"When I think of all the victims killed during nitroglycerine explosions," Ascanio Sobrero wrote, "and the terrible havoc that has been wreaked, which in all probability will continue to occur in the future, I am almost ashamed to be its discoverer."

In spite of these tragedies, nitroglycerin, or blasting oil as it came to be called in popular parlance, had its uses. In western Massachusetts, for example, construction of the Hoosac railway tunnel near North Adams had dragged on for twenty years, with the work crews averaging about 79 feet a month—

gunpowder was not getting the job done. Then, in 1868, George M. Mowbray, a North Adams chemist, began making nitroglycerin at the construction site. The new explosive blasted out so much more rock and earth than gunpowder that the work crews were soon averaging 157½ feet a month. In 1875, the 5 mile tunnel was at last completed, thanks to nitroglycerin.

The birth of dynamite

That nitroglycerin was a powerful explosive no one doubted; the trouble was trying to harness it, to tame it so it could be used safely. George Mowbray had found that freezing it made it less volatile. Alfred Nobel was aware of this, too, but it was not an ideal solution—before it could be used the frozen nitroglycerin had to be melted back to its liquid state, and exposing it to a flame was hazardous.

Nobel believed there must be some substance that could be mixed with nitroglycerin to stabilize it, making it safe to transport and to store. Since nitroglycerin is a liquid, he experimented with porous substances—sawdust, cement, charcoal. Some of these mediums failed to absorb the nitroglycerin; others had a good absorption rate, but reduced the explosive power.

One day in 1867 he tried a substance that was lying about in his laboratory— *kieselguhr* (diatomaceous earth)—a soft, white, clay-like substance composed of the fossils of tiny plants known as diatoms. He had been using the diatomaceous earth as packing material to keep containers of nitroglycerin from bouncing against each other. Now he dumped a handful of the stuff on his worktable, and poured a little nitroglycerin over it. The diatomaceous earth absorbed the liquid beautifully, taking on the consistency of putty, which made it extremely easy to shape.

Nobel rolled the mixture into a stick and used a blasting cap of mercury fulminate to set it off. It caused a powerful explosion, twenty times more powerful than gunpowder.

Next, he tested the mixture's safety—setting it on fire, striking it with a hammer, throwing it against a wall. Luckily for Nobel, nothing caused it to explode except a detonated blasting cap.

Nobel named his new product "Nobel's Safety Blasting Powder." Then he gave a shorter name—dynamite, derived from the Greek *dynamikos*, "power."

Engineers and construction crews who did not want to be anywhere near nitroglycerin were skeptical, not to mention nervous, when Alfred Nobel and his brother Robert began making sales calls to tout the new explosive.

The brothers arranged demonstrations in mines and quarries, and once the skeptics saw dynamite in action, they were astonished: the sticks of dynamite were lightweight, easy to transport, safe to use, yet still packed the explosive wallop of nitroglycerin.

Dynamite comes to France

As much a businessman as he was a scientist, Nobel busied himself selling his new product, but he encountered many obstacles. In France, the government held a monopoly on gunpowder. Dynamite was not gunpowder, but the gunpowder manufacturers persuaded Emperor Napoleon III's government to declare that all explosives must be approved by L'Administration des Poudres et Salpêtres. The bureaucrats reviewed dynamite, then banned it.

Germany, on the other hand, welcomed dynamite, permitting Nobel to rebuild his plant at Kruemmel and manufacture dynamite there. The German government even became one of Nobel's customers.

Then, in 1870, came the Franco-Prussian War, during which France and her emperor suffered a cruel series of shocks and humiliations. Six weeks into the war, at Sedan in eastern France, the Prussian army completely surrounded Napoleon III and his army, forcing the emperor to surrender. As the Prussians drove further into France, the French military learned, to its horror, that the Germans had dynamite and were using it to blow up forts and bridges. With no French army to stop them, the Prussians pressed on to Paris and laid siege to the city.

With the capture of Napoleon III, the imperial government fell and the influential 32-year-old statesman, Léon Gambetta, formed a new government. But as the Germans were certain to capture Paris, Gambetta could not afford to remain in the capital. He escaped in a hot-air balloon to Tours where he established the Third Republic and rallied France to resist the invaders. And he invited Paul François Barbe, Nobel's agent in France, to open a dynamite factory as quickly as possible. Sadly, French resistance at this stage of the war was a hopeless enterprise—the Prussians won, and forced the government of the Third Republic to surrender to Germany the provinces of Alsace and Lorraine.

As for Barbe's dynamite, some of it found its way into the wrong hands. For a short time during the war Paris had been taken over by the Commune, a group of political and social radicals. The Commune acquired a quantity of dynamite

The apparatus used to make nitroglycerin in the late nineteenth century. The apparent lack of safety measures would be unthinkable today.

with which they destroyed monuments to the monarchy, such as the column in the Place Vendôme. They also used it to blow up their political opponents. With these horrors fresh in their minds, the French legislature outlawed dynamite, and Barbe was compelled to close his factory.

Paying an old debt

Nobel also found that breaking into the British market was a challenge. The terms of the *Nitroglycerin Act* were sweeping: it outlawed "the manufacture, import, sale and transport of nitroglycerin and any substance containing it." That last phrase barred dynamite from England, but Nobel was persistent. He convinced the Home Secretary, Henry Bruce, that dynamite was safe, with the result that Bruce issued a license permitting the importation and manufacture of "such high explosive compounds as were proven to be safe." In the end, Nobel's efforts were stymied by Sir Frederick Abel, chief chemist of the War Department; Abel was experimenting with a nitroglycerin substitute, and he did not want any competition. To keep his prospective monopoly intact, Abel convinced the London financiers not to loan Nobel the money to build a factory in England.

Undeterred, Nobel moved on to Scotland, where in 1871 he received permission to establish a factory at Ardeer, on a barren stretch of coast in Ayrshire. The Ardeer factory became one of the most productive in Nobel's industrial empire. Within four years the value of its stock had increased in value tenfold, and it was producing 10 percent of the world's supply of dynamite, shipping most of it to markets in South Africa, East Asia and Australia.

In 1873 Nobel opened his first factory in Italy, at Avigliana outside Turin. He appointed Ascanio Sobrero adviser, a post the frustrated inventor held until his death in 1888.

Dynamite pirates

Nobel had taken the precaution of obtaining a patent for dynamite from the U.S. Patent Office, and in 1868 had licensed the Giant Powder Company in California to manufacture it. American gunpowder manufacturers, like their colleagues elsewhere in the world, realized that dynamite could destroy their business, and so some American gunpowder companies developed their own brand of "exploding powder."

The Nobel Prizes

In March 1888 Alfred Nobel's brother Robert died. Opening up a French newspaper, Alfred saw that the obituary writer had confused his Nobels and written a death notice for Alfred under the headline, "The Merchant of Death is Dead." Deeply disturbed by the idea that he would be remembered only for the destructive capacity of dynamite, Nobel began to consider how he could enhance his reputation after his death.

On November, 27 1895, a little more than a year before his death, Nobel signed his will. In it he left $9 million for the establishment of a foundation that would award annual prizes to individuals who had advanced the sciences of chemistry, physics and medicine, made a significant contribution to the field of literature, and "to the person who shall have done the most or the best work for fraternity between nations, for the abolition or reduction of standing armies and for the holding and promotion of peace congresses."

The first Nobel Prizes were awarded in 1901. Amongst the Nobel Laureates since then have been Marie Curie, Guglielmo Marconi, Albert Einstein, Niels Bohr, Enrico Fermi, Rudyard Kipling, William Butler Yeats, Thomas Mann, Pearl S. Buck, Ernest Hemingway, Boris Pasternak, Martin Luther King Jr., Mother Teresa, Lech Walesa and Archbishop Desmond Tutu.

In 1874 the California Powder Works introduced to the market a high explosive called Hercules Powder. The du Pont family, since 1802 one of the leading manufacturers of gunpowder in America, got into the game with their Atlas Powder. Lammot du Pont, who founded the Atlas Powder factory in Gibbstown, New Jersey, made a faux pas at the groundbreaking ceremony when he declared, "This will one day be the largest dynamite plant in America." Nobel's American competitors were generally careful not to refer to their products as "dynamite," for fear of being taken to court for patent infringement. Hence they sold their sticks of exploding powder under such names as Hercules Powder, Atlas Powder, Ajax Powder, as well as Rend Rock, Vigorite and Nitroleum.

Du Pont's prediction appeared to be accurate: in 1880 the Gibbstown plant produced 228 tons of Atlas Powder; in 1881 production rose to 1,372 tons. Nobel, of course, was livid. He sued the men who had pirated his invention, but all his efforts to protect his interests in the United States proved futile.

In 1885 he gave up all patent infringement cases, vowing never to set foot in America again. And he kept that vow.

By then Lammot du Pont was dead. On March, 18 1884, a worker at the Gibbstown plant noticed smoke rising from a vat of nitroglycerin. The established procedure in such a contingency was to drain the nitroglycerin into a vat of cold water, but the workman panicked and went running for help instead. Du Pont and an associate rushed to the plant, arriving just as the nitroglycerin exploded. Both men were killed instantly.

A multitude of uses

In the 1870s Nobel built fourteen dynamite factories across Europe, where production rose from 11 tons per year to 5,000 tons. Across the globe, engineers found new uses for dynamite. It blasted out tunnels in the gold and diamond mines of South Africa. Dynamite "dug" the Suez Canal, the Corinth Canal and the Panama Canal. It cleared treacherous passages in the Danube and at Hellgate on New York's East River. The sculptor Gutzon Borglum used dynamite to rough out his monumental portraits of U.S. presidents on Mount Rushmore.

Dynamite was also extremely useful for mundane but previously labor-intensive tasks. Lumberjacks used it to clear log jams. Farmers used it to clear tree stumps and rocks from their fields. Dynamite made it easier to lay railways through mountains, and enabled miners to reach rich deposits of gold and silver, copper, lead and zinc that lay buried deep in the earth. Dynamite excavated the foundations for skyscrapers, and demolished old buildings so new ones could be erected on the same site. And for more than a century dynamite has been a favorite tool of robbers, who use it to blow open the doors of bank vaults.

"I write a few lines with effort"

Dynamite made Alfred Nobel a wealthy man. In 1891 he bought a villa in San Remo on the Italian Riviera. It was a splendid house, built in the eighteenth century in an exotic blend of Moorish and Venetian styles, with extensive grounds that ran down to the sea. He retired there at the age of fifty-eight—but only up to a point, building a laboratory near the villa where he invented a new type of varnish and found the formula for artificial silk. And he kept testing explosives— a habit which caused his neighbors to complain about the noise, not to mention the shock of having the peace of this resort suddenly shattered.

On December, 7 1896, Nobel wrote to his friend Ragnar Sohlman, "Unfortunately my health is again so poor that I write a few lines with effort." An hour later he suffered a stroke. The man who had spoken several languages suddenly was almost mute, unable to communicate with his Italian servants or the Italian physician who attended him. Finally he managed to get out the word "telegram" in Swedish. His manservant, Auguste Oswald, understood and wired Nobel's two nephews and Sohlman. By the time they arrived in San Remo, Alfred Nobel was dead. He was sixty-three years old.

Making armies obsolete
Richard Gatling's machine-gun

SCIENTIST: Richard Gatling

AREA OF SCIENCE: Mechanical engineering

MAIN INVENTION: Machine-gun

IN 1864 AN ECSTATIC DR. RICHARD GATLING of Indiana wrote to a friend: "Ben Butler took the guns … to the Battle of Petersburg and fired them himself upon the rebels. They created great consternation and slaughter, and the news of them went all over the world."

Gatling's excitement was understandable; for a year he had been trying to interest the U.S. Army in purchasing his machine-gun for use against the Confederate rebels. But by 1863, army officers as well as officials of the federal government in Washington, DC had had their fill of attending demonstrations of new weapons that eager inventors claimed would markedly increase Confederate casualties and bring a swift end to America's civil war.

Dr Gatling may have been unaware of the army and the government's disenchantment with new "wonder weapons." In any case, in 1863 he sent his entire stock of machine-guns—all thirteen of them—to Baltimore, assuming that his agent there would have no trouble getting an order from the military. The officers who purchased weapons showed no interest in Gatling's gun. But another officer did. General Benjamin Butler, fascinated by any new development in military technology, by chance was in Baltimore at the same time as Gatling's agent. After testing the guns, General Butler used his own money to buy twelve of the thirteen (they were priced at $1,000 apiece). The thirteenth was purchased by Admiral David Dixon Porter, who planned to mount it on the deck of one of his ships that patrolled rivers in the Southern states.

Richard Gatling (1818–1903), American inventor of the first successful machine-gun. Gatling believed that his machine-gun would "supersede the necessity of large armies, and consequently, exposure to battle and disease [would thus be] greatly diminished."

141

In spring 1864 Butler led 30,000 men to Petersburg, Virginia, a railroad hub a few miles south of Richmond, the Confederate capital. Union General Ulysses S. Grant was determined to take the town and the five railway lines that ran into it. Confederate General Robert E. Lee was equally determined to hold the site. The battle settled into a siege that lasted ten months, during which time the North lost 42,000 men and the South 28,000 men.

On or about May, 30 1864, General Butler rolled one of his Gatling guns up to a battery. Across a desolate stretch of ground rose Confederate earthworks, with Rebel soldiers strolling across the top, occasionally calling out to the Yankees hunkered down in their rifle pits. Without warning, General Butler began turning the crank that operated the gun, instantly releasing a deadly spray of bullets, 200 per minute, at the unsuspecting Confederates. This was the first time a Gatling gun was used in combat, and contrary to Gatling's account it did not create "great consternation" Amongst the Rebels—it made them hopping mad. Leaping down behind their earthworks, the Confederates replied with a barrage of artillery that, according to an eyewitness, Lieutenant J.B. Morris of the 4th New Jersey Battery, severely wounded a captain and a private.

Innocent beginnings

Richard Jordan Gatling was born in 1818 in Hertford County, North Carolina. His family owned a cotton plantation of 1200 acres. Some of his twelve slaves worked as house servants, the rest toiled in the fields. But the Gatlings weren't just planters, they were also inventors. Richard's father, Jordan, invented a rotary cultivator and a device that thinned cotton; his brother James tinkered with building a flying machine. As for Richard, by the time of his death in 1903 he would have to his credit nearly fifty patents for such inventions as a steam plough, a flushing apparatus for water closets (as indoor toilets were known at the time), and of course a machine-gun, better known as the Gatling gun.

Gatling received his first patent in 1844 for a seed-planter. For millennia, farmers had walked through their fields scattering seeds over the tilled ground in a long sweeping motion that looked picturesque but was terribly wasteful of seed. Gatling's device was precise and economical: it consisted of a metal hopper or bin mounted on a cart that wheeled across a newly tilled field. As it moved, a roller turned, dropping down one seed at a time into several furrows. Eighteen years later Gatling would apply the same principle to his gun, but in this case it was not a seed that dropped into soil but a bullet that dropped into a chamber.

Batteries and coffee mills

The quest for a weapon that did not require reloading each time it was fired was centuries old, going back at least as far as the fourth century BC in China. But while the Chinese would have been content with a rapid-fire, repeating crossbow, the military of Gatling's generation wanted a repeating firearm.

One of the first machine-guns was invented by a dentist in Rochester, New York. Before he studied dentistry, Dr. Josephus Requa had served as an apprentice to the renowned gunsmith William Billinghurst. Requa imagined a gun consisting of twenty-five barrels; lacking the confidence to build such a weapon himself, he asked Billinghurst to fashion the prototype. Billinghurst lined up the barrels side by side, like a pipe organ. To fire the gun—known as the Requa Battery—the gunner pulled on a lanyard (cord) and the barrels fired in such rapid sequence that to some observers all twenty-five barrels appeared to shoot simultaneously. During a demonstration in 1861, utilizing a crew of three, the Requa Battery was reloaded and fired seven times a minute, an impressive 175 shots in sixty seconds.

A fellow resident of Rochester, Captain Albert G. Mack, could not wait to get Dr. Requa's gun into battle. In 1862 he raised the 18th Independent Battery, New York Light Artillery, promising that the men of the 18th—almost all of whom were from Rochester—would be equipped with the Rochester machine-gun. Several Requa Batteries went with the 18th when they moved south to fight in Louisiana and Alabama, but whoever had been responsible for assembling the equipment failed to send ammunition.

Other regiments had more luck. The 3rd New Hampshire, 39th Illinois and 9th Maine infantry regiments used Requa guns in South Carolina. They were also used at the battle of Fort Wagner where the famous African-American regiment, the 54th Massachusetts, took so many casualties.

Another machine-gun, known as the "Coffee Mill," was invented in 1861, but the person responsible for its creation is a matter of debate. Wilson Ager, an inventor of farm machinery, is usually given the credit, but Joseph G. Bilby, an expert in firearms of the Civil War era, believes the actual inventor was a man named J.D. Mills who, in addition to his gifts as a tinkerer, was a colorful salesman. Somehow Mills persuaded President Abraham Lincoln to attend a demonstration of his machine-gun at the Washington Arsenal.

Mills' weapon was a wooden box set on wheels with a single gun barrel protruding from one end. On top of the box was a hopper full of cartridges. According to a story that may or may not be apocryphal, Lincoln took one look at the machine and called it the "Coffee Mill," a name that stuck. Then Mills went into his sales pitch. What he was offering the president, he said, was "an army in a box." When he operated the Coffee Mill, it fired 120 bullets in sixty seconds. Lincoln was sold, and ordered the Ordnance Department to purchase ten of them. In December 1861 the order was increased to fifty.

Some of Mills' guns were installed in the defensive works around Washington that protected the Yankee capital from a possible Confederate assault. In January 1862 two were assigned to the 28th Pennsylvania Volunteer Infantry on campaign in Virginia. Sadly, by this time the Army had discovered that the mainspring of the gun tended to break. After using the Coffee Mills in combat, Colonel John W. Geary of the 28th Pennsylvania complained that they were "inefficient, and unsafe to use."

Major General John C. Frémont ordered sixteen Coffee Mills that he planned to take along on his raids through Virginia's Shenandoah Valley. The guns happened to be stored at the arsenal in Harpers Ferry when Confederate General Thomas "Stonewall" Jackson captured the town. He carried off the Coffee Mills, at which point they vanish from the historical record. There is no indication that Mills' machine-gun was ever used by the Confederacy.

In addition to a weak mainspring the Coffee Mill had other problems. Paper cartridges that worked without any trouble in rifles caught fire inside it. If the gun became overheated through constant firing, the velocity of the bullets decreased. Ordnance officer Colonel Charles Kingsbury reported to Major General George McClellan that the Coffee Mill's performance in battle was "not equal to the results obtained at the Washington Arsenal." In March 1863 *Scientific American* magazine published a review of Mills' gun and concluded that it had "proved of no practical value".

Hopelessly naïve?

Gatling's machine-gun employed several improvements over Requa's Battery and Mills' Coffee Mill. Firstly, it was compact, just a single cylinder inside of which were six gun barrels which revolved around a central axis. Mounted on the left side of the cylinder was a small hopper-like magazine full of cartridges. Mounted on the right side was a hand-crank. At the rear of the cylinder were several spring-activated firing pins. As the crank was turned, the barrels revolved and the firing pins struck the cartridges in succession as the barrels came around. The bullet shot out of the barrel; the spent cartridge shell was ejected from an

Studio portrait of Richard Gatling demonstrating the operation of a tripod-mounted machine-gun mechanism.

aperture at the bottom of the cylinder; and a new cartridge dropped into place from the hopper.

The Gatling gun could fire as fast as the gunner could turn the crank—about 400 shots per minute. When the magazine was spent, it was only a matter of seconds to slip off the empty hopper and replace it with a new one. Of course, those 400 shots were mowing down men, making the Gatling gun the most dreadful weapon of war since the Chinese discovered gunpowder. It was truly a weapon that changed history.

Yet Richard Gatling claimed that his machine-gun would shorten wars and reduce the number of casualties (being aware that as many, if not more, men died from infected wounds than from a killing shot). Writing to a friend in 1877 he said: "It occurred to me that if I could invent a machine—a gun—which could by rapidity of fire, enable one man to do as much battle duty as a hundred, that it would, to a great extent, supersede the necessity of large armies, and consequently, exposure to battle and disease [would be] greatly diminished." Gatling's biographers, military historians and ordinary readers have never been able to decide whether he was hopelessly naïve, or wickedly hypocritical.

While the Gatling gun saw little action in the Civil War, there was one occasion when it made a significant difference. In July 1863, thousands of the poorest residents of New York City, most of them Irish immigrants, rioted against the draft, which they felt targeted them unduly. For four days angry mobs rampaged through the city, destroying draft offices, looting luxury shops, such as Brooks Brothers, and the homes of well-to-do New Yorkers, and murdering African-Americans. At one point a mob headed for the offices of the *New York Times* to avenge themselves on the newspaper's staunchly Republican and pro-war editor, Henry Jarvis Richmond. Warned that the mob was on its way, Richmond acquired three Gatling guns; two he placed in windows overlooking the street, the third he placed on the roof of the building. As the crowd surged toward the newspaper's offices, they saw the guns, including the one on the roof, its cylinder pointed at them. The rioters stopped in their tracks, then scattered. Once again the Gatling gun did not see action, but it had acted as a deterrent.

Name recognition

Gatling never got rich from government orders during the Civil War, but as his biographer Julia Keller observes, the gun did achieve "iconic status" after the war. "It showed up in poems and novels," she writes, "in paintings, in newspaper columns, and it made cameo appearances in anecdotes and tall tales." William "Buffalo Bill" Cody included Gatling guns in his traveling Wild West Show. In the scene where bloodthirsty Indians attacked a settler's cabin, the U.S. cavalry came to the rescue with a Gatling gun. Invariably the audience cheered as the Gatling gun fired round after round of blanks.

Richard Gatling understood that the poems and newspaper columns and the Wild West Show were all free publicity for his invention—and he was delighted. When he or his agents made sales calls in England, France, Germany, Turkey and Russia, his gun essentially sold itself. Everyone had heard of it and understood how it worked and what would be its advantages on the battlefield. And in 1874 Gatling's invention was embraced at last by the US military. A report on the gun filed that year praised "the lightness of its parts; the simplicity and strength of its mechanism; the rapidity and continuity of its fire without sensible recoil; … its general accuracy at all ranges attainable by rifles; … its great endurance."

For the remainder of the nineteenth century Gatling found a large and diverse market for his guns. Foreign governments and generals of foreign armies placed orders, but so did U.S. state militias, police departments and owners of mines, railroads and other large enterprises.

The British used Gatling guns against Ashanti warriors in what is now Ghana, and against the Zulus in South Africa. A newspaper correspondent covering the Zulu War of 1879 described the aftermath of one battle: "When all was over and we counted the dead, there lay, within a radius of five hundred yards, 473 Zulus. They lay in groups, in some places, of fourteen to thirty dead mowed down by the fire of the Gatlings."

In 1877, Major General Oliver O. Howard turned two Gatling guns on Chief Joseph and 800 Nez Percé men, women, and children who were trying to escape U.S. territory and take refuge in Canada.

That same year the New York Militia rolled out a Gatling gun to quell angry workers on strike against the Erie Railroad. Over the next twenty years, state militias in Connecticut, Kansas, Ohio, Pennsylvania, Tennessee, and California discovered that the easiest way to break up an angry crowd of strikers or rioters was to let them see a Gatling gun.

In 1885, four Gatling guns were sent to British troops in Canada to help them put down the Riel Rebellion.

In 1893, when American residents of Hawaii staged a coup against Queen Liliuʻokalani and seized control of the islands for the United States, American

The Maxim gun

The son of a Maine mechanic, Hiram Maxim (1840–1916) received his first patent at the age of twenty-six for a hair-curling iron. He was one of those ingenious Yankees who churned out gadget after gadget, always hoping the next invention would make his fortune.

By 1884 he had moved to London, where he focused his attention on automatic weapons. His machine-gun, known as the Maxim, was a distinct improvement over the model then available on the market. For one thing, it was water-cooled, which eliminated the problem of overheating. Instead of a box of cartridges, the gun was fed with shells attached to a belt. Most ingenious of all, he harnessed the gas released by the gunpowder when each shell was fired to power the weapon, making the Maxim gun truly automatic. In 1891 he introduced yet another improvement, using smokeless cordite instead of gunpowder in each shell; the cloud of powder smoke that had obscured a gunner's vision became a thing of the past.

While all of these innovations were marvelous, most astonishing of all was the gun's rate of fire—up to 600 rounds per minute.

True to a pattern that inventors have encountered time and time again, the British military could not see the advantage of the Maxim gun; the commanders were thinking in terms of mobility rather than of gun emplacements. Not until 1887 did the British Army place an order, and then for only three. That same year Hiram Maxim demonstrated his gun before Kaiser Wilhelm II of Germany, who was so impressed he ordered his engineers to pirate Maxim's design.

Britain finally saw the advantages of the Maxim gun during the First Matabele War (1893–1894) in South Africa. On a famous occasion, fifty British troops armed with four Maxim guns fought off 5,000 Ndebele warriors.

The incident appears to have been the inspiration for Hilaire Belloc's poem, "The Modern Traveller." In it he describes a British officer confronted by a native uprising:

He stood upon a little mound
Cast his lethargic eyes around,
And said beneath his breath:
"Whatever happens, we have got
The Maxim Gun, and they have not."

troops brought out a Gatling gun—just the sight of it quickly dispersed the queen's supporters.

In 1870 Richard Gatling sold the patent for his gun to Colt's Patent Fire-Arms Manufacturing Company in Hartford, Connecticut; henceforth, Colt's would have the right to manufacture the Gatling gun. Gatling remained president of the Gatling Gun Company, now a subsidiary of Colt's. But Gatling did not degenerate into a semi-retired corporate figurehead; he spent the last decades of his life making sales calls in places as far off as Stockholm, Munich, and St. Petersburg, all the while thinking up improvements to his machine-gun.

In 1874 he introduced a more compact model, which measured 35½ inches and weighed 134½ pounds. This smaller version of the original became popular with police departments, who bolted the gun to small carts, and with navies, where it could be mounted on a ship's gunwale. Gatling guns in the original size—49 inches long, weighing 198½ pounds—were still available and tended to be used as field guns.

In 1877 Gatling introduced the Bulldog, a five-barrel version on a sturdy tripod that could fire an astonishing 1,000 rounds in 79 seconds. The 1889 model introduced metal shields to protect the gunner from enemy fire. Earlier Gatling guns had no such feature, which left the gunner entirely exposed.

Gatling also experimented with guns that were powered by electricity or gas, but these models proved unsatisfactory—especially the electrical type, since it was awkward to carry a power source onto a battlefield.

In February 1903, Richard Gatling, now eighty-four years old, and his wife Jemima were visiting their daughter Ida and her husband Hugh Pentecost at their home in New York City. He had just recovered from a case of the flu, but decided one morning to visit a long-time friend, the editor of *Scientific American* magazine. When he returned a little after 1:00 in the afternoon, he was very tired, too worn out to join his wife and daughter at the table for lunch. He went in to a parlor to rest on the sofa. A short time later Ida entered the room to answer the telephone, and found her father gasping for breath. She called her mother, sent for a doctor, and raised her father to a sitting position, hoping to help him breathe more easily. Richard Gatling died in his daughter's arms before the doctor arrived.

In his eulogy, the Reverend A.R. Benton referred to Gatling's belief that his weapon would save lives, saying:

> Paradoxical as it may seem, it was his contention that the more
> destructive the weapons of war, the fewer are its casualties. In his earnest
> and convincing way he maintained his aim to invent such a weapon was
> humane, beneficent, and philanthropic ... This destructive arm of war
> has become famous on two continents, and promises to perpetuate his
> name and fame to remote generations.

Slow but effective
Robert Whitehead's torpedo

SCIENTIST: Robert Whitehead

AREAS OF SCIENCE: Mechanical engineering and missile technology

MAIN INVENTION: Torpedo

GIOVANNI LUPPIS LOOKED LIKE A CHARACTER from an operetta: high forehead, deep-set eyes, flourishing mutton-chop whiskers set off by a flashy naval uniform complete with gold epaulettes.

Luppis (1813–1875) was born in Fiume (now known as Riejka), in what is now Croatia and was then part of the vast Austro-Hungarian Empire. His father was Italian, his mother was Croatian, so he was known as Giovanni or Ivan depending on which side of the family he was visiting.

Luppis entered the Austrian Imperial Navy, where he became interested in creating a new type of torpedo. In the first half of the nineteenth century torpedoes were not mobile; they floated on the surface of the water, anchored by a long rope or chain to the bottom of a bay, harbor, or river. They could best be described as floating landmines—if a ship brushed up against one of them, a large hole would be blown into its side which might sink the vessel. "Might" was the operative word, however—because the floating torpedo did not damage the ship below the waterline, there was no guarantee that it would go down.

Of course, an enemy fleet could try to skirt around these floating minefields, or its commanders could send in small dummy boats to detonate the mines before an attack. Giovanni Luppis imagined a new type of torpedo that did not sit passively waiting for an unwary ship to bump up against it, but could be directed at a particular ship, and controlled from the shore.

After a bit of experimentation, in the late 1850s Luppis built a torpedo armed with an explosive that went off on impact, that was propelled by a simple engine

English engineer Robert Whitehead (1823–1905) invented the self-propelling torpedo, which was fired from a tube below the waterline.

(based on the same type of mechanism that ran a clock) and was equipped with two rudders so the weapon could turn left or right. The torpedo was controlled from shore, but not by some automated system: very long ropes or wires were attached to it, and its direction was guided by manipulating the lines. In 1860, Luppis demonstrated his new torpedo—which he had named *Salvacoste*, Italian for "Coast Saver"—for Emperor Franz Joseph. The torpedo worked, but if the emperor was impressed, his Imperial Navy was not. They rejected the new weapon because it moved too slowly in the water and the land lines made it too difficult to maneuver.

Although Luppis is often credited with being the first man to conceive of a self-propelled torpedo (this is especially the case in Croatia), it was actually Robert Whitehead (1823–1905) who invented the modern torpedo. Nonetheless, in 1869 Franz Joseph recognized Luppis's contribution by granting him the title Baron von Rammer, *rammer* meaning "to ram" or "to sink."

Robert Whitehead was an English engineer who had come to Fiume originally to help silk manufacturers improve their looms, but later worked for the Austrian Navy. In 1864, Luppis showed his guided torpedo to Whitehead who, like the naval officials, thought the guidance system impractical. It was Whitehead who envisioned a torpedo that was both self-propelled and struck ships below the waterline.

Dud torpedoes

American David Bushnell, the inventor of the submarine, first used the term "torpedo." His inspiration was the torpedo fish, a kind of ray that gives off an electrical charge to stun its prey. Bushnell developed his submarine during the American Revolution specifically to attach torpedoes to the underside of British warships. The pilot of the submarine, using a pedaling system similar to a modern-day bicycle, moved underwater toward his target. On reaching the ship, the intention was that he operate a crank to drill a small hole into the hull, embed the torpedo in the hole, light the fuse, then turn about and pedal away furiously, trying to get far away from the ship before the torpedo exploded. Unfortunately, the invention didn't work; in the 1770s the hulls of British warships were plated with copper, which the submarine's drill could not penetrate.

Between 1797 and 1804 another American, Robert Fulton, attempted to improve on Bushnell's idea of explosives that would damage a ship below the waterline. Initially he tried to sell his torpedo to the French, who were at war with Britain, but the contract was canceled after his creation failed to sink even a single British warship. So Fulton crossed the English Channel and offered his torpedo to the British. They gave him an opportunity, but once again the torpedoes proved to be duds—they did not so much as cause a leak in a French warship. Fulton returned to the United States where at first he tried to keep his torpedo idea alive; ultimately he abandoned it and moved on to the invention that made him famous—the steamboat.

Jousting with torpedoes

Military men never lost interest in the concept of blowing up enemy vessels but, like Bushnell, Fulton and Luppis, inventors in the first half of the nineteenth century failed to hit upon an effective delivery system. About the time the American Civil War began in 1861, the navies of both the North and the South were using spar torpedoes, explosive devices attached to poles or spars 39½ feet long. (The spar torpedo was invented by E.C. Singer, nephew of Isaac Singer, inventor of the sewing machine.) A small boat, steel-plated for its own protection, crept up on enemy warships in the dark of night, placed the spar torpedo beside an anchored ship, then touched it off using an electrical charge. It was about as inelegant (not to mention hazardous) a solution to the torpedo problem as could be imagined. And since it also bore a striking resemblance to a medieval knight's jousting lance, the spar torpedo also looked ludicrous.

The Confederate Navy used a slightly different delivery system. In about 1862 an inventor named T. Stoney of Charleston, South Carolina, developed a small steam-powered submarine armed with a spar torpedo. It was not a true submarine since it was not fully submerged—the exhaust pipe and a pipe that drew fresh air into the vessel both protruded above the water's surface. Stoney christened his vessel the *David*, a reference to the puny navy of the Confederacy that nonetheless went up against the Union's naval Goliath. The *David* crept up on Union ships, brandishing its spar torpedo; when it reached its target the spar struck the underside of the ship and exploded. After witnessing the effectiveness of Stoney's submarine, the Confederate government released funds for the construction of twenty more Davids.

The spar torpedo never became the preferred explosive device of the Civil War; the most common type of torpedo remained the floating mine. One of the most famous encounters between a fleet and these surface torpedoes occurred in 1864 at the Battle of Mobile Bay in Alabama. Union Admiral David Farragut was leading his fleet into the harbor when the ironclad U.S.S. *Tecumseh* struck a floating torpedo and sank. Every ship in the fleet ground to a halt as officers and crew waited for the admiral, aboard the flagship U.S.S. *Hartford*, to call for a retreat. Instead, Farragut gave the famous order, "Damn the torpedoes! Full speed ahead!" By tremendous good luck, the fleet avoided all other mines in Mobile Bay, and captured the two forts that guarded the harbor (although they failed to capture the city of Mobile).

Guarding his patent

Having dismissed as awkward Giovanni Luppis's method of guiding a torpedo with ropes from shore, Robert Whitehead set to work on a self-propelled torpedo. His assistants were his 12-year-old son and an elderly mechanic. The details of the process, and even the appearance of the prototype, are not known. Whitehead refused to publish his notes and sketches, and even many years after the fact he still rejected all requests to show his papers. Very likely he was trying to protect his invention from unscrupulous competitors who would try to pirate his invention; there were several notorious cases of the practice in the nineteenth century—Eli Whitney's cotton gin and Elias Howe's sewing machine being just two examples that were stolen in spite of the patents held by their inventors.

Drawing upon the accounts of eyewitnesses, naval historian Geoff Kirby gives us some idea of what Whitehead's torpedo probably looked like: "blunt nosed like a dolphin with four long fins extending almost along the whole body length. The engine was driven by compressed air stored at 370 psi (2,550 kPa) and regulated to approximately constant speed by a simple valve." It was the air pressure that turned the torpedo's single propeller.

The torpedo was shot from a tube below the waterline. It traveled at about seven knots for 607 feet, then at a slower pace for the next 295 feet By 1868 Whitehead had improved on the design so that the torpedo could keep a steady rate of speed of 7 knots over a distance of 2132½ feet. Whitehead demonstrated his torpedo for representatives of the Austrian Navy, who were so impressed they attempted to buy the patent. Whitehead refused to sell.

The next year, 1869, representatives of the British Royal Navy traveled to Fiume to investigate the torpedo. They, too, were impressed, but instead of trying to acquire the patent invited Whitehead to come home to England where he could continue to make improvements.

*Engraving of an
early Whitehead torpedo
during trials, 1878.*

By the fall of 1870 Whitehead was back in England, where he gave several successful demonstrations, culminating in a dramatic grand finale. A coal hulk had been tied up at Cockleshell Hard in Sheerness Harbor, Kent. The torpedo was fired from 394 feet away, and when it struck the hulk it blew a hole 20 feet wide and 10 feet high. The old boat sank at once, and the impressed representatives of the Royal Navy who were there to witness the demonstration immediately placed an order.

Keeping up with orders

Whitehead had been wise to hold on to his patent. The British Admiralty paid him £15,000 for the right to manufacture his torpedoes. It was not an enormous sum, but the contract was not exclusive—Whitehead was free to sell his torpedoes, should he wish, to other markets. And he did. Orders poured in from France, Germany, and even China. In another respect Whitehead was proved correct—munitions manufacturers overseas did attempt to pirate his torpedo. It must have been very satisfying for him that the pirated versions invariably failed.

The torpedo at this point was still the slow-moving 7-knot missile. Whitehead envisioned that his weapon would be used in close quarters such as a bay or harbor. But the Germans wanted a torpedo they could use in battle on the high seas. They asked whether or not Mr. Whitehead could produce a faster model of his torpedo weapon? Specifically, the Germans wanted a torpedo that could skim through the water at 16 knots. Working with a machine shop in Peterborough, England, Whitehead replaced his twin-cylinder engine with a three-cylinder engine and increased the air pressure to 1,000 psi (6,890 kPa), which revved up the torpedo to 18 knots, up to a range of 1640½ feet.

The Germans were delighted, but also more than a bit envious, and set about manufacturing their own torpedoes—which were of such high quality even the British Admiralty purchased some. It was not that the Admiralty had become disenchanted with Whitehead's torpedoes, it was simply a case of supply and demand—the Peterborough factory could not keep up with the number of orders. By 1881, the company had sold 1,456 Whitehead torpedoes. Its biggest customers were Great Britain (254), Russia (250), France (218), and Germany (203).

"Whitehead's Secret"

Speed was not the only issue; there was also the matter of the torpedo maintaining a predetermined depth. Initially this caused Whitehead more than a few headaches. His early torpedoes were inconsistent: sometimes they rose to skim along the surface of the water, sometimes they plunged too deep, or even leaped in and out of the water like a dolphin following a ship at sea.

By 1868 Whitehead had perfected a simple stabilizer mechanism that kept his torpedoes at a consistent depth. Anxious as ever about his invention being pirated, he never patented this device. Only a handful of employees knew how it was made and operated. So much mystery surrounded the stabilizer that it came to be known as "Whitehead's Secret."

The "Secret" was an airtight compartment called a balance chamber that was positioned behind the warhead. Inside the chamber was a movable disc, known as a hydrostatic valve, and a pendulum. By maneuvering the disc or valve, the depth at which the torpedo was to travel could be set.

Even so, because the valve was flexible, it moved while traveling through the water, which could throw it off target. The real stabilizing device was the pendulum, an upside down T-shaped weight that sensed any movement in the valve and shifted its load to compensate, thereby keeping the torpedo at the desired depth.

The "Secret" worked so well that it remained standard equipment on torpedoes until the end of World War II.

Firing torpedoes

Whitehead and the Royal Navy had a difference of opinion regarding how best to fire a torpedo, Whitehead arguing that firing a torpedo from an underwater tube was optimal. His method, invented about 1880, followed what is known as "the pea shooter principle": using compressed air to shoot the torpedo from its tube. In later years the torpedo would be propelled by the gases released from slow-burning gunpowder packed inside the torpedo.

The Royal Navy preferred firing torpedoes from a kind of cannon located on the ship's deck. (Initially the navy had "launched" torpedoes in the most primitive manner imaginable—by placing a torpedo on top of a mess-hall table set up against a porthole, then shoving it out the porthole and into the sea.)

Even if the torpedo cannon was a technological advance over the out-the-porthole system, it worried Whitehead. After he and his son-in-law and business partner, Count George Hoyos, had observed their torpedoes fired from a deck-mounted cannon, they sent a report to the Admiralty expressing their concern that "such delicate weapons [as torpedoes] are not meant to be fired like shot from a gun." Their fears appear to have been unfounded, for there were no mishaps aboard British ships that employed the torpedo cannon. Nevertheless, in time all navies adopted Whitehead's underwater tube method.

Incredibly, these discussions were purely academic—no torpedo was fired in battle until 1891, during the Chilean Revolution. On the night of April , 23 1891, two ships of the Chilean Navy spotted a rebel vessel, the *Blanco Encalada*. A torpedo fired from the *Almirante Lynch* struck the *Blanco*, tearing open a hole 16 feet by 8 feet below the waterline. The *Blanco* sank, taking 180 officers and men with her. The captain, Don Luis Goni, survived; the impact of the torpedo strike had blown him out of a ventilation shaft and into the sea. He swam ashore with another survivor, the *Blanco*'s mascot, a pet llama. Captain Goni and the llama were both rescued by a British ship that happened to be in the neighborhood, HMS *Warspite*.

The Sound of Music connection

In 1910 James Whitehead, Robert's son, was serving as Great Britain's ambassador to the Austro-Hungarian Empire. That year the Imperial Navy prepared to launch a new submarine, and asked the ambassador's daughter, Agathe, to christen the vessel. At the ceremony she met the submarine's commander, Captain Georg von Trapp. Two years later they married, but their life together was brief: in 1922, after ten years of marriage, Agathe died, leaving behind seven children.

In 1926, Captain von Trapp asked the mother superior of the Benedictine abbey of Nonnberg in Salzburg to send him a young woman to serve as a tutor for one of his daughters, who was recovering from scarlet fever. The Reverend Mother sent the 21-year-old novice Maria Augusta Kutschera. Maria fell in love first with the von Trapp children, and then with their father. In 1927, Maria and von Trapp married.

The von Trapp family became famous through the highly fictionalized musical version of their life, *The Sound of Music*. Almost entirely forgotten is the fact that the von Trapp children were the great-grandchildren of Robert Whitehead, the man who invented the torpedo.

A well-connected family

Robert Whitehead's success was due largely to having invented a weapon that every navy in the world coveted, but he also owed some part of his success to his children and grandchildren, several of whom made well-placed marriages. In 1869 his daughter Alice married Count George Hoyos, who had managed Whitehead's factory in Fiume and eventually purchased it. As a member of the aristocracy, Hoyos had many influential relatives and friends in the hierarchy of the Austro-Hungarian Empire, and his contacts brought Whitehead a string of lucrative orders from Austria's Imperial Navy.

In 1892 Hoyos' daughter Marguerite—Whitehead's granddaughter—married Herbert von Bismarck, the son of the great German Chancellor, Otto von Bismarck. This marriage also increased Whitehead's international business contacts.

Now a wealthy man, Whitehead purchased two homes, one on the fashionable Isle of Wight—one of Queen Victoria's favorite retreats—and another, a large estate, in Berkshire. He retired at the age of eighty, handing over the operation of the torpedo business to his son John, and died two years later. For his invention, Robert Whitehead had been honoured by nine different nations, but his homeland was not Amongst them. His epitaph reads, "His fame was known by all nations hereabouts."

Like a pomegranate
William Mills perfects the hand grenade

SCIENTIST: William Mills

AREA OF SCIENCE: Chemistry

MAIN INVENTION: Hand grenade

IT WAS SUNDAY MARCH, 13 1881, and Czar Alexander II of Russia was riding in his carriage through the streets of his capital, St. Petersburg, on his way back to the Winter Palace after observing a military parade. To an empire accustomed to brutal autocrats, Alexander was an anomaly. He had ended centuries of tradition by liberating Russia's serfs—tens of millions of peasants who were little better than the slaves of the aristocrats and landowners. For this dramatic act he was hailed as "the Czar-Liberator." That Sunday morning he had taken another unprecedented step, approving a plan to establish a national assembly that would advise the czar and his ministers on legislation. At the parade ground Alexander had confided to the Grand Duchess Catherine, "I have determined to summon an assembly of notables." Those "notables" would have been the first step toward representative government in Russia.

The czar's bullet-proof carriage was rolling along the Catherine Canal, heading for the Pevchevsky Bridge—the route always taken after military parades—when a 20-year-old anarchist named Nikolai Rysakov tossed a bomb under the carriage horses. It exploded, killing a Cossack guard and wounding the driver as well as several pedestrians. The carriage was only slightly damaged, however, and the czar was not hurt at all. The blast threw Rysakov against a fence. As he regained his footing, he saw that his bomb had not reduced the carriage to splinters, and he cursed.

U.S. troops in France c. 1917 hurling hand grenades, wearing masks to protect themselves against the enemy's poisonous gas clouds.

The carriage driver begged Alexander to remain inside, assuring the czar that he would be able to drive back to the Winter Palace; the horses were not badly injured. The six surviving Cossack guards also pleaded with their sovereign not to step out of the carriage, but Alexander was determined to comfort the wounded.

By this time Rysakov had been seized. The police chief, Colonel A.I. Dvorzhitsky, traveling in the sleigh immediately behind the carriage, hurried to the czar's side. Alexander made the sign of the cross, and said, "Thank God, I am not wounded." Dvorzhitsky suddenly heard the prisoner shout something, and saw another young man, 25-year-old Ignacy Hryniewiecki, running toward the czar with another bomb in his hands. Crying out, "It is too early to thank God!," Hryniewiecki flung the bomb between the czar's legs. A tremendous flash of flame erupted and shrapnel flew in every direction. Two dozen or more bystanders were struck down by the second bomb, amongst them the police chief, who was scorched by the flames and struck by some shrapnel.

As he lifted himself painfully off the pavement, Dvorzhitsky saw Alexander propped up against a wheel of his carriage. His right leg had been blown off, his left was mangled; his stomach was ripped open, his face lacerated. "To the palace," he whispered, "to die."

As news of the bombing spread across St. Petersburg, members of the Imperial family hurried to the Winter Palace. Priests arrived to give Alexander the last rites of the Russian Orthodox Church. Soon thereafter he died. His son, now Alexander III, and his grandson, the future Nicholas II, were at his deathbed. The trauma of the czar's assassination would define their two reigns: they did not reverse the emancipation of the serfs, but they turned back every other progressive initiative Alexander II had attempted. Under Alexander III and Nicholas II, Russia returned to absolute autocracy until it was swept away by the Bolshevik Revolution of 1918. Thirty-six years of repressive imperial rule followed by seventy-two years of Communist dictatorship were the direct result of two home-made hand grenades.

The first grenades

The Chinese were the first to discover the formula for gunpowder, and so all explosives and firearms have their origin in China. By the tenth century the Chinese military carried into battle hand grenades known as *zhen tian lei* ("heaven-shaking thunder"). They were cast-iron balls packed with gunpowder that was ignited by a fuse. The troops often threw the grenades individually, but sometimes a large number were placed in the bowl of a catapult and hurled en masse at the enemy. The deadly spray of flying shrapnel could have a devastating effect on troops, but it was a risky tactic—if the fuses were too short, the grenades would explode as they were being loaded into the catapult.

A different type of grenade was in use in the Byzantine Empire in the eighth century. The Greeks did not have gunpowder, but they did have Greek fire, the flammable liquid that was Byzantium's secret weapon. Typically the Byzantine

Czar Alexander II was assassinated by nihilists using hand-made bombs (primitive hand grenades) as he drove through St. Petersburg on March, 13 1881.

military used a primitive flamethrower made of bronze or iron and equipped with a hand-pump that spewed the liquid on their enemies; but by the eighth century Byzantine troops were equipped with ceramic and glass containers filled with Greek fire. These grenades were an effective way of spreading panic amongst enemy troops, but the fragility of the containers also made them hazardous for their users: one bump and a supply wagon loaded with the containers, or a foot soldier carrying one, would be consumed in flames.

By the fifteenth century, European armies were using hand grenades that were almost identical to those thrown by the Chinese 500 years earlier. By the early seventeenth century European grenades were packed with gunpowder and

The Molotov cocktail

A staple of violent street protests for more than sixty years, the Molotov cocktail is a home-made bomb that uses ingredients that can be found anywhere. A glass bottle is half-filled with petrol, ethanol, or methanol. A cork, rubber stopper or some other article is jammed into the mouth of the bottle to keep it airtight. A cloth rag that has been soaked in the flammable liquid is tied around the bottle and ignited, and the bottle is thrown at the intended target.

The Molotov cocktail was invented during the Winter War of 1939–1940, fought between Finland and the Soviet Union for possession of Karelia, an isthmus north of St. Petersburg. Finnish troops invented the "cocktail" as an anti-tank weapon, and named it for the Soviet Foreign Minister, Vyacheslav Mikhailovich Molotov, although why he was singled out remains a mystery. For that matter, the Russians dispute that it was the Finns who invented the bomb, claiming it was to their men's credit.

Be that as it may, the Molotov cocktail was adopted by resistance and guerrilla movements in World War II, and was used most famously during the Warsaw Ghetto Uprising of 1943, when poorly armed Polish Jews took on a large detachment of Nazi troops. A member of the Jewish Fighting Organization in the Ghetto described one such incident: "The well-aimed bottles hit the tank. The flames spread quickly. The blast of the explosion is heard. The machine stands motionless. The crew is burned alive. The other two tanks turn around and withdraw. The Germans who took cover behind them withdraw in panic."

The one problem with the Molotov cocktail is the flammable liquid—because it has a low viscosity it runs and splatters. To make the liquid adhere to its target, bomb-makers have taken to adding palm oil, tar, or even dish and laundry detergent, all of which make the Molotov cocktail a more effective grenade.

bullets, making them even more lethal. The bullets inside the ball-shaped bomb resembled a pomegranate, which earned it the name grenade, from the French word for the fruit.

Although effective, the cast-iron, bullet-packed grenades were not easy to use. They weighed a hefty 3 pounds, or thereabouts, and the average infantryman could not throw a 3 pound exploding metal ball very far. Defenders of fortresses and walled cities took to lobbing grenades down onto their attackers, but kings and commanders did not want their use limited to defending towns and bastions, and so recruited men who could throw such a weight a good distance. These special troops were known as grenadiers.

The grenadiers

Grenadiers tended to be tall, strong, and athletic young men. They were also fearless—a necessary quality since their task was to storm entrenchments, hurling grenades as they charged. There were grenadiers who fought for King Charles I during the English Civil War. In 1656, after the defeat of the Royalists and the execution of Charles, a group of these men went to Bruges, in what is now Belgium, where they served as bodyguards for their exiled, uncrowned king, Charles II. They were known as Lord Wentworth's Regiment. When the monarchy was restored in 1660, the grenadiers returned home with Charles. This loyal regiment is the origin of the Grenadier Guards, an elite corps and the most senior regiment of the Household Division, the military units that serve a variety of ceremonial functions but also act as the bodyguards of the British royal family.

King Louis XIV of France introduced grenadiers to his army in 1667, ordering that there must be a grenadier company in each battalion. In 1676 Louis XV organized the first mounted grenadiers. By the end of the seventeenth century there were grenadier companies in the armies of virtually every nation in Europe.

Early in the eighteenth century it became customary for advancing armies to mass their companies of grenadiers in the front line. It was thought that the sight of hundreds of the biggest, strongest, bravest troops would demoralize their adversaries; to increase the effect, French commanders urged their grenadiers to grow large, ferocious moustaches to give themselves a barbarous look. They also wore high pointed hats, which, of course, made these tall men look even taller.

By the 1770s, the British Army had phased out the hand grenade as a weapon. Not only were they cumbersome to carry, but in order to light the fuses each grenadier was obliged to go into battle with a smouldering slow match, or match cord, in a perforated metal box. If it rained, or the grenadiers had to wade through a stream or river, the slow match, and thus the grenades, were rendered useless. But the army did not give up its grenadier regiments—they were still elite military units, but without grenades.

During the Crimean War (1854–1856), British troops re-invented the grenade. In 1855 Colonel Hugh Robert Hibbert wrote to his sister:

> *We have a new invention to annoy our friends in their pits. It consists in filling empty soda water bottles full of powder, old twisted nails and any other sharp or cutting thing we can find at the time, sticking a bit of tow in for a fuse then lighting it and throwing it quickly into our neighbors' pit where it bursts, to their great annoyance. You may imagine their rage at seeing a soda water bottle come tumbling into a hole full of men with a little fuse burning away as proud as a real shell exploding and burying itself into soft parts of the flesh.*

Terrorist bombs

The grenade might have gone out of fashion in military circles, but it found new popularity amongst terrorists. One of the earliest such attacks occurred in Boston in 1721, when an unknown assailant threw a home-made grenade comprised of black powder and turpentine through an open window of the home of Cotton Mather, a prominent Puritan minister. Fortunately, it was a dud.

In 1858 revolutionaries threw three bombs at the carriage of France's Emperor Napoleon III and Empress Eugénie. The explosions killed eight bystanders and wounded more than 140 others, but the emperor and empress were unharmed. In 1886, striking workers gathered for a rally at the Haymarket in Chicago. As police moved in to break up the meeting, someone threw a grenade. The explosion killed one police officer, wounded several others, and started a gunfight in which eight police and an unknown number of workers were gunned down. In 1893, a French anarchist, Auguste Vaillant, threw a home-made grenade into the French Chamber of Deputies. Fortunately it was so poorly made that no one was killed; twenty-two deputies suffered only slight injuries. That same year a Spanish anarchist, Santiago Salvador, threw two grenades into the audience of the Liceu Opera House in Barcelona, killing twenty and wounding many others.

In 1906, Mateu Morral, a Catalan anarchist, concealed a grenade inside a bouquet of flowers and threw it at the carriage of Spain's King Alfonso XIII and his bride, Princess Victoria Eugénie. The newlyweds escaped unharmed, but twenty-four people standing along the crowded street were killed. In 1914, Serbian radicals calling themselves the Black Hand threw a grenade at the car of Austrian Archduke Franz Ferdinand and his wife Sophie. It bounced off the back of the car and exploded, wounding twenty people. Franz Ferdinand and Sophie escaped harm. The Black Hand believed they had botched the assassination, but later that day one of their number, Gavril Princip, spotted the Archduke and his wife. Their driver had made a wrong turn, and as he backed up the car, Princip ran across the street; at point-blank range he shot and killed Franz Ferdinand and Sophie. Their assassination led to World War I, the war that would see the return of the grenade to the battlefield.

The Mills bomb

William Mills (1856–1932) was the son of an established shipbuilder, but his career path was more erratic. As a teenage boy he worked as a butcher, then began an apprenticeship with a marine engineer. After seven years at sea, Mills returned home to take up a new interest—metallurgy. He opened the first aluminum foundry in Britain in 1885, The Atlas Works, at Monkwearmouth in the northern county of Durham (now part of Tyne and Wear). An avid golfer, Mills designed the first golf clubs with metal heads—made of aluminum from his own foundry, of course. In 1892 he received a patent for what he called "Metallic Golfing Instrument Heads."

When World War I broke out in August 1914, Mills opened a munitions factory in Birmingham. It was there in May 1915 that he began to manufacture a grenade of his own design, which came to be known as the Mills bomb. Mills' grenade was the size of a lemon, weighed 1 pound 4 ounces and was made of steel or cast iron with its exterior shell etched into forty-eight small squares. It was easy to operate: a soldier held down the curved handle that was connected to the top and ran down the side, pulled the pin and hurled the grenade at its target. As it flew through the air the handle disengaged from the grenade, releasing a coiled spring inside that ignited the fuse. Three to four seconds later it exploded, sending forty-eight deadly little squares of metal flying.

Following pages: Under the watchful eyes of officers, American Army recruits in a World War I training camp practice throwing hand grenades.

Initially each battalion was required to train a platoon of bomb throwers. Very soon the high command realized that any man who could throw a rock could throw a Mills bomb, so the special training was suspended. It is estimated that in 1915 British munitions factories produced between 250,000 and 500,000 grenades per week, and that by the end of the war in November 1918 the Allies had thrown 70 million Mills bombs, and about 35 million other varieties of grenades.

Improvized grenades

It was trench warfare that revived the demand for grenades. As historian William Weir has written, "The Western Front in World War I was a massive siege—the longest siege line in the history of the world with the most besiegers and defenders (each side had both)." Within the narrow confines of a trench, where there was no place to hide or to dive for cover, a grenade could be especially lethal.

In 1914 the Germans had a stockpile of 70,000 grenades, but the British had none. To compensate, the men in the trenches made their own improvized grenades, using any materials that were at hand. They packed empty shells, bits of shrapnel, bent nails, any type of useless metal, inside an empty jam tin (with lid still partly attached) already partly filled with some explosive such as gun-cotton or dynamite. Then they punched a hole in the lid, ran a fuse through it, wrapped wire around the can to keep the lid down, ignited the fuse, and threw it into the nearest German trench. The home-made fuses were the main trouble with the jam-tin grenades: some burned too fast, blowing up in the soldier's hand. Others burned too slowly, giving the Germans time to lob the grenade back into the British trenches, "with dire results," as Arthur G. Empey, a machine-gunner who served in France, observed in his memoir.

The arrival of the Mills bomb was welcomed in the British trenches. "The Mills has the confidence of the thrower," Empey said, "in that he knows it will not explode until released from his grip."

Immediately, the Mills bomb became popular with the Allied troops. The Australians took to carrying about half a dozen in their pockets and inside their shirts as standard equipment. The British, whose closely tailored uniforms did not permit them to stuff grenades into their pockets, made do with canvas buckets, which may have been clumsy to carry around but had the advantage of being able to hold as many as two dozen grenades.

An icon of World War I

In Mexico in 1915 Pancho Villa was at the pinnacle of his fame and success. He was a complicated character: a general, revolutionary, bandit, with a touch of Don Corleone and Robin Hood. When he learned that one of his rivals, General Álvaro Obregón (a man Villa regarded as a bourgeois pipsqueak), had fortified the town of Celaya, Villa summoned 25,000 of his Los Dorados (The Golden Ones) and attacked the town, expecting an easy victory. They were the finest cavalrymen in Mexico, and on the day of the battle, April, 13 1915, they employed their usual tactic—a headlong charge. But before they could get near Celaya, Los Dorados found themselves and their horses painfully entangled in coils of barbed wire. Obregón had surrounded the town with the wire, and placed his artillery and machine-gun nests behind it. As Los Dorados struggled to free themselves, Obregón's field-guns and machine-guns mowed them down. Pancho Villa lost 10,000 men that day: 4,000 killed, 6,000 captured.

Barbed wire was the brainchild of Joseph F. Glidden (1813–1906), a farmer from DeKalb, Illinois. In the late nineteenth century cattle ranching had become big business in Texas, Kansas, and all across the Great Plains. But keeping their herds off neighbors' land and fields proved difficult. Conventional wooden fences were time-consuming to build, and wasted effort as the cattle just broke through them at will. But Glidden's fencing was different.

He created sharp barbs which he wrapped at intervals around a smooth wire, then twisted the wire together with another wire to keep the barbs in place. Cattle soon learned to shy away from the barbs. All a rancher had to do was string the wire from a few fence posts and he had a simple, inexpensive, effective method to keep his cattle where he wanted them.

The military caught on early to the usefulness of barbed wire. During the Spanish-American War of 1898, Spanish commanders strung barbed wire around their fortresses. During the Second Boer War (1899–1902) in South Africa, the British used tangles of barbed wire to impede Afrikaaner horsemen. And during the Russo-Japanese War (1904–1905), both sides fought from behind great coils of barbed wire.

Barbed wire became as associated with World War I as trenches and hand grenades. It stretched from one end of the Western Front to the other, snaring men and forming a virtually impassable bulwark. True, the barbs were no defense against a wire-cutter, but by the time a soldier had cut enough wires to get through the tangle, he was almost invariably torn to pieces by enemy machine-gun fire.

By the end of the war the Germans had introduced a cheaper, modified version of barbed wire—razor wire. It was not really wire at all, but coils of thin ribbons of metal with jagged edges. It did much more damage to human flesh than barbed wire, and no ordinary wire-cutter could snip through it.

German grenades

Over the course of World War I, Germany manufactured a variety of grenades. The least popular was the percussion grenade: the German troops, like the Allies, did not trust them. There had been too many deadly accidents in the trenches when a percussion grenade had detonated after being dropped, or even when a soldier carrying such a grenade had been jostled by another.

Most German grenades had a time-release mechanism, usually with a 5- to 7-second delay. Stormtroopers were armed with grenades that had only a 2-second delay; since these grenades gave their Allied targets no time to take cover, they were brutally effective in clearing out the trenches.

The most characteristic of the German grenades was the *Stielhandgranate*, or stick grenade—nicknamed the "Potato Masher" by the British. It was an explosive canister mounted atop a wooden stick, activated by jerking on a pull-cord, after which the grenade would explode in five seconds. The stick to which the grenade was attached actually enabled a German soldier to throw his grenade further than a British soldier could throw a Mills bomb: on average, a Mills bomb traveled about 49 feet, while a stick grenade could fly 98½ to 131 feet.

Rifle grenades

There was one drawback to the Mills bomb—its range was limited by the strength of the individual soldier's throwing arm. In an attempt to achieve greater distance, the rifle grenade, a grenade mounted on a long metal rod, was developed. The rod was slipped down the rifle barrel and the rifle loaded with a blank cartridge; when fired, the charge would shoot the grenade and rod out of the rifle toward its target. Unfortunately, rifle grenades rarely came anywhere near their targets. Perhaps it was the rod that threw off the trajectory, or perhaps it was the weight of the grenade, but Allied troops routinely complained that even their best marksmen could not hit the broad side of a barn with a rifle grenade.

And the rifle grenade had another flaw—it had a tendency to split the rifle barrel. Both soldiers and munitions manufacturers gave up on rifle grenades. Effective grenade launchers would not be developed until after World War I.

After the war, in 1922, William Mills received a knighthood in recognition of his contribution to the war effort through his hand grenade. He also received a grant from the British government in the amount of £27,750. Mills insisted that since this was a gift from the government, he should not be obliged to pay income tax on it. The British Inland Revenue department disagreed and forced him to pay up. Sir William Mills died in 1932.

—⋙—

Since World War I, the grenade has been basic equipment for infantry. It was used in every theatre of World War II to clear out bunkers, machine-gun nests and trenches. By the time of the Vietnam War in the 1960s, American munitions manufacturers had designed a new, lighter, more lethal grenade that on detonation sent thousands of tiny metal shards flying in every direction. It could kill anyone within a 15 metre (49 feet) radius, and wound anyone within a 35 metre (115 feet) radius.

Today, a variety of grenades is available on the military and law-enforcement market: illuminating grenades for night-time use to reveal the location of the enemy; incendiary grenades to start fires; and smoke and tear-gas grenades to clear rioters from city streets. The grenade has become one of the most effective and versatile weapons in an army's arsenal.

Perverting chemistry
Fritz Haber's poison gas

SCIENTIST: Fritz Haber

AREA OF SCIENCE: Chemistry

MAIN INVENTIONS: Poison gas and Zyklon

IT WAS ABOUT 5:00 IN THE AFTERNOON on April, 22 1915 when the wind over Ypres shifted. It no longer blew in from the sea over the Allies' trenches toward the German lines; now the wind was at the Germans' backs. Such a modest meteorological change was hardly worth anyone's notice, particularly on a battlefield where approximately 195,000 men were dug in. Then the Allies saw rolling toward them a large dense cloud, variously described as yellowish or greenish or blueish, and the road that led south from the Yser Canal was suddenly filled with panic-stricken men. They were Canadians, Algerians, and Moroccans, some riding two or three to a horse, most running as fast as they could, throwing away their guns and their gear, even stripping off their tunics in an attempt to escape … something. Anthony Hossack of the Queen Victoria Rifles witnessed the pandemonium: 'One man came stumbling through our lines. An officer of ours held him up with levelled revolver, "What's the matter, you bloody lot of cowards?" says he. The Zouave [Algerian] was frothing at the mouth, his eyes started from their sockets, and he fell writhing at the officer's feet.'

The Allied troops who were too slow to follow their comrades' example suddenly felt the taste of something sharp; their eyes reddened, burned and began to water; then there was an unpleasant tickle in the nose and throat. Soon they were lurching forward, gasping, vomiting, trying to escape the horrible cloud.

Five thousand Allied troops died that day, asphyxiated by poisonous chlorine gas. An untold number were injured, some suffering permanent lung damage, while others went blind when they or their friends tried to relieve their eyes

Fritz Haber (1868–1943) won the 1918 Nobel Prize in Chemistry but is better remembered for perfecting the use of poisonous gases as a weapon of war during World War I.

by bathing them in water—when it comes in contact with water, chlorine gas becomes as bad as acid, burning any tissue it touches.

A favoring wind

It started on March, 10 when the Germans, working at night, began burying in advance of their trenches nearly 5,000 canisters filled with poison gas, each 5 feet long and weighing 189½ pounds. Because the wind was against them—in the part of Belgium where Ypres is located the wind blows almost continuously from the sea—the Germans were obliged to delay their attack by more than a month. Once the wind was in their favor it would carry the poison cloud into the Allied trenches. After the chlorine had done its work, massed German troops equipped with protective gas masks would move in and wipe out the remaining Allied troops. With their new, unstoppable weapon the Germans would move rapidly from victory to victory until they had won the war on the western front.

Kaiser Wilhelm II was enthusiastic about the new weapon, but many of his commanders and officers did not share his attitude. Crown Prince Rupprecht of Bavaria warned that if they used poison gas, the Allies would respond in kind. Another commander, in a letter to his wife, complained, 'War has nothing to do with chivalry any more. The higher civilization rises, the viler man becomes.'

For six weeks the Germans waited for the favoring wind. In the meantime, from time to time, lucky shots or bits from shrapnel from the Allied lines struck the occasional canister, sending a small poisonous fog into the faces of the Germans. Several times German commanders massed troops in preparation for an assault, but each time the wind failed to co-operate, and most of the troops were sent to the Eastern Front to battle the Russians.

When the auspicious moment at last arrived, the assault did not work as perfectly as the Kaiser had hoped. After the gas had done its job, the German troops, not fully confident in their gas masks, moved in very cautiously—too slowly, in fact, to roll up the Allied line. As they crept toward the Allied trenches, Canadian troops who had escaped the gas attack fired into the German flank.

There was no general rout of the Allies at Ypres, but Kaiser Wilhelm was nonetheless pleased with the results. He sent Champagne to the officer in charge of the line where the gas canisters had been detonated, then summoned the inventor of the new weapon to court and awarded him the Iron Cross.

Stretching a point

The man who invented the poison gas released at Ypres was chemist Fritz Haber, who was born in 1868 in Breslau in eastern Germany (now Wroclaw, Poland). His mother died when he was a week old. His father, who owned a successful dye and paint factory, showed little interest in his son.

The Habers were Jews, but Germany in the late nineteenth century was not the Germany that it became under the Nazis. The hostility that Jews endured in France, the violent pogroms that targeted them in Poland and Russia, were unknown in Germany. German Jews were active in the arts; they built prosperous careers for themselves as industrialists, attorneys, journalists, doctors, and scientists; they were admitted to the universities as students and as faculty. German Jewish children played with their German Gentile neighbors. And intermarriage between Jews and Gentiles was on the rise in Haber's day: by 1915, 30 percent of marriages in the Jewish community involved a non-Jewish bride or groom. This is not to say that anti-Semitism did not exist in Germany: it survived amongst the aristocracy and in the military, and in the slurs and slights Jews endured from the ordinary people.

Like many other assimilated German Jews, Fritz Haber tended to think of himself as German first and Jewish second. Nonetheless, a year after receiving his doctorate in chemistry in 1891, Haber removed what he considered the final obstacle to his full assimilation into German society—he converted to Christianity. But baptism failed to open every door. The Officer Corps remained closed to him; in the eyes of the military, and of the Kaiser, Haber was still a Jew. But the invention of poison gas so delighted Kaiser Wilhelm that he was willing to stretch a point and grant Haber the rank of honorary captain, which permitted him to wear a dashing military uniform complete with saber and spiked helmet.

Harmless, almost laughable

Using gas, or at least fumes, as a weapon was not entirely Fritz Haber's idea. The ancient Greeks had tried to harness sulfur fumes with the thought that the unmistakable rotten egg stench would drive away the enemy. Leonardo da Vinci, whose genius as a weapons designer ranged from the sublime to the improbable, sketched a bomb packed with sulfur and arsenic powder. With advances in chemistry and weaponry in the nineteenth century, a chemical weapon became less and less of a pipe-dream. To forestall such a weapon actually being used in battle, the Hague Convention of 1899 outlawed "the use of projectiles the sole object of which is the diffusion of asphyxiating or deleterious gases." Britain, Russia, France and Germany all signed this accord, but within a decade the British, the Germans and the French had all developed tear gas. While Britain felt honor-bound not to add tear gas to its arsenal, France and Germany experienced no such qualms. When World War I broke out in 1914, the Germans began lobbing tear-gas grenades at the Allies, and the French responded. Writing in *Military History* magazine, historian John P. Sinnott speculated that the French tear-gas grenades may have been defective, because if the French had truly used them, "[they] had gone completely unnoticed by the Germans!."

The Germans had a similar problem in October 1914 at the Battle of Neuve Chappelle, where they fired 3,000 howitzer shells packed with sneezing powder. The irritant had no effect on the Allied troops, who did not learn that the Germans had turned a 'deleterious' weapon against them until after the war, when Allied commanders read through defeated Germany's military archive.

Both the Germans and the French continued to use tear gas against each other, fired from artillery, but the results were insignificant, and sometimes almost laughable. At Bolymov on the eastern front in January 1915 the Germans fired tear gas at the Russians, but the temperature was so cold the gas froze, rendering it harmless.

That year Fritz Haber, now a reserve sergeant-major in the German cavalry and artillery, began to study the possibility of releasing gas from canisters rather than artillery shells. And he went a step further, suggesting the German military retire their supplies of harmless tear gas and sneezing powder and instead use a poison gas against the Allies. The gas Haber recommended was chlorine; it was highly toxic, and it was readily available.

As the son of a dyer Haber knew that chlorine was used to make dyes. The war had all but eliminated the demand for new dyes; dye factories were sitting idle, and stockpiles of chlorine were available across Germany. Haber collected some of the finest chemists in the country to assist him in perfecting his new weapon: amongst them were James Franck, Otto Hahn, and Gustav Hertz—all of whom, like Haber, would one day win Nobel Prizes for Chemistry (although not for their work with poison gas).

Late in 1914 Haber attended field tests of the effectiveness of the canisters, the gas, and the gas masks manufactured to keep the troops safe. Once, in an incautious moment, he rode too close to a chlorine cloud; he and his horse were engulfed and nearly choked to death. He survived the mishap, and within a few weeks his new weapon was ready for use against the Allies.

Two shots in the night

An unintended victim of the chlorine gas attack at Ypres was Fritz Haber's wife, Clara. Like her husband, Clara Immerwahr was from a Breslau Jewish family. They became close friends at Breslau's university where both were studying chemistry. Clara was a gifted student who continued her studies until she earned a doctorate in chemistry—the first female student of the Breslau University to receive such an honor. The next year Fritz and Clara married, and the year following, 1902, she gave birth to their son, Hermann.

The marriage deteriorated quickly. Fritz expected Clara to give up her interest in chemistry and become a full-time housewife and mother. When Clara rebelled against such a restricted life, Fritz was mystified. "Women are like lovely butterflies to me," he confided to a friend. "I admire their colors and glitter, but I get no further." Fritz became ever more absorbed in his work and ignored his wife and son. The lack of affection and attention hurt Clara; writing to one of the professors who had directed her doctoral studies she lamented, "I'd rather write ten dissertations than suffer this way."

When Fritz went to Ypres with his canisters of chlorine gas, Clara remained at home with Hermann. One day she told a friend that when she thought of what her husband was doing she was overwhelmed by despair. To pervert chemistry, the science she loved, to kill thousands of human beings was obscene.

Although the gas attack had killed "only" 5,000 men, far fewer than Haber had expected, officials of the German government and military were delighted. Fritz became the guest of honour at a series of congratulatory dinners and parties; Clara remained at home.

On the night of May, 2 1915, only ten days after the attack at Ypres, Clara Haber went into the garden, taking with her Fritz's service revolver. From the house 12-year-old Hermann heard two shots ring out. Running outside, he found his mother lying on the grass, badly wounded, bleeding profusely, but still alive. He roused his father, who had gone to bed, and rushed back to the garden. By the time Fritz came downstairs, Clara was already dead in her child's arms.

Biographers of Fritz Haber have suggested that Clara killed herself because her marriage was unhappy and because she had no career as a chemist, but there was almost certainly more to her despair than a failing marriage and a frustrated career. A friend of the family, James Franck, who had assisted Fritz in preparing the chlorine gas, believed that "the fact that her husband was involved in gas warfare certainly played a role in her suicide."

Haber had orders to leave the next day for the eastern front to supervise a poison gas attack on the Russians. He could have appealed to the government for a delay so that he could bury his wife and console his son, but he made no such request. He would later write, "For a month [after Clara's suicide] I doubted that I would hold out, but now the war with its gruesome pictures and its continuous demands on all my strength has calmed me."

The British fight back

The British were the first to retaliate for the gas attack at Ypres. Lieutenant-Colonel Charles Foulkes was placed in command of the Special Gas Companies—an odd choice of name since the men were strictly forbidden to use the word "gas" when referring to what was inside the canisters they carried. The canisters themselves were to be called "accessories."

The British commanders had selected Loos as the site for the first gas attack against the Germans. After dark on September, 24 1915, British troops deployed 400 canisters filled with chlorine gas along their front lines. At 5:20 the next morning, the men of the Special Gas Companies crept forward and turned the valve on each canister that released the gas. The plan called for the British to wait forty minutes, then the infantry would attack the German trenches.

Everything began well: a light breeze carried the poison gas toward the German line. Then, unexpectedly, the wind shifted direction and blew the gas back into the British trenches. The British suffered approximately two thousand, six hundred casualties, including seven deaths, from their own cloud of poison gas. German casualties are unknown, although they are believed to be fewer.

A stealth weapon

It was clear to commanders on both sides that the airborne delivery system diminished the effectiveness of poison gas. The wind could not be relied upon to carry it where the military wanted it to go, and so the Germans, French, and British all began studying ways of delivering poison gas via artillery shells.

British casualties blinded by German mustard gas in a battle at Bethune in France shuffle to an aid post.

Scientists working for both sides discovered that phosgene gas was effective when delivered by artillery shell. Placed under pressure, the gas liquefied and could be sealed inside a shell. When heated, the liquid returned to the gaseous state—and firing the shell from an artillery gun created enough heat for the purpose. On impact the shell would burst open, releasing the toxic gas.

Poison gas casualties

COUNTRY	DEATHS	INJURIES
Russia	56,000	363,000
Germany	9,000	191,000
British Empire	8,100	180,600
France	8,000	182,000
Italy	4,600	60,000
Austria-Hungary	3,000	97,000
USA	1,500	72,800
Others	1,000	10,000

In addition to being ideal for artillery, phosgene gas had another advantage—it was a stealth weapon. Unlike chlorine gas, which was visible and odoriferous and instantly caused violent bouts of coughing, choking, and vomiting, the colorless phosgene gas, which had a faint smell of freshly cut grass or hay, was difficult to detect. It was not unusual for twenty-four to forty-eight hours to pass before a soldier showed symptoms of having been exposed to phosgene.

The worst weapon

Chlorine gas and phosgene gas killed or injured anyone who inhaled them. As the Allied armies acquired effective respirators (popularly known as gas masks), chlorine and phosgene became less effective on the battlefield, with the result that in 1917 Germany introduced mustard gas.

Mustard gas is comprised of carbon, sulfur, chlorine, and hydrogen. It is believed that it was invented in 1860 by a British physicist named Frederick Guthrie, although the evidence is not conclusive. While all the poison gases used during World War I were dreadful, mustard gas was especially terrible. Even a soldier equipped with a gas mask could still be horribly wounded because the gas was an alkylating agent, which meant the chemicals in it caused painful blisters anywhere on the body. The eyes were especially vulnerable; if a high dose of mustard gas came in contact with the eyes, the unfortunate individual usually suffered permanent blindness. If mustard gas was inhaled, the blisters it created on the interior of the lungs and nasal passages could close the air passages, suffocating the victim. Men who were affected often suffered lifelong, debilitating respiratory trouble.

Once it was released, mustard gas remained active for weeks. A soldier who dived into a foxhole contaminated with mustard gas would suffer burns, or blindness, or both. A soldier who tramped through a muddy puddle laced with mustard gas would find his feet and legs covered with agonizing blisters. Mustard gas was one of the most feared weapons in a war notorious for introducing so many terrible new ways to kill.

A casualty of mustard gas was an Austrian soldier, Adolf Hitler, serving with the Bavarian Reserve Regiment 16. He suffered temporary blindness.

It has been estimated that by the end of the war in 1918, the Germans had used 68,000 tons of poison gas, the French 36,000 tons, and the British 25,000 tons. Although the Americans entered the war late, U.S. production of poison gas was astonishing: at Verdun on November, 1 1918, just ten days before the armistice, the U.S. artillery fired shells bearing mustard gas—36,000 of them—into the German lines. After the war the United States continued to manufacture and stockpile the deadly gas, producing 200 tons a day.

No remorse

The abdication of Kaiser Wilhelm II and Germany's surrender to the Allies was a crushing blow for an ardent patriot like Fritz Haber. But his situation became much worse in the summer of 1919, when a friend warned him that as the mastermind behind the use of chlorine gas on the battlefield, the Allies had included his name on a list of war criminals. By this point Haber had remarried—a woman twenty years his junior—and had another child, a daughter. He assembled his family, including Hermann, now seventeen years old, and fled to Switzerland where he succeeded in acquiring Swiss citizenship. The Habers had settled in St. Moritz when Fritz received word that it had all been a false alarm—the Allies were not after him, and he was free to return to his home in Berlin.

In Germany, Haber, the recent fugitive, learned that he had won the Nobel Prize for Chemistry—not for his invention of chlorine gas, but for discovering a method to produce ammonia (up to that time, a substance devilishly difficult

Following pages: German stormtroopers wearing gas masks emerge from a thick cloud of phosgene gas laid as cover for an attack on British lines.

to manufacture) on an industrial scale. There were protests from France and the United States, but the Nobel Committee did not back down—Haber had been nominated several times already and his ammonia process deserved recognition.

Haber never expressed any remorse for creating a chemical weapon. In fact, he displayed in his office a framed photograph of the first gas attack at Ypres. Secretly he was involved in further research into chemical weapons, in preparation for the day when Germany would re-arm and resume her place amongst the world's great nations. Furthermore, he often traveled abroad, advising heads of state and generals on the most effective methods of gas warfare.

—⁂—

In the 1930s, when Germany did rise again, the resurrection was led by Adolf Hitler. With horror, Haber watched as Hitler assumed the powers of a dictator under the title of chancellor. In power at last, the Nazis began to implement their anti-Semitic agenda. They ordered Jewish judges to resign; they dismissed all Jews from the civil service. It did not matter if any of these Jews were converts to Christianity—under Nazi law, Jews were a racial group, not a religious group.

During the Easter holiday of 1933, the national newspaper for the sciences published an article about Haber's research institute in which the author claimed:

> The founding of the Kaiser Wilhelm Institute in Dahlem was the prelude to the influx of Jews into the physical sciences. The directorship of the Kaiser Wilhelm Institute for Physical and Electrochemistry was given to the Jew F. Haber, the nephew of the big-time Jewish profiteer Koppel. The work was reserved almost exclusively to Jews.

But as Haber's biographer, Thomas Hager, points out, "Haber was not related to Koppel and three-quarters of the workers in his institute were not Jewish." Rather than be forced out, Haber resigned. All across Germany Jews were expelled from their posts at universities and scholarly institutes, which were also forbidden to admit Jewish students. "I am bitter as never before," Haber wrote to a friend.

Now Haber spent his days trying to find a position outside Germany. Late in 1933 he received the offer of a research post in Cambridge, England. The offer came with the promise of British citizenship, and Haber accepted at once.

In Cambridge, Haber was often ill and depressed—some of his colleagues at the research institute who were veterans of World War I shunned him.

After only two months in Cambridge he decided to travel to Switzerland for medical treatment. While staying at a hotel in Basel, he suffered a heart attack and died.

When Hermann Haber opened his father's will, he found that it had been written very recently, in Cambridge. Amongst his instructions, Fritz Haber asked for this epitaph on his headstone: "He served his country in war and peace as long as was granted him."

Zyklon B

Fritz Haber also invented Zyklon B, the deadly cyanide gas the Nazis used to murder more than one million people in Auschwitz and other concentration camps. Unlike the chemical weapons he had developed for Germany during World War I, Haber created Zyklon B as an innocent substance intended as an insecticide, and until the 1940s that is how it was used—to fumigate vermin-infested buildings and clean lice-infested clothing.

Being cyanide-based, Zyklon B is an extremely dangerous compound, and on exposure to the air releases poisonous fumes. It was manufactured in small, soft pellets that looked like bits of cotton, and was stored in airtight metal canisters.

By 1941 the Nazis were searching for a more efficient method to dispose of Jews, Slavs, Gypsies, Russian prisoners of war, and other persons they considered undesirable or subhuman. German troops assigned to the execution squads frequently suffered nervous breakdowns—the mental and emotional strain of shooting hundreds of civilians, especially women and children, was more than many of these men could bear. Early on the Nazis had initiated a euthanasia policy, killing mentally disabled individuals by locking them in a sealed van and pumping in carbon monoxide. While carbon monoxide poisoning was effective, it took a long time—up to twenty minutes—and the Nazis intended to exterminate millions. Poison gas was the answer, but they needed a fast-acting one. It is believed that it was Adolf Eichmann of the SS who learned about Zyklon B and recommended a trial of its effectiveness.

At Auschwitz on September, 3 1941, a group of Russian prisoners of war was herded into a windowless room. The doors were locked and sealed, and Zyklon B was released through grates in the ceiling. The deadly fumes spread quickly and within minutes all the prisoners were dead.

The Nazis were encouraged by these results and went on to establish gas chambers at Auschwitz-Birkenau, Majdanek, Mauthausen, Sachsenhausen and Dachau, amongst other places.

The flaming coffin
The Wright brothers build the first military aircraft

SCIENTISTS: Wilbur and Orville Wright

AREA OF SCIENCE: Aeronautics

MAIN INVENTION: Aircraft

THREE DAYS AFTER GERMANY INVADED Belgium en route to northern France, Lord Kitchener, Secretary of War, rushed the British Expeditionary Force (the BEF) to France to help the Belgians and the French repulse Kaiser Wilhelm's army. Amongst the BEF's equipment were thirty-seven aircraft, none of which was armed.

That changed on August, 22 1914, when a 23-year-old Dorset farmer, Lieutenant Louis A. Strange, mounted a Lewis machine-gun on a Farman aircraft and took to the skies. This was the first armed aircraft in history, and Strange had not been aloft long before he encountered a German observation plane. Strange attacked, firing his machine-gun. The German pilot returned fire with the only weapon he had on board—his pistol. Even so, the German had the upper hand—his plane could rise to 5,000 feet, while Strange's Farman could not climb above 3,500 feet.

The German got away, and when Strange returned to base his commanding officer assumed it was the weight of the machine-gun that had kept the Farman from achieving a higher altitude. He ordered Strange to leave the machine-gun behind on future missions.

The bizarre short-sightedness of Lieutenant Strange's commander was a temporary anomaly. In April 1915 Strange was back in the air, this time in a Martinsyde S1 fighter armed with a Lewis machine-gun. Once again he

The Wright brothers, Orville (left) and Wilbur (right), American aviation pioneers, pictured in 1909, were always formally dressed even when working alone.

encountered a German observation plane, and once again he attacked, his Lewis gun blazing. He spent all forty-seven rounds without hitting the enemy, but Strange would not give up. He decided to reload—a tricky business aboard a Martinsyde. To replace the machine-gun's drum, Strange had to unbuckle himself from his seat, stand up in the cockpit, remove the empty magazine and replace it with a fully loaded one, all the while keeping the flight controls steady with his knees.

Strange pulled at the empty ammunition drum, but it would not come loose. As he yanked at the thing he lost control of the plane: it flipped upside down and went into a tailspin. Fortunately, Strange was still hanging on to the immovable drum. In what must be a classic example of nerves of steel, he let go of the drum, strapped himself back into the cockpit, righted his plane and brought it back to base. His approach to the landing strip was too fast—he struck the ground with such a jolt that the wicker pilot's seat splintered and pieces flew into the controls, ruining them. But Lieutenant Strange climbed out of his battered cockpit unharmed.

"A surge of joy"

In 1908 the Wright brothers received a contract from the U.S. Army to produce military aircraft. The price was $25,000, but the army stipulated that the plane must carry two men, have enough fuel to travel a distance of 125 miles, and fly at a top speed of 40 miles an hour. Furthermore, the Wright brothers and their team would be obliged to train three pilots. But the army also offered a bonus— for each mile per hour the Wrights' plane flew above the 40-mile benchmark, the army would pay $2,500.

The first flight school candidate to go up in the air was Lieutenant Benjamin Delahauf Foulois, a 29-year-old aviation enthusiast, who was also a perfect physical specimen as a pilot—he weighed only 130 pounds, an important consideration at a time when an aircraft could not lift much weight. The lessons were held at Fort Myer, an army post adjacent to Arlington National Cemetery across the Potomac River from Washington, DC. Foulois described his plane as "only a bag of air holding me up and four Oregon spruce bars held together by wire holding me in. But being airborne, with the controls in my hands and the hot engine blasting me in the face sent a surge of joy through my whole body that defied description." The flight lasted only ten minutes, and Foulois was euphoric during every moment.

The presence of the Wright brothers and their flying machines attracted throngs of visitors to Fort Myer. Orville Wright complained to his sister Katharine that he could scarcely get any work done, because "I have to give my time to answering the ten thousand fool questions people ask about the machine." Orville's patience had a limit, and as he and his team of mechanics set to work they learned to ignore the crowds around them and pay no heed to the questions. Lieutenant Foulois recalled that Orville and his mechanics "talked only to each other, as though they were on a desert island miles from civilization." They had much to keep them focused on the job, not least the problem of getting the airplane up to the required speed of 40 miles per hour. Just as the army offered a bonus if the aircraft surpassed that speed, it exacted a monetary penalty if the speed fell short. But luck was on the Wright brothers' side. As Tom Crouch, their biographer, tells it, "Some higher octane gasoline, a set of new oil cups, and a bit of tinkering with the magneto solved the problems."

On September, 9 1908, Orville took up the prototype of the military aircraft to see how the tinkering had paid off. It must have been a tense moment, since three members of President Theodore Roosevelt's cabinet had showed up to watch the flight. Orville took off and remained aloft for 57 minutes, 13 seconds—the world record for the longest plane flight. Delighted with the results, after a few minutes on the ground Orville decided to go up again. This time he remained aloft for 62 minutes, 15 seconds. The third time, he took along one of his student pilots, Lieutenant Frank Lahm, and once again set a record, this time for flying with a passenger—6 minutes, 24 seconds.

In the days that followed Orville repeatedly broke his old records and set new ones. Everyone involved with the project was excited. On September, 17 Orville invited Lieutenant Thomas Selfridge, another of his student pilots, to join him on a test flight. They were circling Fort Myer at an altitude of about 100 feet when the plane began to shake violently. As Orville tried to cut the power, the left wing dipped and the plane plunged toward the ground, crashing outside the gates of Arlington National Cemetery.

Mechanics and observers raced to the site, where they found Orville and Selfridge bleeding and unconscious amid the tangle of debris. They were carried on stretchers to the post hospital, where Orville was treated for a broken hip, several broken ribs, a back injury, and lacerations to the head. Selfridge was in worse shape, with a severely fractured skull. He was rushed into surgery, but died minutes after the operation was completed. Thomas Selfridge became the first person to die in a powered airplane crash.

The bicycle shop

The Wright brothers, Wilbur (1867–1912) and Orville (1871–1948), were the two youngest of the Wright family's five children. They were a close-knit group: their father Milton Wright's attachment to his family led him to keep in touch by visits or letter-writing with even his most distant relations, and after he married Susan Koerner he visited and wrote to her relatives as well as his own.

A bishop of the Church of the United Brethren in Christ, Milton Wright was often away from home, preaching to far-flung congregations or attending to church business. In 1878 he returned home from one of his journeys with a gift for Wilbur and Orville—a toy helicopter made of bamboo and paper, with a rubber band that was twisted to turn the propeller. In the hands of eleven- and seven-year-old boys the toy soon broke, but the brothers made themselves a new one.

Young Wilbur was a natural athlete, especially good at gymnastics. Orville had an entrepreneurial streak. Pulling his wagon up and down the streets of Dayton, Ohio—their hometown—he collected bones that he sold to the fertilizer factory and scrap metal that he sold to the junkyard. In their teens the boys teamed up to make money by repairing bicycles (as a boy, Wilbur had saved his money and purchased a high-wheel bicycle). The late 1880s and early 1890s saw a bicycle craze sweep across the United States. In 1890, some 40,000 bicycles were manufactured to meet the rising demand, and by 1895 that number had soared to 1.2 million. With so many bicycles on the road, the need for bicycle repairmen increased.

In 1893, Wilbur and Orville opened the Wright Cycle Exchange in Dayton, where they sold new bicycles from the showroom in the front and repaired damaged bicycles in the shop at the back.

At the same time that they were building their bicycle business the Wrights had become interested in aviation, particularly the work of Otto Lilienthal, a German who perfected manned flight aboard a glider. His death in a crash in 1896 troubled the brothers, and they began to study the possibility of powered flight. They wrote to the Smithsonian Institution in Washington, DC, asking for a list of the best books on aviation. One of the titles recommended was Chicago engineer and aviator Octave Chanute's *Progress in Flying Machines*, a work that made such an impression on the Wrights that they began to correspond with the author—the beginnings of a professional and personal friendship that would last for years.

Three problems

Through their reading, their discussions with Chanute, their own observations, and several trial-and-error experiments, the Wrights narrowed down the difficulties of manned flight to three primary problems: the shape of the wings that would lift the aircraft off the ground, balancing the aircraft once it was in the air, and finding a method of propulsion.

In October 1900 Wilbur and Orville and a team of mechanics traveled to the high sand dunes of Kitty Hawk on the coast of North Carolina, a spot

Orville Wright at the controls of the Wright Flyer as it takes off from a sand hill at Kitty Hawk, North Carolina on December, 17 1903. On this day the brothers took turns at flying the machine.

recommended to them by the Weather Bureau in Washington, DC, because of the strong winds and open space. Here they built and tested unmanned gliders that were in essence very large kites which they controlled from the ground with long lead-lines. They hoped these experiments would help them sort out the problems of designing a manned, mechanically propelled aircraft, but their tests only spotlighted new problems. At one point Wilbur lamented, "Nobody will fly for a thousand years!."

At Kitty Hawk, and back in Dayton, the Wright brothers focused on the shape of the wings and various methods to control them so that a pilot could turn the aircraft left or right, up or down. In 1902 they discovered that if they linked the wing mechanisms with the rudder, the aircraft would turn smoothly in any direction the pilot required. The next problem they had to face was building an engine.

A bumpy ride

Incredibly, the press paid almost no attention to the first manned, engine-powered flight.

After the success at Kitty Hawk, Orville Wright telegrammed his father, urging Bishop Wright to "inform the press" of their achievement. A newspaper in Norfolk, Virginia, published a story on the flight, but got so many of the facts wrong that Wilbur and Orville issued a press release to the Associated Press. Their announcement did not set off the firestorm of excitement and publicity they had expected. Newspaper publishers had been bamboozled so often by other "inventors" claiming that they had been "the first to fly" that they were reluctant to publish yet another unsubstantiated account.

In the spring of 1904, the Wrights invited members of the press to a demonstration of their aircraft to be held at a cow pasture outside Dayton. On the day appointed, unfavorable winds combined with a balky engine forced the brothers to cancel and reschedule the demonstration for the next day. A few reporters turned up again, but as the aircraft was about to lift off the engine failed and the tail of the flyer dropped to the ground with a dull thump. After this debacle, the local press wrote off the Wrights as just two more charlatans.

As a result of the Wrights' failure to win recognition as the first men to fly, in October 1906 the Frenchman Alberto Santos-Dumont managed to get his odd-looking tailless biplane off the ground, and as a result proclaimed to France and the world that *he* was the first man to fly.

All previous would-be inventors of a manned aircraft had been thwarted by the weight of the gasoline engines available at the time. The engine the Wrights built was no lightweight—it tipped the scales at more than 198½ pounds—but the brothers were convinced that the speed generated by this 12 horsepower engine would be enough to lift their 705½ pound aircraft, its pilot and of course the engine itself. And they found something useful in their own bicycle shop—two long bicycle chains, which they used to connect the aircraft's twin propellers to the engine.

In December 1903, the Wright brothers and their team packed up their latest aircraft and traveled back to Kitty Hawk. The aircraft they would be testing measured 21 feet 1 inch in length, stood 9 feet high, and had a wingspan of 40 feet 4 inches. With its water-cooled, four-cylinder, 12 horsepower engine the Wright Flyer—as it has come to be known—weighed 745 pounds. The Wright brothers calculated that it could fly—if it did fly—at 30 miles per hour.

The morning of December, 17 1903 was bitterly cold, with an icy 24 mile an hour easterly blowing in off the Atlantic. A few spectators had climbed to the top of the sand hill to see if the aircraft would get off the ground: they included men from the Kill Devil Hills Lifesaving Station and some young boys from the neighborhood. At 10:35 in the morning, Orville Wright climbed into the pilot's position and started the engine. With a jerky motion the aircraft went forward and lifted off the ground into the headwind, remaining airborne for 12 seconds and traveling a distance of 39 metres. At that moment the dream of Icarus was fulfilled—man could fly.

Orville alone

In 1912 the Wright brothers were still manufacturing planes for the U.S. military, delivering them one at a time (mass production was not possible at this stage). In mid-May 1912, Orville went to Washington with a new plane; back in Dayton, his brother Wilbur, who had been ailing with what doctors believed was malaria, felt very ill and called for an attorney to help him prepare his will. On May, 18 Wilbur fell into a coma; the family telegrammed Orville, who hurried back to Dayton. Over the next ten days a stream of doctors visited Wilbur, prescribing opiates amongst other medications, all of which proved useless. At 3:15 on the morning of May, 30 1912, Wilbur Wright died. His father recorded in his diary his son's age: "45 years, 1 month, and 14 days", and added this brief eulogy:

"A short life, full of consequences. An unfailing intellect, imperturbable temper, great self-reliance and as great modesty, seeing the right clearly, pursuing it steadfastly, he lived and died."

The loss was doubly tragic for Orville. The brothers had been inseparable since boyhood, and as pioneers in the field of aviation it was Wilbur who had managed the business side of their affairs. A natural leader, Wilbur had been perfectly at ease giving orders to mechanics, presiding over board meetings or courting wealthy New York investors. Orville, although a charming man amongst family and friends, felt uncomfortable amongst strangers and disliked being the one who had to make all the decisions. He accepted the presidency of the family aircraft manufacturing firm, the Wright Company, because he had no choice, but he kept his distance—literally. Rather than move into an office at the aircraft factory, Orville worked out of the office above the brothers' bicycle shop. Instead of visiting the factory, he issued orders through his secretary, Mabel Beck. One of his closest friends, Grover Loening, said of Orville, "He certainly did not have any 'big business' ideas or any great ambition to expand. He seemed to be lacking in push." Three years later, in 1915, Orville sold the Wright Company for an undisclosed sum (although the *New York Times* reported the sale price as $1.5 million).

Orville had unburdened himself of a job he hated and at the same time made himself a very wealthy man. But he could never give up the desire to tinker, to invent, to produce wonderful new machinery. By 1918 he and several friends had joined together to establish a new aircraft manufacturing firm, the Dayton-Wright Company. When the United States entered World War I, the American military ordered 4,000 warplanes from Dayton-Wright.

Luck and daring

When World War I broke out in August 1914, Germany had 1,200 fighter aircraft, while Britain and France had a combined air fleet of about 1,000 planes. Amongst the aircraft that were put into action during the first year of the war were the BE-2, a reconnaissance biplane built by Captain Geoffrey de Havilland (founder of the De Havilland Aircraft Company); France's Nieuport scouting biplane; and the German Albatross, also used for scouting. Initially, aircraft were seen as an innovative way to gather intelligence about an enemy's strength and position. It did not take long, however, for the combatants to recognize the possibilities of armed aircraft.

In February 1915, Roland Garros, a French pilot, mounted an automatic rifle on the cockpit of his Morane monoplane, right behind the propeller which he had armored with protective steel plates. If one of the bullets struck one of the propeller's plates, there was an excellent chance that it would ricochet back to the cockpit, wounding or killing Garros. Somehow, in defiance of the odds, it never happened.

Garros was as lucky as he was daring. In the space of sixteen days he shot down five German planes, becoming the first Allied flying ace of the war. On April, 19 1915, engine trouble forced him to land behind enemy lines; both Garros and his plane were captured by the Germans, yet even under these circumstances his luck held up—Garros escaped.

The loss of Garros did not trouble the Germans—it was his plane that fascinated them. How could he fire that rifle without hitting his propeller?

The plans patented in 1908 for the Wright brothers' airplane; the drawings were made by W. B. Robinson from the brothers' specifications.

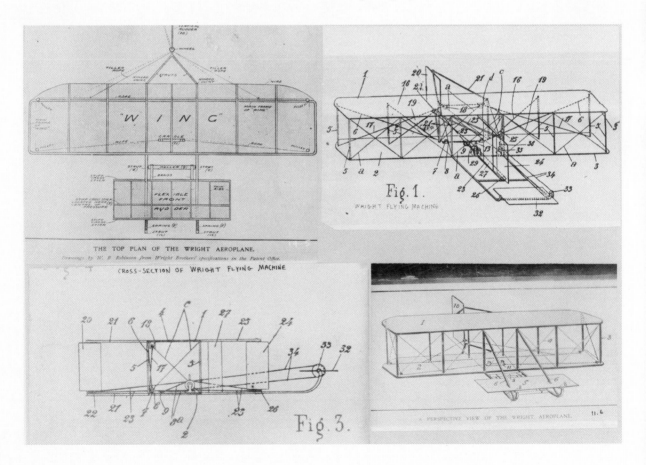

197

At the war's start the Germans had hired Anthony Fokker, a Dutch aircraft designer, to build warplanes. Now they called on him to examine Garros' plane and find a safe method of using a forward-firing gun. Within two days Fokker had the solution—a rod-and-lever mechanism that synchronized the firing of the gun with the propeller's spin so that each shot went between the blades.

A few high-ranking German officers insisted on a real-life demonstration. Although he was a non-combatant from a neutral nation, Fokker acquiesced. He took the plane to the air, where he spotted a French aircraft. He was about to fire, but suddenly stopped. "I had no wish to kill Frenchmen for the Germans," he explained later. "Let them do their own killing!"

The Germans put Fokker's new design into production, and called the plane the Fokker Eindecker, German for monoplane. With the Fokker, Germany had its first two aces—Lieutenant Oswald Boelcke and Lieutenant Max Immelmann. It was Immelmann who developed the distinctive loop and roll maneuver—known ever since as the Immelmann Turn—to evade a pursuer. With seventeen kills to his credit, Immelmann was a German hero. His death in June 1916—shot down by the English pilot George McCubbin— so demoralized Kaiser Wilhelm II that he grounded Lieutenant Boelck rather than put at risk another German ace. But four months after Immelmann's death, Boelcke was back in the air. During a dogfight in October 1916, another German plane accidentally struck the wing of Boelcke's aircraft. It spun out of control and crashed, killing Boelcke instantly.

"The Flaming Coffin"

In spite of the Wright brothers' pre-eminence in aviation and their early contracts to build military aircraft, the fighter planes Dayton-Wright manufactured during World War I were not as good as, let alone superior to, the aircraft being produced in Europe. Thus in 1917, as the United States prepared to enter the war, the military felt it could not wait for new American-designed fighter planes and bombers and had a British De Havilland 4 (DH-4) two-seater bomber delivered to Dayton-Wright as a model.

Orville Wright, his engineers and mechanics, redesigned the British plane to accommodate the American Liberty engine (the British model came equipped with a Rolls-Royce engine). It took time—the first American-made DH-4 did not arrive in France until May 1918, and did not fly its first combat mission until August.

Wilbur and Orville Wright, with Charlie Taylor, placing their plane on the launching rail at Fort Myer, Virginia in July 1909. Smooth launching rails were used to help develop momentum before a wheeled undercarriage was developed.

The American made DH-4 was armed with two .30-calibre Marlin machine-guns in the nose, two .30-calibre Lewis machine-guns in the rear, and 1322 pounds of bombs. With its 400 horsepower Liberty engine it could cruise at 90 miles per hour, reach a maximum speed of 127 miles per hour, and had a range of 397½ miles. Fully loaded with weapons and fuel, the DH-4 weighed 3,565 pounds. The going price was $11,250 per plane.

Back in Ohio, Dayton-Wright put Orville to work as a one-man public relations device. Before crowds of journalists and newspaper photographers he made demonstration flights in the Dayton DH-4 planes, but his celebrity status and all the positive publicity couldn't mask the drawbacks of the Dayton-Wright design. The fuel tank was positioned between the pilot and his crewman/gunner in the rear seat, increasing the distance between the two and making it difficult for them to communicate in mid-flight. Much worse was the fuel line's tendency to burst into flames, and the engine's propensity to explode. American airmen nicknamed the DH-4 plane from Dayton "the Flaming Coffin."

A new kind of warfare

If the American-made DH-4 was disappointing, British, French, and German designers created the best planes of World War I. Especially popular with the British Royal Naval Air Service was the Sopwith Pup, a fast plane, easy to maneuver, that could outclimb every other fighter plane in 1917. France produced the SPAD S.XIII, a powerful fighter plane that became the favorite of American ace Eddie Rickenbacker.

Both the British and the Germans produced heavy bombers. In Britain the twin-engine Handley Page 0/400 carried 1,808 pounds of bombs. The German Gotha G.V. carried a payload of 3,307 pounds, yet was surprisingly agile for its size, which made it difficult to shoot down. By the end of the war the British had built a four-engine bomber that could carry 7,518 pounds of bombs; they intended to use it to bomb Berlin, but before this giant could be deployed against the enemy, the Armistice ended the war.

Arguably the most important and innovative aircraft of World War I was the German Junker J.I. It was the first mass-produced all-metal aircraft, constructed of duralumin 9 (an alloy of aluminium and copper, manganese, magnesium, iron, and silicon). The engine and the two cockpits were protected by 5.5 millimetre plates of sheet steel. While this armored plane was almost impervious to anti-aircraft fire on the ground, the Junker's weight—4,729 pounds—made it difficult for the aircraft to achieve lift-off. A Junker required a very long runway.

—⁓—

The dogfights between aces blessed with nerves of steel and lightning-fast reflexes are part of the lore of World War I, and by the final weeks of the war the Allies had learned how to use air power against ground forces. Waves of Allied fighter planes targeted masses of German infantry; Allied bombers attacked railways and supply depots. It was a new kind of warfare that challenged the privileged place infantry and artillery had held in land wars for at least two centuries, and it took the German commanders by surprise. Had the war lasted longer and had the British sent their heavy bombers over Berlin, the Germans might have suffered an even greater shock, although how effective those bombers would have been is open to debate—in 1918, precision bombing did not exist.

Fighter planes and bombers changed warfare forever. As historian Arthur Gordon writes in *The American Heritage History of Flight*, there was a new maxim for commanders: "If you hold the air, you cannot be beaten; if you lose the air, you cannot win."

Traveling caterpillar fort
Lancelot de Mole's tank

SCIENTIST: Lancelot de Mole

AREA OF SCIENCE: Mechanical engineering

MAIN INVENTION: Tank

THE SIGHT OF THE PHARAOH cut off from his troops, with only the royal bodyguard to defend him, filled the Hittite king's heart with fierce elation. He urged on his charioteers, certain not only of victory, but of making Ramses II his prisoner.

Driving at full speed, the Hittite charioteers smashed into the first rank of the royal bodyguard, splintering the Egyptians' wood-and-leather shields and crushing the men beneath their wheels. Some members of the bodyguard threw themselves at the chariots, seizing the horses' reins in a desperate attempt to drag them to a stop. The wild courage of these men inspired their comrades to mount a counterattack against the Hittites. They fought on foot—for in the entire Egyptian camp only one chariot, that of Ramses, had its horses standing ready in the traces. The 25-year-old pharaoh called his driver, Mennu, to prepare to attack the Hittites, but Mennu refused to obey his king—the fear of being slaughtered outweighing his fear of what Ramses might do if, by some miracle, he turned back the enemy and won the battle.

Enraged, Ramses climbed into his chariot alone, tying the reins around his waist so his hands would be free to fight. Then, calling on Amun, the king of the gods, to give him strength, the pharaoh drove toward the Hittite ranks. But he met no resistance. Having scattered the Egyptian forces, the Hittites had dispersed to loot the Egyptian camp. While they hunted for valuables, a handful

Lancelot de Mole, little-recognized designer of the first caterpillar-tracked armored vehicle, enlisted in the 1st Australian Imperial Force (AIF) in September 1917.

of Ramses' bodyguards harnessed horses to a number of other chariots; they were joined by a few charioteers who initially had fled but now returned to fight with their king. With this small band, Ramses attacked the eastern flank of the Hittite army, taking it by surprise and driving it back across the Orontes River where the Hittite king, Muwutallis, watched the battle with his reserve infantry and 1,000 additional charioteers. Muwutallis ordered the 1,000 to launch a counteroffensive and, as they splashed into the river, Ramses saw his opportunity. The chariots would have to climb a steep muddy bank before they could get into formation to attack the Egyptians. While they were in this awkward position, they were vulnerable.

With his few charioteers Ramses raced across the plain, reaching the riverbank just as the Hittite chariots tried to scramble up. Bogged down in the mud, the Hittites were in no position to defend themselves against the onslaught. After taking heavy casualties, they retreated. For three hours the Hittites made one attempt after another to cross the Orontes, each time being driven back while their losses mounted: amongst the dead were Muwutallis's two charioteers, the commander of the royal bodyguard, the royal scribe and the king's brother, Metarama.

Suddenly the Division of Ptah, approximately 8,000 men led by the pharaoh's vizier, rushed out of the Forest of Robaui. The men of Ptah had become separated from Ramses' force, but they arrived at just the right moment and at precisely the best location—at the Hittites' rear. Unable to cross the Orontes and now under attack by fresh Egyptian troops, Muwutallis ordered his men to retreat to the safety of the walled city of Kadesh. As the Hittites fled, Ramses proclaimed that he alone had won a great victory over the king of the Hittites. The Egyptian historian–poet Pentaur quotes the pharaoh as saying:

> *Not one of my princes, of my chief men and my great,*
> *Was with me, not a captain, not a knight;*
> *For my warriors and chariots had left me to my fate,*
> *Not one was there to take his part in fight.*

The first tanks

The chariot was the tank of the ancient world. It was invented in Mesopotamia about 3000 BC as an engine of war; while a skilled driver maneuvered the chariot across the battlefield, an archer kept up a barrage of arrows into enemy ranks.

That arrangement was still the rule when the first tank rolled out onto a World War I battlefield—there were men to drive the tank and operate its gears, and men to fire the cannon and machine-guns.

Since a chariot did not have shock absorbers, its jouncing and jolting over the most hospitable of terrain made it difficult for even the greatest archer to shoot accurately. To compensate, commanders took to massing their chariots, which elevated the volume of arrows fired at the enemy and increased the chances of doing some real damage. The sight of a single chariot drawn by two or four horses thundering toward them could break up an infantry formation and send the troops scattering; the spectacle of hundreds of chariots at full stretch must have been truly terrifying.

In the fifth century BC the Persians added a new element to their chariots—a long, sharp scythe blade attached to the hub of both wheels. As the chariot advanced the blades rotated, causing horrible wounds to the legs of any man or cavalry horse unlucky enough not to get out of the way. It's possible that these blades could have severed limbs.

At the Battle of Gaugamela in 331 BC, the Persian king, Darius III, sent his scythed chariots against the army of Alexander the Great. But Alexander was ready for them—he had already drilled his men to break formation, let the chariots drive harmlessly through their ranks, then close ranks, surround the chariots, and kill the drivers and the archers.

In order to be effective, chariots required flat ground. Terrain that was rocky, full of tree roots or soggy could cause breakdowns. At the Battle of Kadesh,

The tank of the ancient world: the chariot of Pharaoh Ramses II leads the Egyptian charge against the Hittites at the Battle of Kadesh in 1274 BC. (Based on a temple relief in Abu Simbel.)

Ramses II took advantage of the terrain—in this case, the steep pitch of the Orontes riverbank—to immobilize Muwutallis's chariots.

Even more effective than chariots was a kind of living tank—the war elephant. They were used in India, Burma, and Thailand, but most famously war elephants were employed by the Carthaginians in North Africa. War elephants had many advantages over chariots. In the first place, the smell of the elephants tended to terrify horses that had not been trained to accept the odor—one whiff, and the cavalry horses and the chariot teams were bolting in every direction. Secondly, a charging war elephant had no fear of a battalion of troops bristling with javelins. With its trunk the elephant could hurl a man 29½ feet. Its ivory tusks could gore, skewer, and toss. And its huge feet crushed everything in its path.

In 202 BC, at the Battle of Zama during the Second Punic War, the Carthaginian commander Hannibal lined up eighty war elephants and sent them charging into the Roman ranks. Like the troops of Alexander the Great, the Romans had been trained to move aside and let the elephants run through their ranks; despite this, some of Hannibal's elephants attacked, spreading panic amongst the legionnaires and killing and wounding an untold number.

Sixteen years earlier Hannibal had brought two or three dozen war elephants along on his invasion of Italy. Some were drowned trying to cross the flooded Rhone River. Many more died during the Carthaginians' passage through the Alps. Ultimately, when Hannibal entered Italy only a handful remained, which demonstrated that elephants were as subject to the terrain as chariots.

The traveling caterpillar fort

In 1911 Lancelot de Mole, an Australian engineer and inventor, was surveying in rugged country near Geraldton in Western Australia. Being jolted across the difficult terrain gave de Mole the inspiration for a tracked vehicle that would move effortlessly over all obstacles. As he developed the idea he imagined it as an armored vehicle for the military. In 1912 he sent drawings and a model of his "traveling caterpillar fort" to the British War Office in London.

De Mole's plans called for a tank 39 feet long with a wheelbase of 32 feet that ran on a caterpillar track constructed of hinged steel plates. It could cross a trench 16½ feet wide, was easy to steer, and could travel forward or in reverse. The chain track, attached to the steering mechanism, was encased in armor, making it more difficult for the enemy to put the vehicle out of action.

When several months had gone by and de Mole had not heard back from London, his colleague G.W.D. Breadon wrote to the Secretary of State for War, John E.B. Seely, endorsing de Mole's invention as a marvel that "can travel over broken ground, climb embankments, span canals, streams and trenches with the greatest of ease, and … if armored and manned with small quick firing guns and maxims, will quickly turn the most stubborn of armies, even if they be strongly entrenched."

Breadon received no response either. Then in June 1913 de Mole received a letter stating that the War Office had no interest in his invention. Friends urged him to take his design to the German consul in Perth, but de Mole dismissed the suggestion. If he had presented his idea to the Germans, and if the Germans had had the foresight to recognize the advantages of the tank and begun manufacturing it in quantity, ready to be deployed when World War I began, the outcome might have been very different.

On January, 5 1915, less than two years after de Mole received his rejection letter, Winston Churchill, First Lord of the Admiralty, wrote to Herbert Asquith calling for the development of armored "steam tractors" built along the lines of the "caterpillar system [which] would enable trenches to be crossed quite easily, and the weight of the machine would destroy all wire entanglements". But Breadon's letter recommending de Mole's invention—which met all Churchill's requirements—and de Mole's unwanted plans and model were gathering dust in their respective pigeonholes at the War Office in London.

Tanks and armored cars

Before there were tanks there were armored cars. They were, as the name suggests, automobiles that had been covered with boilerplate about ¼ inch thick and outfitted with machine-guns. One of the first cars to be armored in Britain was a six-cylinder Rolls-Royce Silver Ghost. Unlike the Ford automobiles, which were built inexpensively on an assembly line in America, the Silver Ghost was a bespoke, or custom-made, luxury vehicle. But it was also a sturdy, dependable car, widely regarded as the best in the world. Of course, for use in wartime it was stripped of all its luxurious doodads and fitted instead with a revolving turret armed with a .303 Vickers machine-gun. The first armored Silver Ghost was ready for military service within weeks of the war's outbreak in August 1914, and by the end of September the British government had requisitioned every Silver Ghost chassis in private hands.

British veteran Frank Canvin, who drove an armored Ghost in the Middle East during the war, recalled, "As a fighting vehicle, the design was adequate, although the traditional comfort left much to be desired." The celebrated Rolls-Royce engine still ran quietly, but an armored Ghost was much more difficult to drive than the luxury touring-car models, and had a tendency to overheat. Furthermore, the armored cars were entirely unsuited to the mire of the western front, so they were sent to North Africa, where the British were fighting in the German colonies, and to the Near East, where nine were put at the service of T.E. Lawrence—better known as Lawrence of Arabia—in his war against the Turks. Lawrence declared these armored Ghosts were "more valuable than rubies."

Tanks at the Somme

Late in 1915 a British officer, Lieutenant-Colonel Ernest D. Swinton, developed something that could traverse the no-man's-land between the trenches, and grind coils of German barbed wire into the muck—the Mark I tank. Constructed of boilerplate half an inch thick, the Mark I weighed 28 tons. It was armed with two 6-pound cannon and four machine-guns. Its eight-man crew was equally divided—four men fired the weapons, the other four drove the tank and operated its gears. With its 105 horsepower Daimler engine revving at top speed, the Mark I could race along at 4 miles per hour.

Inside, the crew suffered the torments of the damned. With almost no ventilation the tank became a rolling sweat-box. And with no suspension system, the men were jarred by every rock, log, and rut. If the tank traveled over especially rough ground, the crew could be tossed about like rag dolls, ricocheting off the steel walls. But when the Mark I first rolled onto a battlefield on September, 15 1916, stunned and frightened German troops fled or surrendered—before noon that day 8,000 men had laid down their arms. Very quickly the British introduced a improved tank, the Whippet: it weighed 14 tons, could travel at 8 miles per hour, and required a crew of three.

The tanks were assigned to the Heavy Section of the Machine Gun Corps. In September 1916, thirty-six Mark I tanks arrived in France and were put in action at the Battle of the Somme. Swinton had argued that the tanks would be most effective if they attacked the enemy positions en masse, but he was overruled by his superiors, who sent out two or three tanks at a time against various strongpoints along the German line.

Some of the tanks fell into craters. The driver of one stopped the engine and steadfastly refused to run over a road full of bodies. But elsewhere the tanks performed very well, capturing a heavily fortified German position at Courcelette, taking large numbers of prisoners in and around the village of Martinpuich, and liberating another village called Flers. The chaplain of the 151st Infantry Brigade, the Reverend Canon Cyril Lomax, reported that the

An American soldier walks ahead of an MKIV British-made tank during World War I.

tanks "certainly put the wind out of the Bosch. His favorite strong places were as nothing and they crossed trenches with ease."

A weapon with no future

The French also created a tank, the Renault FT-17; it weighed about 7 tons, traveled at approximately 5 miles per hour and had armor that was

Swinton's "Mother"

Lieutenant Colonel Ernest D. Swinton's tank prototype was christened Mother because from her all future tanks would come. In January 1916, under the cover of night, Mother was transported to a field near Hatfield Park in Hertfordshire, near a private golf course belonging to Lord Salisbury. In an effort to replicate the terrain along the Western Front, trenches had been dug across the field, and a stream dammed up so the ground would turn swampy.

On February, 2 1916, Minister of Munitions David Lloyd George, First Lord of the Admiralty A.J. Balfour, Chancellor Reginald McKenna and the Chief of the Imperial General Staff, Lieutenant-General Sir William R. Robertson, gathered at the field for a demonstration. Swinton later recalled:

It was a striking scene when the signal was given and a species of gigantic cubist steel slug slid out of its lair and proceeded to rear its gray bulk over the bright-yellow clay of the enemy parapet,

before the assemblage of Cabinet Ministers and highly placed sailors and soldiers collected under the trees.

Minister for War Lord Kitchener may have had no faith in the tank, but the observers, especially Sir William, were impressed as they watched Mother cross a 10 foot trench. After being given a ride in the tank, Balfour, one of the other observers reported, reacted with "an almost childlike pleasure." Six days later King George V came to Hatfield Park so he too could ride in the tank. Within days, the British military placed an order for 100 tanks; Swinton was given command of the new Tank Detachment and was authorized to recruit men for this new branch of the service. He advertised in *Motor Cycle* magazine, believing it was the best place to find men who had experience driving motorized vehicles. The advertisement called for men who knew how to operate "light cars"; the recruits discovered, however, that they were expected to operate a machine that weighed 28 tons.

not quite 1 inch thick. In 1917, when the United States entered the war on the side of the Allies, General John "Black Jack" Pershing ordered 400 Renault tanks. This Light Tank Service, as the Americans called it, was assigned to Lieutenant George S. Patton Jr., an aggressive 32-year-old cavalry officer who months earlier in Mexico had used three Dodge touring cars to hunt down and kill some of Pancho Villa's men. Never a shy man, Patton volunteered to lead the tank corps, arguing that he was "the only American who has ever made an attack in a motor vehicle." In a forest outside Compiègne, Patton took a Renault for a test drive, and was delighted by the machine. "It is easy to do after an auto and quite comfortable though you can see nothing at all," he reported. Then he added, "It is funny to hit small trees and see them go down."

Patton trained his tank corps at Bourg, but they waited long weeks before the first shipment of Renaults arrived. When they did, it was in time for the 1st Tank Brigade to participate in the Battle of St. Mihiel. Patton's orders were simple: "American tanks do not surrender." Unlike the French, who held their tanks in reserve at the rear, Patton brought his tanks out front, leading a reconnaissance in force—the first such maneuver ever made by tanks. But the Tank Brigade encountered no Germans—their generals had been pulling them out of the trenches at St. Mihiel to reinforce the Hindenburg Line, a vast system of fortifications erected to defend Germany's border with north-eastern France. Frustrated, Patton sent three tanks under the command of Lieutenant Ted McClure to find some Germans. An hour later he heard the sounds of battle, and an hour after that McClure returned to report that he had attacked a German battery, destroyed its guns, and penetrated the thought-to-be-impregnable Hindenburg Line. Patton was euphoric.

Soon thereafter, at the Battle of the Argonne, Patton's tanks performed less well. The dense forests and steep ravines of the Argonne were virtually impassable, and the Germans put up such a determined defense that at least half the officers of the 1st Tank Brigade were killed or wounded—the Germans' anti-tank guns, such as the 77 mm, pierced the Renaults' armor easily. Furthermore, whenever the tanks advanced, the Allied infantry held back. Without infantry support to help them knock out German batteries, the tanks were taking the full brunt of the battle.

The Germans, once they became accustomed to the sight, were not persuaded that the tank had a future in warfare. It was not until the 1920s that two officers, Erwin Rommel and Heinz Guderian, convinced the German military otherwise.

They developed the idea of a fully motorized division in which tanks, supported by infantry and artillery in armored cars and on motorcycles, would launch a *blitzkrieg*, a lightning war, against the enemy. On September, 1 1939, Adolf Hitler put Rommel and Guderian's theory into action when he launched the devastating—and successful—blitzkrieg against Poland.

"An armed caterpillar"

The secret to the success of the tank was simple: it was a tracked vehicle rather than a wheeled vehicle. The track was a series of hinged steel segments that ran in a continuous loop, like a conveyor belt. As the tank advanced, it laid down this track as if it were paving its own road. And because it moved over its own track the tank covered much more surface area while exerting much less force per unit area on the ground beneath it than an ordinary wheeled vehicle such as a truck or a jeep, or especially an armored Rolls-Royce.

Precisely who invented the tracked vehicle is a subject of debate: amongst the contenders are Fyodor Abramovich Blinov of Russia, and Americans Charles Dinsmore of Pennsylvania, Alvin O. Lombard of Maine, and Benjamin Holt of California. Whether the last named was the first to invent such a vehicle is immaterial, however—when war broke out in Europe in 1914, both the English and the Austrians wanted to purchase tracked tractors from him.

Holt had built his tractor in response to the demands of farmers who wanted to take advantage of a large fertile area of California known as the Delta. This 50 mile stretch of superb farmland covered an area north of San Francisco at the point where the Sacramento and San Joaquin rivers converged. The Delta offered some of the richest soil in the state, but the presence of the two rivers made the ground so sodden that ordinary farm equipment sank into the muck. In 1904, to alleviate this problem, Holt invented a tracked vehicle which became known as a tractor. He found a huge market for his tractors, not only in California but also across the United States, and overseas in countries that had vast areas of rich farmland, such as Argentina, Hungary, and Russia.

When war broke out in 1914, Austro-Hungarian noblemen who owned Holt tractors put them to work hauling heavy siege guns. The Imperial Army tried to place new orders with Holt, but although the United States was not yet in the war, Holt declined to do any business with the Central Powers (the collective term for Germany, Austria-Hungary, the Ottoman Empire, and Bulgaria), and instead sold his tractors to the British. It was Lieutenant-

Colonel Ernest D. Swinton of the Royal Engineers who married the armored car to Holt's track-laying mechanism and thereby brought about a new war machine—the Mark I tank. When the idea was presented to Lord Kitchener, the War Minister, he derided the tank as "an armed caterpillar [that] would immediately be shot up by the guns."

An inventor with no traction

After the war, Lancelot de Mole filed appeals requesting that his invention of the tank be recognized formally, and in some measure rewarded. And he found some support. The head of the British Commission on Awards to Inventors declared: "De Mole made and reduced to practical shape, as far back as the year 1912, a very brilliant tank invention, which anticipated, and in some respects surpassed, that put into use in the year 1916." Trevor Watson, counsel for the Ministry for Munitions, concurred: "De Mole's suggestions would have made a better article than those that went into action."

In spite of these endorsements, de Mole never received the credit he believed he deserved. The creators of the Mark I tank were awarded £18,000. De Mole received £965 in compensation for his expenses and was named an honorary corporal. In 1920 he was made a Commander of the British Empire.

De Mole's career as an inventor never got any traction. After the war he took a job as an engineer for the Sydney Water Board. At the start of World War II he brought to the Army Headquarters Invention Board a plan for steel-wire shields or screens to be used as a defense against enemy bombs. The Australian Invention Board thought the idea was promising and forwarded the proposal to military authorities in London. They examined the design, then dismissed it as "impracticable."

Lancelot de Mole died in Sydney in 1950. Today, outside his native Australia, he is virtually unknown.

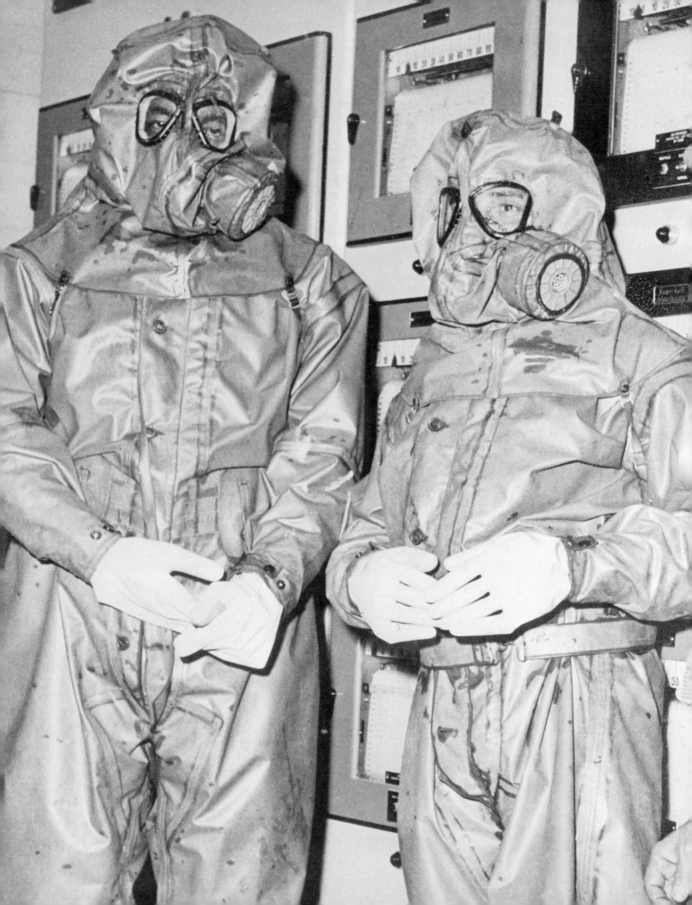

The plague zone
Ishii Shiro and the germ warfare scientists

SCIENTIST: Ishii Shiro

AREA OF SCIENCE: Bacteriology

MAIN INVENTION: Biological weapons

THE MONTHS OF MAY AND JUNE 1763 had been difficult ones for the settlers and garrisons of western Pennsylvania. American Indian tribes had captured or destroyed every English fort between Lake Ontario and Lake Erie. They had burned settlers' cabins, slaughtered any troops they met and now were laying siege to Fort Pitt (erected on the site of the present-day city of Pittsburgh).

The fort was crowded with refugees, some of whom had brought with them smallpox, causing a minor epidemic amongst the pioneer families and the garrison. In spite of these serious disadvantages, Fort Pitt's commander, Captain Simeon Ecuyer, believed that with his 250 troops plus the many frontiersmen who had sought shelter, he could drive off the Indians. His confidence was shaken when, from the parapet, he saw hundreds of warriors surging out of the forest. This was no simple war party; this was an Indian army.

On June, 24 two chiefs of the Delaware tribe stood outside the walls and asked to speak with the captain. The gates swung open, and the chiefs entered. The Delawares greeted Captain Ecuyer, then presented their terms: surrender, or face a massacre. Ecuyer refused to surrender. William Trent, a trader amongst the refugees inside the fort, recorded in his diary what happened next. As a gesture of good faith, Ecuyer presented the chief with gifts. "Out of our regard for them," Trent wrote, "we gave them two Blankets and an Handkerchief out of the Small Pox Hospital. I hope it will have the desired effect."

These "Man from Mars" suits provide protection from contamination by biological or chemical substances and were designed in the 1950s as a result of experiments in biological warfare during World War II.

No one knows where Captain Ecuyer got the idea to wage what we would now call biological warfare. We do know that his superior, Sir Jeffrey Amherst, commander of British forces in North America, approved of such measures. By chance, on July, 7 1763, while Ecuyer was waiting for his infected blankets to set off an epidemic, Sir Jeffrey wrote a letter in which he said, "Could it not be contrived to Send the Small Pox amongst those Disaffected Tribes of Indians? We must, on this occasion, Use Every Stratagem in our power to Reduce them." A week later he wrote to Colonel Henry Bouquet in Philadelphia: "You will Do well to try to Innoculate the Indians by means of Blanketts as well as to try Every other method that can serve to Extirpate this Execrable Race." (Amherst used the term "inoculate" as it was used at the time, meaning "infect." Only much more recently has it acquired the meaning of "protect against.") We do know that during the summer of 1763 smallpox raged amongst the tribes in the Ohio Valley; whether Ecuyer's two infected blankets and handkerchief were the cause is impossible to determine.

If Ecuyer, Amherst and Trent strike us as men without pity, we must bear in mind that the Indians could be just as ruthless. In 1763 Indian warriors killed approximately 2,000 settlers—men, women, and children—as well as about four hundred soldiers. In speaking of atrocities on the American frontier, there has always been more than enough guilt to go around.

A man of unshakable loyalty

In 1915, physician Anton Dilger (1884–1918) rented a house only 6 miles from the White House in Washington, DC, and set about building a laboratory in the basement.

Dilger's father Hubert had emigrated to the United States from Germany; he identified so strongly with his new homeland that when the American Civil War broke out in 1861, he enlisted in the Union army. Hubert Dilger fought at Gettysburg and Chancellorsville with such heroism and distinction that he was awarded the Medal of Honor. After the war he purchased some 1,730 acres in Virginia's lush Shenandoah Valley, one of the most fertile regions in the east and a place of great natural beauty, set at the foot of the Blue Ridge Mountains. Anton Dilger was born on this farm.

When Anton was ten years old his sister married a wealthy businessman from Mannheim in Germany. The Dilger family agreed that Anton should go to Germany to live with his sister and brother-in-law and acquire the kind of education that was not available in rural western Virginia. In Germany Anton immersed himself in his studies, was admitted to the University of Heidelberg, and received a degree in medicine. In 1902 he went back to America to visit his parents, and almost immediately became disenchanted with life on the idyllic farm at the foot of the mountains. There was no intellectual or cultural life in the Shenandoah Valley, and the Dilgers' neighbors struck Anton as provincial if not just plain ignorant. He decided to make his home in Germany, where very quickly he found work as a surgeon.

Although the younger Dilger had lost any emotional attachment he may have had to the United States he had not relinquished his citizenship, and as an American expatriate was not obliged to serve in the German Army. Just two weeks after the start of World War I, however, his German-born nephew was killed in action—and it appears that this family tragedy motivated him to volunteer as an army surgeon.

In 1915 Germany had used chemical weapons—poison gas—against the Allies; now Kaiser Wilhelm's government wanted to develop biological weapons as well. Germany's primary target was the United States. In 1915 America had not yet entered the war, but was sending the Allies weapons and supplies, as well as horses for the cavalry and mules to haul goods and heavy guns to the battlefields. The General Staff in Berlin searched for a medical man, unshakably loyal to Germany, who could enter the United States without raising suspicion, develop biological weapons, and disseminate them amongst German agents who would infect the American horses and mules before they were shipped to Europe. Anton Dilger met these criteria perfectly. As an American citizen who had been living in Germany it would seem perfectly logical that he would return home to escape the horrors of war.

In his basement laboratory Dilger cultured the bacilli for anthrax and glanders. He bottled them, literally, producing liquids infected with the diseases. Of the two, glanders would be easier to disseminate: anthrax had to be injected into the animals, but glanders would do its work as soon as it was poured over their feed or into their drinking water.

During the winter of 1915–16, German saboteurs collected their bottles of anthrax and glanders from Dilger, then traveled to three nearby ports where horses and mules were assembled for shipment to Europe—Baltimore in Maryland and two ports in Virginia, Newport News and Norfolk. All that winter army veterinarians filed anxious reports about a severe epidemic that killed approximately 3,000 horses and mules.

Dilger's act of sabotage had been a success, but the infection of the horses and mules was more of an inconvenience than a coup—it had no substantial effect on the outcome of the war. Meanwhile, in Germany, several physicians and scientists were urging the government to use biological weapons against the Allies. One medical officer proposed sending zeppelins across the English Channel to drop bombs filled with the plague bacillus on the civilian population. The government rejected the proposal as unworthy of a civilized nation.

Anton Dilger's career as a developer of biological weapons was cut short. He died in Spain in 1918, about four weeks before the Armistice, one of the first victims of the Spanish flu pandemic.

Total war

On June, 17 1925, in Geneva, Switzerland, the representatives of the United States, Great Britain, the Soviet Union, Japan, and France signed "The Protocol for the Prohibition of the Use of Asphyxiating, Poisonous or Other Gases, and of Bacteriological Methods of Warfare," declaring that "all analogous liquids materials or devices [have] been justly condemned by the general opinion of the civilized world" and that a ban against the use of such weapons "shall be universally accepted as a part of International Law, binding alike the conscience and the practice of nations." It would be no more effective than the 1899 Hague Convention had been against the use of "asphyxiating or deleterious gases."

By the time the 1925 Protocol was signed, France was already developing a biological weapons program, a situation which led the nation's representatives to insist upon an exception—that France could use biological weapons only if such weapons were used against her first. This led to the "no first use" policy, which permitted nations to develop chemical and biological weapons, but only for defensive purposes, the thought being that if all nations promised never to be the first to deploy such weapons, then no nation would ever use them. But "no first use" was also a loophole that signatories such as the Soviet Union and Japan exploited to legitimize their ongoing chemical and biological weapons programs. In the United States, too, the Senate failed to ratify the Protocol, which left both the military and private industry free to develop these terrible weapons.

In the Soviet Union, medical officer Jacov Fishman, with the encouragement of General Mikhail Tukhachevsky, produced biological weapons as part of a program designed to modernize the Soviet Army. During the purges of the 1930s Josef Stalin, whose paranoia extended to almost everyone in Russia, turned on the scientists who worked on the biological weapons program. In 1937, Fishman was imprisoned and Tukhachevsky was executed.

About the same time that Fishman and Tukhachevsky were being purged by Stalin, Adolf Hitler was re-arming Germany. In Canada, Sir Frederick G. Banting, a medical scientist, one of the co-discoverers of insulin and a Nobel Laureate, concluded that the Nazis really would be ruthless enough to use germ warfare against their enemies. Shortly before Hitler invaded Poland in 1939, Sir Frederick traveled to England where he visited members of the government, trying to persuade them that Britain's survival depended on having biological weapons it could use in its own defense. Sir Frederick's advice was not well received at first, but during the Blitz of 1940 a former cabinet secretary, Maurice Hankey, threw his support behind Sir Frederick and convinced the Minister of Supply to open a biological weapons research facility at the military science complex at Porton Down near Salisbury.

Paul Fildes, a microbiologist, was named director of the facility and began working on a bomb that would be armed with the anthrax bacillus. Fildes enjoyed the support not only of Sir Frederick but also of Prime Minister Winston Churchill, who showed an eager interest in any weapon that would ensure England's survival in the war against the Nazis. British scientists set up a germ warfare research station on the Scottish island of Gruinard, where they attempted to make massive quantities of the anthrax bacillus. The island's soil became so infected that for decades afterwards no one was permitted to set foot there.

Sir Frederick was an advocate of "total war," a doctrine that erased the distinction between soldiers and civilians. He was not alone: during World War II the Germans and the Japanese would attack civilian as well as military targets; German bombers would devastate London and other British cities; Allied bombers would level Dresden and Cologne, to name just a few; and in August 1945 the United States would drop two atomic bombs, one on Hiroshima, the other on Nagasaki. Surprisingly, Adolf Hitler, who called for the extermination of Jews, Poles, Gypsies, Russians and anyone else who opposed his will or whom he considered subhuman, was implacably opposed to germ warfare.

"Seven pounds of toxins"

By 1942 the United States was developing biological weapons, led by Theodore Roseberry and Elvin Kabat of Columbia University in New York, and Ira Baldwin of the University of Wisconsin. It was Baldwin who assured the U.S.

military that if pathogens could be created safely in a test tube, they could be created safely in a 10,000 gallon vat. The idea of unleashing germ warfare on enemy troops, or even on civilian targets, did not trouble Baldwin's conscience. Speaking with an interviewer after the war he said, "The immorality of war is war itself. You start out with the idea in war of killing people, and that to me is the immoral part of it. It doesn't make much difference how you kill them."

The Chemical Warfare Service, as it came to be known, was established at a 91 acre deserted airfield near Frederick, Maryland, some 50 miles from Washington, DC. The site was christened Camp Detrick.

The staff's first task was to manufacture 7 pounds of dried *Clostridium botulinum* toxin (which causes the disease of the nervous system known as botulism) for the British military. The deadly bacteria multiplied so quickly that the order was ready in two days. By the end of the war, Camp Detrick was home to approximately 250 army officers and 1,457 enlisted army personnel, 87 naval officers and 475 enlisted naval personnel, and nine civilians. While at one end of the camp Baldwin supervised the production of the anthrax and botulism toxins, at the other end scientists worked to create vaccines that would protect American troops and civilians in the event the Axis Powers used biological weapons against the United States.

Baldwin tended to be offhand about the dangers of working with so much toxic material. Ed Regis, a British scientist who worked at Camp Detrick, recalled a conversation in which Baldwin said, "I'm not really worried about whether you get killed or not. If you do, we'll feel sorry about it and we'll take a couple of hours off and we'll go to the funeral and we'll come home and go to work again. But if we let organisms out into the air and Farmer Jones' cows over here get anthrax and they die, we'll have a Congressional investigation that will probably shut down the whole post. So I really am not as much interested in you as I am in protecting the community."

Reaching the emperor's inner circle

In 1924 the inhabitants of the Japanese island of Shikoku were ravaged by a mysterious illness whose symptoms were emaciation and uncontrollable chills, followed by paralysis and death. Ishii Shiro, a brilliant, ambitious, 32-year-old expert in pathogenic microbiology, was sent to Shikoku to identify the disease and perhaps find a cure. He discovered that the disease was a previously unidentified mosquito-borne virus, now known as Japanese encephalitis.

Before he pinned down the culprit, approximately 3,500 people had died and the island's medical community, local government officials, and the general population lived in a state of constant terror. His experiences on Shikoku taught Ishii the power of an epidemic, and led him to contemplate whether there might be a way to harness and even direct such a disease against the enemies of Japan.

The son of a wealthy family which owned extensive property in Chiba prefecture, Ishii grew up proud and supremely self-confident, and studied medicine at Kyoto Imperial University. During the 1920s he studied the new chemical and biological weapons that had been developed during World War I; by the latter part of the decade he was urging Japan's War Ministry to initiate a program for the creation of biological weapons. His appeals went largely unheard, but once the ultra-nationalists came to power his plans for germ warfare found a more sympathetic audience.

In 1952 Soviet delegate Yacov Malik (front right) reacts enthusiastically to the UN Security Council president's demand that the United States ratify the 1925 Geneva Protocol outlawing germ warfare—which Russia had ratified way back in 1928.

In 1930 Ishii was given the rank of major and assigned to the Tokyo Army Medical College, where he was placed in charge of the Epidemic Prevention Research Laboratory. The lab's name suggested that his responsibility was to safeguard Japanese troops against disease, and in fact there were researchers devoted to that task. The lab's true function, however, was to create biological weapons that could be used in Japan's efforts to build an empire (the Greater East Asia Co-Prosperity Sphere) across Asia. Ishii immersed himself in his work, and his initial experiments were so successful that soon he was welcomed into the upper ranks of government, even gaining access to the inner circle of Emperor Hirohito.

Prison break

Like all medical researchers, Ishii had conducted his experiments with lab animals, but to ensure that his pathogens would be effective against the enemies of Japan he required human guinea pigs. It was unthinkable to conduct such dangerous experiments in Japan itself or on Japanese civilians, but as luck would have it the nation controlled all of Manchuria in northern China, a vast, underpopulated area. Assisted by the High Command, Ishii settled on a village called Beiyinhe, about 62 miles from the city of Harbin. In the summer of 1932 Japanese troops took over the village, burned every hut, and forced the villagers and other Chinese laborers they had conscripted into service to build a new facility on the site that became known as the Zhong Ma Prison Camp.

The complex was impressive—100 brick buildings that included laboratories, living quarters, a secure unit with cells for 1,000 prisoners and a crematorium. A 10 foot brick wall topped with high voltage wires encircled the camp.

In one of Ishii's first experiments three Chinese Communist guerrillas were infected with the plague bacillus. The Zhong Ma medical staff closely monitored the progress of the disease as it ravaged each subject; and when death was near, and the men fell unconscious, Ishii had all three vivisected in order to see the disease's effect on the bodies of its victims.

Zhong Ma remained in operation for less than a year. In 1933, during the Mid-Autumn Festival, when the Chinese celebrate the overthrow of the Mongol Yuan Dynasty in the fourteenth century, the camp guards drank until they passed out. Those prisoners who could get out of their cells staged a break, and although Japanese troops recaptured most of them, about a dozen had the good fortune to stumble on a band of Chinese partisans who hurried them away to a safe place. The escapees' stories of what was happening inside Zhong Ma spread rapidly across the region. Back in Tokyo, there were discussions on whether the biological warfare research unit ought to be shut down, but once again luck was with Ishii. At the same time as the prisoners escaped from Zhong Ma, Japanese military police had captured five Russian saboteurs in Manchuria: they were carrying bottles filled with the bacteria that cause dysentery, cholera, and anthrax. That persuaded the High Command—if the Soviet Union had biological weapons, then Japan must have them, too.

A plague zone

The Japanese government ordered Zhong Ma abandoned and built Ishii a new, larger facility 43½ miles away at Pingfan. Known as Unit 731, it could hold 3,000 prisoners. Jeffrey A. Lockwood, author of *Six-Legged Soldiers: Using Insects as Weapons of War*, writes that thanks to the goodwill Ishii had cultivated with the Japanese government, he was granted an annual budget of 10 million yen, an appropriation that rivaled the budget the U.S. Congress granted to the Manhattan Project. Unit 731 was an enormous facility, and required a much larger research staff than Zhong Ma. According to Lockwood, during the time Unit 731 was in operation, "Ishii routinely spent three months a year in Japan, enticing top scientists with promises of unfettered research in unparalleled facilities and valued service to the nation."

The challenge for Ishii and his fellow researchers was to find an effective delivery system for lethal diseases. They tested various methods of transmission on human subjects—men, women, children, even infants. The victims were injected with various deadly bacteria, forced to inhale them, or have them smeared into open wounds. At a minimum, at least 600 human subjects were killed each year during Unit 731's twelve years of operation. Most of the victims were Han Chinese, but there were also Koreans, Czarist Russians and Jewish refugees, as well as Allied prisoners of war. And Ishii kept up the practice of vivisection, but now he no longer waited until his victim was unconscious. One medical technician who worked at Unit 731 described the process:

> *The results of the effects of infection cannot be obtained accurately once*
> *a person dies because putrefactive bacteria set in. Putrefactive bacteria*
> *are stronger than plague germs. So, for obtaining accurate results, it*
> *is important whether the subject is alive or not … As soon as the*

symptoms were observed, the prisoner was taken from his cell and into the dissection room. He was stripped and placed on the table, screaming, trying to fight back. He was strapped down, still screaming frightfully. One of the doctors stuffed a towel in his mouth, then with one quick slice of the scalpel he was opened up.

By 1940 the scientists of Unit 731 had discovered an effective method for contaminating a human population—fleas. They sprayed clouds of plague-infested fleas over the western Chinese city of Quzhou, setting off an epidemic that ravaged the city and surrounding area for six years. They repeated the attack on the southern city of Changteh and the north-eastern city of Ningbo, then on at least a dozen other cities and towns until at least 100,000 Chinese civilians were dead. The high casualty rate impressed his supporters in Japan, but Ishii was disappointed—a recent famine had taken the lives of three million Chinese, and he wanted a biological weapon that would deliver results on that scale.

Ishii's next project was to find a way to spread cholera, an especially virulent disease. Epidemiologists had found that the microscopic hairs on the common housefly can carry as many as 4 million bacteria. He created a bomb packed with a slurry of cholera bacteria and hundreds of live flies. The cholera bombs were tested over Yunnan province in the south, where the Allies had established a supply line to Chiang Kai-shek's Nationalist troops who were fighting the Japanese. After dropping explosive and incendiary bombs over the city of Baoshan—an important hub along the supply line—the aircraft returned in a second wave with their cholera bombs. The survivors of the first bombing run were infected with disease by the second bombing run, and as they fled into the countryside they carried the infection with them. Ishii's man-made cholera epidemic took the lives of 410,000 Chinese, made Yunnan a plague zone, and shut down the supply line to the Nationalists.

Escape from retribution

By 1944 the Allies were convinced that the Japanese had the most technologically advanced biological weapons on the planet, and Britain and the United States especially were anxious to ensure that this technology did not fall into the hands of the Soviets. Consequently, after Japan surrendered in August 1945, Ishii Shiro and his colleagues were offered immunity from prosecution for war crimes if they agreed to share the results of their research with the Allies. Although they had conducted inhuman experiments on helpless prisoners and developed biological weapons that took the lives of hundreds of thousands of innocent civilians, Ishii and the other scientists of Unit 731 would not face a Nuremberg-style tribunal. The offer was made by General Douglas MacArthur who, as Supreme Commander of the Allied Powers, exercised virtually unlimited authority in post-war Japan.

MacArthur's willingness to let Ishii and his fellow scientists off was part of his strategy to reconstruct Japan as a democracy, with the role of the emperor reduced to that of a figurehead. The general exerted himself not to alienate the Japanese people, so much so that many MacArthur biographers believe he alone kept Hirohito from being tried as a war criminal. Since Ishii had published articles, delivered lectures, and shown films of his work at Unit 731 to audiences that included members of the Imperial Family, it is reasonable to suspect that the emperor knew of the gruesome experiments that were being conducted there in the name of science and national security. By granting Ishii immunity, MacArthur obtained for the United States the results of the Unit 731 research, and kept his Japanese democratization plan on track.

In the years following the war, American scientists worked to create biological weapons that would almost rival the effectiveness of atomic weapons. One of the handful of voices raised against their manufacture was that of one of the first men recruited to develop them at the onset of World War II—Theodore Rosebury, who headed the airborne pathogen laboratory at Camp Detrick. In 1949 he published a book entitled *Peace or Pestilence: Biological Warfare and How to Avoid It*, in which he argued for a global ban on all biological weapons. Rosebury's timing was poor: in 1949 China fell to the Communists, while the Western democracies and the Soviet Empire had squared off in the stalemate of the Cold War. Given the volatile political situation, very few governments were willing to listen to an argument for disarmament of any kind.

On May, 3 1946, a tribunal convened in Tokyo to try fifty-five Japanese political and military leaders for "crimes against peace, conventional war crimes, and crimes against humanity." After proceedings which lasted two-and-a-half years, twenty-five were found guilty: seven of these men were condemned to death, sixteen to life in prison and two to shorter prison terms. Ishii Shiro and his colleagues were not amongst the prisoners in the dock, nor were their names or their crimes ever mentioned in court. After the war Ishii lived quietly in Tokyo, where he died of throat cancer in 1959.

The destroyer of worlds

Robert Oppenheimer, father of the atomic bomb

SCIENTIST: Robert Oppenheimer

AREA OF SCIENCE: Physics

MAIN INVENTION: Atomic bomb

AT 2:45 ON THE MORNING of Monday August, 6 1945, a B-29 taxied down one of the lengthy runways on Tinian Island in the Northern Marianas, bound for the Japanese city of Hiroshima. The pilot, Colonel Paul Tibbets, had named the aircraft *Enola Gay* after his mother. Since American troops had captured Tinian from the Japanese on August, 1 1944, hundreds of B-29s had taken off from this airfield for bombing raids over Japan, but the *Enola Gay*'s mission was unique—it carried an atomic bomb, the first ever to be used in war.

The flight took seven-and-a-half-hours, and the weather could not have been better—a sunny morning with clear skies. From a height of 31,598 feet, Colonel Tibbets released the bomb, then sped away to escape the shock wave. At 1,900 feet above its target, the bomb detonated with a tremendous flash of light and heat—directly over the parade ground of a military base where Japanese soldiers were performing morning callisthenics.

Two shock waves rocked the *Enola Gay*, the first from the explosion, the second from the force of the blast ricocheting off the ground. Tibbets and his crew looked back toward Hiroshima. "The city was hidden by that awful cloud," Tibbets recalled later "boiling up, mushrooming, terrible and incredibly tall."

The bomb's payload, equal to an explosion of 15,000 tons of TNT, obliterated 60 percent of Hiroshima instantaneously. Inhabitants who were directly beneath the blast were reduced to little heaps of ash and what looked

Manhattan Project–Robert Oppenheimer (1904–1967), pictured in 1954 in pensive pose at the Institute for Advanced Study at Princeton.

like charcoal. The heat was so concentrated it burned the shadows of pedestrians onto the walls of buildings. People 2½ miles away from ground zero suffered terrible burns. Out of a population of approximately 350,000, some 71,000 were killed outright in the blast and 68,000 were injured. And as the years passed, the death toll mounted as Hiroshima residents succumbed to a host of diseases, the result of exposure to intense radiation. In the final analysis, it is likely that the atomic bomb dropped on the city took the lives of over 200,000 people.

In Tokyo neither the government nor the military High Command had any idea what had happened at Hiroshima, except that all communication with the city had ended abruptly at 8:16 a.m. Rumors trickled in of a massive attack, which was confirmed when a staff officer was sent by plane to inspect the situation. From a distance of 99½ miles he could see an immense cloud of smoke hovering above the ruined city. Exactly what had occurred was revealed by U.S. President Harry Truman. In a pre-recorded radio address he announced that a single atomic bomb had been dropped on Hiroshima. He promised to drop more atomic bombs on other cities if Japan did not surrender immediately.

On August, 8 and 9 American planes scattered leaflets all over Japan that ominously declared:

> *We are in possession of the most destructive explosive ever devised by man. A single one of our newly developed atomic bombs is actually the equivalent in explosive power to what 2,000 of our giant B-29s can carry on a single mission. This awful fact is one for you to ponder and we solemnly assure you it is grimly accurate. We have just begun to use this weapon against your homeland. If you still have any doubt, make inquiry as to what happened to Hiroshima when just one atomic bomb fell on that city.*

Splitting the atom

What we call "atomic theory" was developed by the Athenian philosopher Democritus (*c.* 460–370 BC), who put forward the idea that everything in the universe is composed of atoms, the unchangeable, indestructible basic building blocks of nature which are always in motion (the literal translation of the Greek term *atomos* is "that which cannot be divided"). For more than two thousand years Democritus' theory remained only a theory until, in the late nineteenth and early twentieth centuries, it was proved to be essentially correct by such physicists as Ernest Rutherford, James Chadwick, and Albert Einstein. It was Rutherford, writing in 1903, who conjectured that if an atom could be split, a tremendous amount of energy would be released. "Could a proper detonator be found," he said, "it was just conceivable that a wave of atomic disintegration might be started through matter, which would indeed make this old world vanish in smoke." Science-fiction writer H.G. Wells picked up this idea and made it the theme of his futuristic novel, *The World Set Free*, in which he imagined a war fought with atomic bombs. The book was published in 1914, and its premise became reality in 1945.

The world took a giant step closer to splitting the atom in 1932 when James Chadwick, a protégé of Rutherford, bombarded beryllium with radium alpha rays and discovered previously unknown particles which he called neutrons. Inspired by Chadwick's work, Enrico Fermi, professor of theoretical physics at the University of Rome, collected a team of ambitious physicists and began bombarding various elements with neutrons to see if the atoms would disintegrate. It is said that Fermi and "his boys," as he called his colleagues, published a new article on their research almost every week. And in 1938 Fermi won the Nobel Prize for Physics.

As for splitting the atom, for most of the 1930s most physicists regarded the proposition as a daydream. And as for the hope that the energy released by a split atom would become a new source of power, Einstein and Niels Bohr were just two of the most distinguished physicists who dismissed the possibility as hopelessly remote.

At the end of 1938, Otto Hahn and Fritz Strassman of Germany, with Austrian-Swedish physicist Lise Meitner and her nephew Otto Frisch, succeeded in using neutrons to split uranium atoms in two. Such a thing had never happened before, and physics had no term for it, so Frisch borrowed from biology the term "fission" (which describes asexual reproduction, in which a single-cell organism divides itself into two or more parts).

As Rutherford had speculated more than thirty years earlier, the fission, or splitting, of the uranium atom did release energy, but it also released more neutrons. Physicists began to calculate: if the newly generated neutrons were split, and the next wave of newly generated neutrons were also split, and so on and so on in a chain reaction, the energy released could conceivably exceed that produced by the largest electrical power plants. Then again, it might also be possible to harness that energy and use it in a bomb.

A warning from Einstein

Shortly after New Year's Day 1939, Lise Meitner and Otto Frisch disclosed their findings to Niels Bohr, who was about to sail to the United States to attend a conference on theoretical physics in Washington, DC. During the ocean crossing Bohr reviewed and confirmed Meitner and Frisch's findings. At the conference he brought the news of their breakthrough to American and European émigré physicists—amongst them Enrico Fermi and a brilliant Hungarian named Leo Szilard. Following the conference, Bohr went to Princeton University in New Jersey, where he conducted more experiments with nuclear fission; at the same time Fermi and Szilard were working at Columbia University in New York, studying the possibility of producing a chain reaction. The physicists who had attended the conference all believed their colleagues in Nazi Germany were working feverishly to create an atomic bomb, and they feared what would happen to the world if Adolf Hitler had such a weapon.

In August 1939, as it became increasingly obvious that the Nazis were ready to plunge Europe into war, Szilard urged Albert Einstein to write to President Franklin D. Roosevelt to warn him that German physicists had split the atom and were trying to develop a bomb unlike anything the world had seen before.

Two months passed before Roosevelt replied to Einstein's letter. After careful consideration the president had concluded that the threat was real, and that the world could not run the risk of Hitler acquiring atomic weapons. Roosevelt set in motion government funding for a massive research effort that went by the code name of the Manhattan Project.

The man Roosevelt named as director of the project was Colonel, soon-to-be General, Leslie Robert Groves, a career army man with a solid background in the sciences—he had earned a degree in engineering at the Massachusetts Institute of Technology before entering West Point, the U.S. Army's military academy. While Groves had the right credentials, personally he was so abrasive and difficult to deal with that his own second in command confessed that he "hated his guts." He seemed an especially odd choice for this assignment, since he was outspoken about his dislike for scientists whom he regarded as obstinate, opinionated, and thin-skinned. On the other hand, as a colonel in the Army Corps of Engineers he had experience administering large building projects and handling large budgets—but he would still need someone to direct the work in the facility's laboratory.

A self-confident charmer

As scientific director Groves chose J. Robert Oppenheimer, a tall, gaunt, genius with a gift for languages, a fascination with Eastern philosophy and religion, and a penchant for Communism. In the security questionnaire he was obliged to fill out before he could be accepted for the Manhattan Project, he candidly admitted that he had been "a member of just about every Communist Front organization on the West Coast." Despite this, Oppenheimer was accepted and given security clearance—although he was kept under constant surveillance.

The shattered framework of Hiroshima's Prefectural Industrial Promotions Hall shortly after the first atomic bomb was detonated almost directly overhead in 1945.

Julius Robert Oppenheimer (1904–1967) was born in New York City. His father, Julius S. Oppenheimer, was a German Jew who had emigrated to the United States where he founded a textile import company and became very wealthy. The Oppenheimers' luxurious apartment overlooked the Hudson River, and they owned a summer home on Long Island.

As a child Robert was sickly, which kept him at home, away from other children. As a result his social skills were negligible and he spent a good deal of time alone—a condition that persisted into his twenties. He would later lament his "almost infinitely long adolescence."

At seventeen he entered Harvard University, then moved on to Cambridge University in England and Göttingen University in Germany. It was in Europe that he discovered his career as a theoretical physicist. By the time he was in his thirties the tongue-tied boy was gone; in his place was a self-confident charmer. Many women found Oppenheimer attractive, and his students adored him. Back in the United States he held two professorships, one at the California Institute of Technology, the other at the University of California.

"Absolutely essential to this project"

The first order of business for the Manhattan Project was to find a suitable location. Groves and Oppenheimer made a list of what they required in the site for their atomic research facility: it must be remote but accessible, free from extreme weather, and there must be an ample water supply nearby. The site they chose was a mesa in the New Mexico desert; they named the top-secret facility Los Alamos. This is where the atomic bomb would be invented and built.

For a time, it was anyone's guess whether Robert Oppenheimer would actually be permitted to join the Manhattan Project. His status as a Communist fellow traveler troubled the military, but Groves exercised his authority and pushed through his security clearance. "In accordance with my verbal instructions of July 15 [1943]," he wrote to the appropriate authorities in the U.S. Army, "it is desired that clearance be issued for the employment of Julius Robert Oppenheimer without delay, irrespective of the information which you have concerning Mr. Oppenheimer. He is absolutely essential to this project."

The two men never became close friends, but they developed an excellent working relationship. Groves had complete confidence in Oppenheimer's abilities, and Oppenheimer delivered. Although more a theoretician than a lab man, and despite limited experience in directing fellow scientists, Oppenheimer learned very quickly how to administer a large-scale government project, manage the staff of scientists, smooth over the clashes of culture and personality that sprang up between the scientists and the military, and inspire confidence in everyone he met. Victor Weisskopf, one of the physicists at Los Alamos, recalled: "It was his continuous and intense presence, which produced a sense of direct participation in all of us; it created that unique atmosphere of enthusiasm and challenge that pervaded the place throughout its time."

In January, February, and March of 1943 Oppenheimer was on the road continually, recruiting physicists for Los Alamos. He proved to be astonishingly persuasive, for one by one the finest scientific minds in the country—many of them recent refugees from Hitler—packed up and moved to the New Mexico desert to help beat the Nazis in the race to build an atomic bomb. Enrico Fermi, Leo Szilard, Edward Teller, Richard Feyman, Victor Weisskopf, and Robert Wilson were just a few of the great minds Oppenheimer brought to Los Alamos.

And they worked fast. By the spring of 1945, Oppenheimer and his colleagues were ready to test their bomb.

The destroyer of worlds

In southern New Mexico lies a pitiless, waterless, 74½ mile stretch of alkaline desert known as the Jornada del Muerto, the Dead Man's Trail. In the middle of this wasteland the U.S. Army built a field laboratory complete with barracks, a reinforced concrete bunker and a viewing platform for movie cameras. In the center of the site was a 98½ feet steel tower which would house what the scientists of Los Alamos called the "gadget"—the first atomic bomb. Historian Richard Rhodes described how the gadget came to the Jornada: "The core—two silver-plated plutonium hemispheres the size of a baseball and a little walnut-sized initiator of gold-plated beryllium and polonium—rode down from Los Alamos on July 12, 1945, in a shock-mounted carrying case in the back seat of an Army sedan, like a visiting general."

On the morning of Friday July, 12 1945, Oppenheimer and his assembly crew began constructing the explosive. It took all day. On Saturday its multiple detonators were attached and the gadget was winched to the top of the steel tower. On Sunday Oppenheimer made one final inspection.

All through the weekend government officials from Washington, DC, and high-ranking army men had joined the scientists from Los Alamos. At

You can't scare Stalin

The Allied leaders at Potsdam were in their second week of discussions regarding the fate of the world after the war when U.S. President Harry Truman strolled over to Prime Minister Josef Stalin of the U.S.S.R. and told him that the United States had a "new weapon of unusual destructive force". Stalin showed no hint of interest in the president's announcement, saying only that he hoped the Americans would make "good use of it against the Japanese."

If Stalin appeared blasé it was because Truman's news was not news to him. Soviet agents had infiltrated Los Alamos and other facilities associated with the development of the atomic bomb virtually from the beginning. For nearly four years the Soviet government had been receiving high-quality intelligence about the atomic bomb program, and the Manhattan Project in particular, from American members of the Communist Party and even from some of the émigré scientists who had found refuge in the United States.

Many members of the Communist Party in America, and many Communist sympathizers (known as fellow travelers) had advanced degrees and quite a few of them worked in sensitive war-related industries. One of the Soviet Union's sources was the British physicist Klaus Fuchs who, in 1941, offered his services. One of the physicists recruited to work at Los Alamos, Fuchs provided the U.S.S.R. with an enormous amount of detailed information about America's fledgling atomic weapons program.

Thanks to the intelligence passed on by American and British spies, the Soviet Union acquired an atomic bomb some twelve to eighteen months earlier than it might have done if Soviet physicists had been obliged to develop it entirely on their own. On August, 29 1949, when the Soviet Union tested its first atomic weapon, the "gadget" they used was almost an exact replica of the one detonated in the Jornada del Muerto four years earlier.

2:00 in the morning of Tuesday July, 16 they gathered at the control bunker, 2 miles from the steel tower. Quite unexpectedly a violent storm broke over the desert—howling winds, driving rain, flashes of lightning, and crashes of thunder. One of the Los Alamos physicists, Isidor Rabi, said later that everyone in the bunker was "really scared [that] this object there in the tower might be set off accidentally."

After an hour the storm cleared and the team prepared to go ahead with the test. At 5:29, when it was still dark but with a few glimmers of light on the horizon, the gadget was detonated. Said Rabi:

Suddenly, there was an enormous flash of light, the brightest light I have ever seen. It blasted; it pounced; it bored its way right through you. It was a vision which was seen with more than the eye. It was seen to last forever. You would wish it would stop; altogether it lasted about two seconds. Finally it was over, diminishing, and we looked toward the place where the bomb had been; there was an enormous ball of fire which grew and grew and it rolled as it grew; it went up into the air, in yellow flashes and into scarlet and green. It looked menacing. It seemed to come toward one ... A new thing had just been born, a new control; a new understanding of man, which man had acquired over nature.

Robert Oppenheimer recalled that at the test, "a few people laughed, a few people cried, most people were silent." As he witnessed the bomb explode with the force of 18,000 tons of TNT, a line from the Hindu sacred text, the *Bhagavad Gita*, suddenly occurred to him: "I am become death, the destroyer of worlds."

Truman's order

For more than sixty years historians and ethicists have debated President Harry Truman's decision to drop the bomb on Hiroshima. During the summer of 1945, for Truman and his advisers at least, the answer to that question was much clearer. Japan showed no sign that it was interested in negotiating surrender terms. In the Pacific the Allies were still taking heavy casualties from Japanese submarines and kamikaze pilots. And then there had been the Battle of Okinawa in the spring of 1945. For the first time Allied troops had set foot on one of the Japanese home islands, and the result was a bloodbath: the death toll ran to 12,000 American troops, 100,000 Japanese troops, and another 100,000 Okinawan civilians, some of whom had killed their families and themselves rather than live under American occupation. That experience convinced Truman and his military advisers that a full-scale Allied invasion of Japan would cost hundreds of thousands of lives. Truman came to believe that using atomic weapons against Japanese cities might shock Emperor Hirohito and his High Command into surrendering.

On July, 25 the day after he failed to alarm Stalin with his revelation about the United States' new bomb, Truman approved an order issued by Secretary of War Henry Stimson and General George Marshall instructing the Army Air Force's 509th Composite Group to drop atomic bombs on Hiroshima, Kokura, Niigata, or Nagasaki. If these attacks did not bring about Japan's immediate surrender, the 509th was authorized to continue making nuclear strikes as the bombs became available (the U.S. had only two at the time).

Almost unconditional surrender

The destruction of Hiroshima did not immediately convince the Japanese military to surrender. On August, 9 at 3:47 in the morning, another B-29, *Bock's Car*, piloted by Major Charles W. Sweeney, took off from Tinian for Kokura, an industrial city with a large arsenal. Dense cloud cover obscured the city, so Major Sweeney headed for his secondary target, the port city of Nagasaki. The crew encountered zero visibility over Nagasaki, too, but suddenly there came a break in the clouds and bombardier Captain Kermit K. Beahan spotted the city stadium. They were over their target; Captain Beahan dropped the bomb.

The bomb exploded at 1755 feet above the surface, almost exactly midway between the Mitsubishi Steel & Arms Works and the Mitsubishi-Urakami Torpedo Works. Nagasaki is a city of hills, and these reduced, to some degree, the force of the explosion. There was no firestorm such as had swept across Hiroshima, but the devastation and loss of life was still terrible. Every living thing within 1 square mile of ground zero perished. Of the city's 52,000 homes, 14,000 were destroyed outright and 5,400 seriously damaged. The explosion killed approximately 40,000 people and injured 60,000. Ultimately, as many as 140,000 people died as a direct result of the bomb.

The day after the destruction of Nagasaki, Japanese officials offered to surrender to the Allies, but on one condition—Emperor Hirohito must be permitted to remain as the nation's ceremonial head of state. That same day General Leslie Groves reported that another atomic bomb would be ready in a week or so, just in case negotiations broke down.

Rough justice

After the war President Truman appointed Robert Oppenheimer chairman of the Atomic Energy Commission, a post he held from 1947 to 1952. His opposition to the development of the hydrogen bomb, which would be even more powerful than the bombs he had helped to develop at Los Alamos, was impolitic—now that the Soviets had atomic bombs, many in the government and military believed that the United States must have an even more destructive weapon as a deterrent to Soviet aggression.

Oppenheimer's troubles were exacerbated in 1953 when his leftist sympathies and previous close associations with Communism came back to haunt him. It was a time of widespread fear in the United States that Communists had infiltrated the federal government, the military and the atomic weapons program. From this perspective, Oppenheimer's leftist politics outweighed all he had accomplished at Los Alamos. He lost his security clearance and his position as chairman of the Atomic Energy Commission.

There was a certain rough justice in Oppenheimer losing his security clearance because of his past involvement with Communist Front organizations—in hearings in the late 1940s and early 1950s he had testified against former colleagues who, because of their ties to Communism, he believed were security risks. One of the men he testified against was Bernard Peters, who had worked with him at Los Alamos. Before the House Un-American Activities Committee, Oppenheimer described Peters as "quite a Red."

Oppenheimer spent the rest of his life as director of Princeton University's Institute for Advanced Study, where he continued to study and teach theoretical physics. In 1963, President John F. Kennedy announced that he would present Oppenheimer with the Enrico Fermi Award, which honors scientists who have made significant contributions to the development and use of energy. Kennedy was assassinated before he could make the presentation, and Oppenheimer received the award from President Lyndon B. Johnson.

Oppenheimer retired from Princeton in 1966. He died on February, 18 1967, of throat cancer.

For rescue missions

Igor Sikorsky builds the first helicopter and invents vertical flight

SCIENTIST: Igor Sikorsky

AREA OF SCIENCE: Aeronautics

MAIN INVENTION: Helicopter

NINE-YEAR-OLD IGOR SIKORSKY sat curled up in a large armchair, reading yet again his favorite book, Jules Verne's *The Clipper of the Clouds*, the tale of Robur, a scientific genius who had built an electrically powered ship named the *Albatross* that rose straight up off the ground and sailed swiftly through the skies—the world's first helicopter. Once more young Igor was fascinated by this passage:

> *Torpedo-boats do their twenty-two knots an hour, railway trains do their sixty miles an hour; the ice-boats on the frozen Hudson do their sixty-five miles an hour; a machine built by the Patterson company, with a cogged wheel, has done its eighty miles; and another locomotive between Trenton and Jersey City has done its eighty-four. But the Albatross, at full speed, could do her hundred and twenty miles an hour, or 176 feet per second. This speed is that of the storm which tears up trees by the roots … In a word, as Robur had said, the Albatross, by using the whole force of her screws, could make the tour of the globe in two hundred hours, or less than eight days.*

Aeronautical engineer Igor Sikorsky followed up a distinguished career designing regular and amphibious aircraft with the invention of the first practical helicopter.

Like countless other youngsters—and adults—Igor Sikorsky was captivated by the novels of Jules Verne, who had married the classic adventure story to the technological marvels there were appearing so rapidly during the late nineteenth and early twentieth centuries. Igor's family encouraged his interest in scientific innovations—his father Ivan was a university professor who specialized in the new field of psychiatry. New ideas, like congenial guests, were always welcome in the Sikorsky family's home in Kiev.

A year later, in 1899, ten-year-old Igor built his first helicopter, using springs to propel it. For the first time he experienced the thrill of realizing an idea.

A ballooning craze

The model helicopter reflected Igor's interest in heavier-than-air flying machines. In this respect he was either ahead of his time or out of step with it, depending on one's perspective. In his native Russia the science of aeronautics still focused almost exclusively on lighter-than-air flying machines such as balloons and dirigibles. In fact, one of the most distinguished Russian balloonists of the period was Dmitri Mendeleev, better known today as the man who compiled the periodic table of the elements.

In 1899, balloons were not cutting-edge technology; in fact, balloons were more than a century old. On June, 3 1783, the two Montgolfier brothers, Joseph-Michel and Jacques-Étienne, carried a cloth bag 37½ feet in diameter into the marketplace of their hometown, Annonay, in France. The bag consisted of four pieces of linen, held together by 1,800 buttons. A rope net covered the bag, reinforcing the linen. Before a crowd of curious shoppers, the Montgolfiers suspended the bag over a fire; when it had "ballooned" to its full size, they cut it loose. Awestruck, the crowd saw the balloon soar to 1607½ feet, then travel swiftly out of sight. It was found 1½ miles from the marketplace.

The experiment in Annonay set off a craze for ballooning. In Paris, on September, 19 1783, before a crowd of 300,000 that included the renowned American polymath Benjamin Franklin, the Montgolfiers sent up a balloon that carried in its wicker basket a rooster, a duck and a sheep. This time the balloon traveled 6 miles before its hot air dissipated; the basket landed gently in a field, its animal passengers unharmed.

Two months later came the first manned balloon flight. Jean-François Pilâtre de Rozier, a teacher of chemistry and physics, accompanied by the

Marquis D'Arlandes, flew 9,514½ feet above Paris; the winds carried them 5½ miles outside the city.

Since there was no other method of flight, ballooning monopolized air travel for more than one hundred years. In 1885 the Russian Army established a ballooning school outside St. Petersburg, with the intention of using balloons as reconnaissance vehicles. Around 1905, aeronautics specialists in Russia urged the military to adopt the dirigible, invented by Count Ferdinand von Zeppelin in Germany. Touring Germany in 1908, Igor Sikorsky attended a Zeppelin demonstration. It was during that trip that he first read about the Wright brothers' successful flight in a heavier-than-air flying machine. When the Wrights traveled to Europe later that year to demonstrate their new aircraft, Sikorsky followed their progress closely.

But as much as Sikorsky admired Wilbur and Orville Wright, he did not plan to imitate them. He dreamed of a flying machine like Jules Verne's *Albatross*, a helicopter that could rise vertically into the air, hover where it liked and veer away in any direction, untroubled by wind currents.

The first failure

At the age of twenty, a year after his visit to Germany, Igor Sikorsky (1889–1972) tried to build his first helicopter. Finding himself short of cash, he borrowed money from his sister Olga to buy the materials he needed. He already had an Anzani 25 horsepower engine; he would build his helicopter around it.

He worked alone for nearly all of May and June 1909, constructing a wooden frame reinforced with wire, a transmission comprising pulleys and belts to drive the coaxial shafts, and two linen-covered steel pipes that were the twin-bladed rotors. Then came another two months of experimentation and tinkering. Despite all the effort he put into it, Sikorsky's first helicopter never got off the ground. He had failed to do some simple arithmetic: the engine could generate 150 pounds of thrust, but the entire contraption weighed 452 pounds.

He tried again in 1910, trimming the weight down to 182 kilograms (401 pounds) and adding four more blades, hoping they would counteract the weight. They did not. Years later Sikorsky pulled out the designs for those two helicopters, studied them closely and declared, "Very fine except for one thing— they couldn't fly."

Since he was getting nowhere with helicopters, Sikorsky shifted his focus to aircraft, designing monoplanes and biplanes in his trademark S-series (S for Sikorsky). His breakthrough was the two-seater S-5, which could climb to an altitude of 1607½ feet.

The Russian government was keen to add aircraft to its military arsenal. Grand Duke Alexander, the brother-in-law of Czar Nicholas II, had witnessed the Wright brothers' demonstrations in France in 1908 and returned to his homeland an ardent advocate for heavier-than-air flying machines. He told the czar that the flying machine had the potential to be a decisive weapon. Under the influence of the Grand Duke, the Imperial All-Russian Aero Club shifted their enthusiasm from balloons and zeppelins to airplanes.

An airplane with a view

In the early 1910s, Sikorsky built larger, faster aircraft. The S-6A could carry three passengers and travel at 68½ miles per hour. His success attracted the attention of M.V. Shidlovskiy, a wealthy Russian industrialist who moved amongst the top echelons of government. He invited Sikorsky to St Petersburg to take charge of a new airplane factory; Sikorsky leapt at the opportunity. There, he designed and built the giant aircraft, the S-21 Russky Vityaz, which became known as the Grand. Powered by four 100 horsepower engines, the Grand featured an enclosed cabin with large windows. There was a table and wicker chairs for passengers, and the cabin was illuminated by electric lights. And outside the cabin was a balcony. It was an aircraft straight out of a Jules Verne novel. It caused such a stir that Czar Nicholas II came to inspect it.

A month after the czar's visit, the Grand set a new world record, flying for 1 hour and 44 minutes while carrying eight passengers.

Sikorsky followed the Grand with an even larger aircraft, the S-22 Ilya Muromets, named for a Russian folk hero. This plane was 20 percent larger than the Grand, could accommodate sixteen passengers, was furnished with a toilet and, of course, had a balcony.

When Russia entered World War I in August 1914, Sikorsky's patron, Shidlovskiy, received an army commission as a major-general and was instructed by the government to build Ilya Muromets aircraft for the military. Shidlovskiy charged Sikorsky with building Russia's first air force; before the war was over, Sikorsky would receive his own army commission, also as a general. Sikorsky redesigned his luxury airbus into a flying fortress. And in aerial combat, it did very well. In July 1916, Captain G.I. Lavrov was piloting an Ilya Muromets when he was attacked by four German fighter planes. After Lavrov shot down three, the fourth German plane retreated.

When the Bolsheviks came to power in November 1917, both Sikorsky and Shidlovskiy knew they must escape the country. As a wealthy industrialist Shidlovskiy was a target for the Bolsheviks, but so also was Sikorsky—he was Shidlovskiy's colleague, an army general, and he had ties with the Romanov dynasty. Shidlovskiy decided to flee to Finland; Sikorsky chose Paris. He escaped by steamer from Murmansk, but Shidlovskiy was not so fortunate. While he and his son were trying to cross the Russo-Finnish border, they were captured by Bolsheviks and executed.

The Flying Clipper

Sikorsky's life as an émigré was not easy. In Paris he received a commission to design a bomber for the Allies, but before he could complete the design the Armistice was signed. Unable to find work in aeronautics in France, Sikorsky traveled to New York in 1919 where job opportunities also proved meagre. At one point, through the influence of some fellow Russian émigrés, he took a job teaching mathematics. Even so, his salary was so scanty that for a time he survived on bread and beans.

The large Russian émigré community in New York was Sikorsky's rock. He was a link to pre-revolutionary Russia, a man whose flying behemoths were still a source of pride for the émigrés. Although most of the Russians in New York were also short of cash, a group pooled their resources to help Sikorsky get back into the aeronautics business. Thanks to these investors, and a gift of $5,000 from the renowned Russian composer Sergei Rachmaninoff, Sikorsky started the Sikorsky Aero Engineering Corp to build commercial and passenger aircraft.

In the meantime Sikorsky married Elizabeth Siemon, a fellow Russian émigré who had lost her mother and father during the civil war that followed the Russian Revolution. Sikorsky's two sisters, Olga and Helen, along with Helen's two children and Sikorsky's daughter from his first marriage, also managed to escape Russia and come to New York.

At the farm of the Utgoff family on Long Island, working out of a chicken coop that had been converted into a machine shop, Sikorksy revived his S-series airplanes. His S-29A (A for America) was an all-metal transport plane and the forerunner of all future aircraft. One of his greatest successes came with the S–38, a twin-engine amphibious aircraft that could land on water. Pan American Airways purchased several S–38s for its new flights to Central and South America.

Sikorsky also built the S–42 Flying Clipper, a true luxury aircraft that flew Pan Am's routes across the Atlantic and the Pacific. It was a flying hotel, complete with dressing rooms for the passengers and a separate dining room where chefs prepared gourmet meals and, like the S–38, was amphibious. Travelers considered the Flying Clipper the most beautiful aircraft of its day.

The first flight

In 1938 Igor Sikorsky returned to the project he had put aside almost thirty years earlier—the creation of a helicopter. He was not alone: engineers in the Soviet Union, Nazi Germany, and France were all working on the challenge of vertical flight. Inventors in the United States, however, were receiving little encouragement—in the 1920s the U.S. Army had sunk $200,000 into a plan to build a helicopter, but none of the prototypes would fly. That unhappy experience led the military to walk away from the project, writing off the helicopter as an impossible pipe-dream.

In the late 1930s Sikorsky was working for United Aircraft Corporation, supervising construction of the Flying Clippers. Upper management agreed to permit Sikorsky to pursue this new area of aviation research, and even reassigned his engineering team to the helicopter project.

Sikorsky wanted to build a single-rotor helicopter because he was convinced that such an aircraft would satisfy the three most important criteria—control, speed, and hovering capability. Control would be his biggest challenge, as he admitted: "The main problem was control, and the difficulty was threefold. First, we had little knowledge of helicopters in general; second, we were building the first helicopter in the world with a single rotor; and third, we knew practically nothing about how to pilot a helicopter."

In a workshop in Stratford, Connecticut, Sikorsky and his team labored for months designing and building their prototype, the Vought-Sikorsky VS–300. On September, 14 1939, Sikorsky was ready for a test flight. It was a frame of steel tubing mounted on four wheels. Overhead was a single rotor with three blades. At the rear, to counterbalance the thrust of the overhead rotor, was a wooden tail-rotor. The helicopter was powered by a 75 horsepower Lycoming engine. In flight, the main rotor would turn at 255 rpm, the rear rotor at 1,700 rpm.

Sikorsky climbed into the cockpit for the first test flight. He pulled the control lever and the tethered helicopter rose into the air—only a few yards into the air, but still, it got off the ground. Then Sikorsky and Serge Gluhareff, a member of the engineering team, made tiny test flights all day long. Sikorsky described the experience as "a wonderful chance to relive one's own life." He was not being mawkishly enthusiastic; what he meant was that each little flight seemed to place him in so precarious a position that he expected to see his entire life flash before

Sikorsky at the controls during the first (tethered) flight of the VS-300 helicopter on September, 14 1939.

his eyes. He admitted that he had been a little mad to "climb into the pilot's seat and try to fly … without ever having flown a helicopter before!"

Learning how to control the machine took time. In December, Gluhareff was making a test flight when a strong crosswind flipped the helicopter. Gluhareff climbed out from under the damaged flying machine unhurt, but the crash impressed upon everyone involved in the project that they still had not found a safe way to fly their new invention.

The army comes calling

Between the first successful lift-off in September 1939 and October 1943, Sikorsky and his team made eighteen major improvements to the VS-300. It was during this period that the U.S. Army came calling. Captain H. Franklin Gregory had visited Sikorsky's workshop shortly after the VS-300 first got off the ground. Gregory was the man Sikorsky had been waiting for: someone who appreciated the possibilities of the helicopter, and had absolute faith that Sikorsky and his team would work through the problems that plagued the prototype. In July 1940, Sikorsky let Captain Gregory fly the VS-300. After an eight-minute flight, Gregory landed the helicopter almost exactly on the spot where he had taken off. Sikorsky and his team gathered around, showering the captain with effusive praise. An army man who had accompanied Gregory to the Stratford factory whispered in the captain's ear, "Don't let it go to your head, Frank. They're not congratulating you on your flight, they're just damned glad that you got the thing down again in one piece."

In January 1941, thanks to Gregory's mediation, the U.S. Army signed a contract with Sikorsky, instructing him to build a helicopter powered by a Warner 165 horsepower engine. This military helicopter, the first ever made, was named the XR-4.

That year was a memorable one for Sikorsky and his team. In April he set a world record for vertical flight, hovering for 1 hour 5 minutes. In October he began construction of the XR-4, with a single overhead rotor and a single tail-rotor. And on December, 8 1941, the day after the Japanese attack on Pearl Harbor, the XR-4 made its first flight.

Early in May 1942, pilot Les Morris took the XR-4 prototype on a long-distance demonstration flight from the Sikorsky factory in Stratford, Connecticut to Wright Field in Dayton, Ohio. He covered 757 miles in five days. By the end of the month, the U.S. military had placed its first order for Sikorsky helicopters. By the end of World War II, Sikorsky had sold 425 helicopters to the U.S. Air Corps, the Coast Guard and the Navy.

The test

The next question was: How would the helicopter be used? It was a natural for reconnaissance, but Sikorsky and his team believed it was especially well suited for rescue missions. In a demonstration staged for a group of visiting military personnel, an 26 foot rope ladder was dropped from a hovering helicopter; a man on the ground climbed on, and the helicopter flew off with the man holding onto the ladder in midair.

The strength, speed, and stability of the helicopter were put to the test in January 1944. There had been an explosion aboard a destroyer docked at Sandy Hook, New Jersey; medics were in desperate need of blood plasma for the wounded. There was a large supply of plasma in New York City, but a howling snowstorm made it impossible for cars, trucks, or any type of aircraft to reach Sandy Hook. U.S. Coast Guard Commander Frank A. Erickson decided to try a helicopter. He flew his Sikorsky through the storm from his base on Long Island to Battery Park on the southern tip of Manhattan, where he picked up the blood plasma, then continued to the waiting medical team in Sandy Hook.

For the U.S. Navy, Sikorsky's team developed amphibious helicopters: they covered the helicopters' "feet" with large inflatable rubber tubes that enabled them to land on and lift off from any body of water. The Navy used the amphibious helicopters for ocean search and rescue missions, as well as for spotting enemy submarines and convoys.

The first combat rescue mission

On April, 21 1944, Sergeant Edward F. Hladovcak was ordered to fly his Vultee L-1 Vigilant aircraft to Burma to pick up three wounded British soldiers trapped deep inside Japanese-held territory. The 23-year-old pilot retrieved the wounded men, but as he was flying back to base his plane was shot down by Japanese anti-aircraft guns. Hladovcak made a crash landing in a rice paddy; all four men scrambled out of the wreck and crawled into the jungle to hide.

For four days they suffered in stifling humidity, tormented by hunger, thirst and clouds of mosquitoes. Their situation was desperate—they were 99½ miles behind enemy lines, their wounds were infected, but no airplane could use a rice paddy as an airstrip. Their spirits lifted after the pilot of an L-5 Sentinel spotted them: he returned to drop supplies, along with a note directing them to a clearing where they were to watch for a helicopter.

Lieutenant Carter Harman had learned how to fly a helicopter at the Sikorsky factory in Connecticut. On the day Hladovcak and the British soldiers were shot down, Harman was 497 miles away in Lalaghat, India. Nonetheless, he was ordered to fly his YR–4B helicopter to the Allies' Aberdeen airstrip in Burma, and from there head to the crash site and rescue the four men. It was a hair-raising flight over mostly Japanese-held territory, not to mention crossing a 5,249 foot mountain range. And every 99½ miles Harman had to find an Allied base where he could refuel.

On April, 25 Harman reached Aberdeen and was ready to begin the final stage of his mission, flying over 62 miles of jungle to where the men were waiting. But the YR–4B was not responding properly. The intense heat and humidity of the jungle was hampering its performance. Nonetheless, Harman got his machine into the air, located the downed men, and evacuated them, one at a time, to safety at Aberdeen.

The helicopter in war

In terms of helping to win World War II, the impact of helicopters was negligible. They were important in reconnaissance, in delivering needed supplies, and rescuing troops, but otherwise their usefulness was limited.

During the Korean War, helicopters were used primarily for medical evacuations, ferrying the wounded to field hospitals, but some U.S. military leaders believed larger helicopters could be useful in transporting large numbers of men to battlefield hot spots, then evacuating them back to base after the battle had been won. That concept was put into practice in 1962 during the Vietnam War with the Bell UH-1 Iroquois, a turbine-powered helicopter popularly known as the Huey. As a troop transport vehicle, the Huey worked beautifully— it was fast, easy to maneuver, and could drop troops almost anywhere. Initially the Viet Cong panicked every time they saw a Huey coming, but soon they realized that the helicopter was extremely vulnerable to ground fire, and went so far as to issue field guides that explained exactly how to bring a Huey down. By the end of the war, the United States had lost about 2,400 Hueys in combat.

In spite of the Huey's vulnerability, the military did not withdraw helicopters from combat; in fact, they sent bigger, faster, more powerful turbo-charged helicopters to Vietnam—including armed helicopters. For the first time in history, helicopters became a firing platform. These battlefield helicopters were armed with machine-guns, grenade launchers, even guided missiles. The helicopter became the symbol of the Vietnam War, so much so that in the musical stage play *Miss Saigon*, set at the end of the war, the visual climax is the descent of a helicopter onto the stage.

In the 1980s armed forces across the globe developed heavily armed helicopters equipped with infrared and night-imaging systems. The Soviet Union used attack helicopters against civilians and guerrillas during its decade-long (1979–1989) war in Afghanistan, and the United States and its allies used them against Iraq in the First Persian Gulf War. In the Falklands War of 1982 Britain used helicopters against Argentinean submarines. Helicopters were still used as troop transports—for example, the Black Hawks that the United States and the United Nations employed in Somalia in 1993.

Although indisputably another form of airpower, the real contribution of the helicopter has been in transforming ground wars. For thousands of years infantry entered enemy territory on foot. Today, an armada of helicopters can carry thousands of troops to where they are needed, where they will be most effective, where they can take the enemy by surprise. And whether the battle is lost or won, those same helicopters stand ready to lift the troops out of the battle zone and back to safety.

—⚶—

During the last years of his long life the deeply religious Sikorsky grew increasingly unhappy that his invention had become a weapon. After his death in 1972, his family discovered that he kept a large file of newspaper clippings, all of them accounts of helicopter pilots who rescued men, women, and children from sinking boats, from floods, and fires.

Waiting for an echo
Robert Watson-Watt invents radar

SCIENTIST: Robert Watson-Watt

AREA OF SCIENCE: Physics

MAIN INVENTION: Radar

IN 1932, IN A CHEERLESS SPEECH before the House of Commons, British Prime Minister Stanley Baldwin assured the honorable members: "It is well for the man in the street to realize that there is no power on Earth that can protect him from being bombed … The bomber will always get through."

At the time the only advanced warning system against enemy aircraft was the combination of the human eye and the human ear. Of course, by the time a bomber was within eyesight or earshot, it was too late to do anything about it. And if bombers attacked by night, the situation was that much worse. In 1916 the Committee for the Scientific Study of Air Defence had suggested using electric lights to illuminate the night sky. The committee members suggested beginning with an area approximately 18½ miles wide and 99½ miles long. Of course, enemy planes could simply skirt around the illuminated area and come out of the darkness elsewhere, and to illuminate the entire island of Britain was not feasible.

Two years after Prime Minister Baldwin's speech, as Adolf Hitler came to power in Germany, members of the British government and the British military who were concerned that Europe was about to be plunged into another war appealed to the scientific community to exert themselves in inventing new defensive weapons. The Air Ministry knew exactly what type of weapon it wanted—a death ray.

British physicist Robert Watson-Watt experimenting with a kite and a wireless transmitter in Berkshire in 1931.

Taken straight from a *Flash Gordon* serial, the death ray, as the Air Ministry imagined it, would release a powerful beam of energy that would blow falling bombs to smithereens and kill fighter pilots in their cockpits. In his article "Robert Watson-Watt, the Father of Radar," R. Hanbury Brown describes the death ray as "a hardy annual amongst optimistic inventors" at this time. As a sweetener, the Air Ministry offered a prize of £1,000 to the scientist who produced a death ray that could kill a sheep at 100 yards. No realistic proposals were submitted.

By January 1935, some in the British government were wondering whether asking scientists to invent a death ray was perhaps a bit silly. H.E. Wimperis, director of scientific research at the Air Ministry, asked the chief of the National Physical Laboratory, Robert Watson-Watt, if a death ray were within the realm of possibility. Watson-Watt did not commit himself either way; instead, he turned the question over to his assistant, Arnold Wilkins.

According to Wilkins' calculations, to kill a man would require a beam of mega-thousands of kilowatts, and there was no technology in the 1930s that could generate such power. After reviewing and confirming Watkins' figures, Watson-Watt said, "Well then, if the death ray is not possible, how can we help them [the Committee]?" On presenting Wilkins' negative findings to the Committee, Watson-Watt offered an additional observation—even if such a beam could be created, it could not pass through metal, so enemy pilots and crews would be immune to it.

Some consolation

Robert Watson-Watt (1892–1973) was born in Brechin in the county of Angus in eastern Scotland. His father was a deeply religious man, an elder of the local Presbyterian church and a Sunday-school teacher. Robert's mother was motivated by social reform: she was an advocate of temperance, and campaigned for women's rights, particularly the right to vote. Robert's father and grandfather were carpenters, but the boy was drawn to the sciences. In 1912 he received a degree in electrical engineering from University College in Dundee. One of his physics professors, William Peddie, suggested that he could make a career studying radio, or wireless telegraphy as it was known at the time.

Watson-Watt's first job was as a meteorologist at the Royal Aircraft Factory at Farnborough, where in 1916 he came up with the idea that, using cathode ray oscilloscopes, radio waves might be used to pinpoint the position of advancing thunderstorms; the information could be radioed to airplane pilots, who could then adjust course to avoid storms. The idea became reality in 1923.

In 1927, when the Radio Research Station was established at Ditton Park in Slough, Watson-Watt was named superintendent. He still held the post in 1935 when Wimperis consulted him about the possibility of building a death ray. Although a death ray was not possible, Watson-Watt was exploring a different type of defensive method that would detect incoming enemy aircraft. He mentioned it, as a kind of consolation, at the end of his report to the Air Ministry: "Meanwhile attention is being turned to the still difficult, but less unpromising, problem of radio detection and numerical considerations on the method of detection by reflected radio waves will be submitted when required."

The principle of reflection

A very primitive form of radar—a term not used at the time—was attempted during World War I. It involved mounting highly sensitive microphones on sound detectors that stood 197 feet high. These microphones could detect a plane 18½–25 miles away. If the enemy aircraft was traveling at about 199 miles per hour, that would give the military and civilians a four-minute warning. Very few civilians could reach shelter in such a short time, and the set-up was useless as far as the RAF was concerned, for it took a minimum of twenty minutes to mobilize a fighter squadron and get the planes into the air, flying in the direction of the enemy.

There had been something infinitely closer to radar as early as 1904—but in Germany, not in England. One of the first attempts to use electrical waves to detect far-off objects was made by Christian Huelsmeyer (1881–1957) of Dusseldorf, who in 1904 applied for a patent for a machine which he called a *telemobiloscope*. Huelsmeyer intended his invention to prevent ships from colliding in the dark or in heavy fog.

On May, 18 1904, he gave a public demonstration. Standing on the Hohenzollern Bridge in Cologne, Huelsmeyer aimed his device at a ship on the Rhine River. An electrical wave from the telemobiloscope bounced off the metal ship, causing a small bell on the invention to ring. When the ship moved out of the electrical wave, the bell fell silent. The device could detect ships at a distance of nearly 10,000 feet, and Huelsmeyer was working on an improved version that could detect a ship at a distance of approximately 33,000 feet. But the German Imperial Navy had no interest in the invention, perhaps because in a harbor full of ships the radio waves became "confused" and sent back false readings. Nonetheless, the principle of reflection was established and by the 1930s was well known in the scientific community.

One of the leaders in the field was Edward V. Appleton, Wheatstone Professor at the University of London and chairman of the Radio Research Board's Propagation of Waves Committee. Given his credentials and his international reputation as one of the foremost experts in the science of radio, it would seem natural that the British government would have consulted with Appleton rather than Watson-Watt. Louis Brown, author of *A Radar History of World War II*, has proposed that Wimperis went to Watson-Watt instead of Appleton because Watson-Watt was a government employee and therefore obliged to keep all military matters secret while Appleton, as a private citizen, was under no such obligation. Whatever the government's reasons, Appleton resented being passed over and harbored a deep dislike for Watson-Watt from that day forward.

"Pure theatre"

Hugh Trenchard, Marshal of the RAF, like Prime Minister Baldwin was convinced that "the bomber will always get through." Most RAF men agreed with him, but Hugh Dowding, Air Vice-Marshal, was more optimistic. When Watson-Watt approached Dowding with his and Wilkins' idea to use radio waves to detect incoming bombers, the air vice-marshal listened, but insisted that the scientists must produce something more substantial than "speculative arithmetic," as he put it. Watson-Watt agreed to a demonstration, but had a condition of his own—if the initial experiment failed it must not be considered definitive since he and his team would have very little time to perfect a working model. Dowding promised to give them some latitude.

On February, 26 1935, the same day that Hitler established his air force, the Luftwaffe, Watson-Watt and Wilkins were in Daventry in Northamptonshire, seated inside a van, staring intently at a small screen. Outside, an RAF aircraft flew back and forth across a BBC Empire transmitting station.

The envious Appleton derided the demonstration as "pure theater," but Watson-Watt had devised something new. Following long-understood science, he sent radio waves which reflected off the RAF plane and sent back echoes which appeared as a line of green light on the screen. But Watson-Watt had taken a major step forward, setting up a receiver with crossed antennae that identified the direction of the moving object—in this case, the aircraft.

Radio waves travel about 984 feet per microsecond. If some obstruction gets in the wave's way, the act of the wave bouncing off the object creates an echo. Watson-Watt discovered that, based on how long it took for the echo to be picked up by a radio transmitter, one could calculate how far the object was from the source of the radio wave. If it was a moving object, such as a German warplane, one could also calculate (using the crossed antennae) the direction in which it was moving and how fast it was traveling.

The British named Watson-Watt's device "radio detection finding," or RDF. It was the Americans who gave the invention the name that stuck—radar, short for "radio detection and ranging".

Dowding declared the demonstration a success, and after Watson-Watt assured him that his device could locate enemy planes from 43½ to 59 miles away, Dowding approved a budget of £12,300 for the development of his invention.

Watson-Watt explains the working of the original apparatus he developed to detect reflected radio echoes from enemy aircraft.

It was Dowding, too, who understood that this new device must be more than an early warning system; it must also be able to send information about the location of the enemy to fighter pilots. Thanks to Dowding, radar would enable Allied fighter squadrons to find and intercept Nazi aircraft in mid-flight. Because the German military had rejected Huelsmeyer's invention, the Luftwaffe did not have its own radar system, nor did it understand that radar gave a tactical advantage to any air force that possessed it.

Within weeks of the Daventry demonstration, Watson-Watt and his team moved to Orford Ness, a remote site on the coast of Suffolk, to begin experimenting with radar and to design the first radar station. The prototype radar station was erected at the Bawdsey Research Station near the mouth of the River Deben. It consisted of a steel transmission tower 384 feet high, and a wooden receiving tower of 239½ feet. Operating at a frequency of 22 MHz,

Robert Watson-Watt's famous ancestor

If a gift for scientific invention is genetic, then Watson-Watt probably inherited his from his famous ancestor, James Watt (1736–1819).

James Watt's life spanned the Scottish Enlightenment, a period when men such as Joseph Black, William Cullen, David Hume, Robert Adam, and Robert Burns stood at the forefront of science, medicine, philosophy, architecture, and poetry.

Born in Greenock, Scotland, and educated at the university in Glasgow, Watt relocated to London where he made mathematical instruments for the University of London. He was also an ingenious engineer, contracted as a surveyor for the Caledonian and Forth and Clyde canals; and he devised improvements for the harbors of Ayr, Port Glasgow and his hometown of Greenock.

Watt was one of several scientists at the time interested in the possibilities of steam power, the invention that was the catalyst for the Industrial Revolution. A shrewd businessman, Watt worked out a unique method for charging customers who wanted to buy one of his steam engines. He calculated that a horse could pull 181 pounds. Using this as his base figure, he worked out the capability in horsepower of the particular sized steam engine the customer wished to buy—it might be a 10 or 20 horsepower engine. Next he tabulated what the customer would save by using a steam engine rather than horses. Once he had worked out all these figures, Watt demanded a fee of one-third of the savings, paid annually, for twenty-five years. James Watt died a very wealthy man.

the transmission tower could detect aircraft 81 miles away in clear weather, and at about 40½ miles on rainy days. Encouraged by the initial results, the government called for five such stations to be constructed along the Thames Estuary. By September, 1 1939, when Hitler invaded Poland, a chain of radar stations extended from Southampton to north of the Firth of Forth in Scotland. By August 1940 the chain reached along England's southern coast, through Wales, and up to the Orkney Islands.

No idle boast

In August 1939, just days before the outbreak of World War II, the captain of the airship *Graf Zeppelin* reported seeing a 295 foot steel transmission tower on the English coast. The German High Command was unconcerned—they assumed that Britain, like Germany, had a radio-wave ship-detecting device. No one in Germany recognized the tower as a radar transmitter.

Radar was Britain's secret weapon, and it was sorely needed. By 1939 Germany had developed a Heinkel bomber that could fly at a top speed of 214 miles per hour. The Air Ministry calculated that once a fleet of Heinkels reached southern England, they could be over Buckingham Palace in about twenty minutes. It took RAF pilots and flight crews twenty minutes to get their planes into the air; if Britain still relied on the eyes and ears of coastwatchers for advance warning, by the time the RAF fighters got into the air London would be in flames. A military theorist of the 1930s, Colonel J.F.C. Fuller, worked out that if London had no warning, "a fleet of 500 airplane s, each carrying 500 ten-pound bombs … might cause 200,000 minor casualties and throw [London] into panic within half an hour of their arrival."

Radar let air defense "see" and "hear" German bombers as they left France or the Low Countries, so the RAF had the time it needed to intercept the attackers, and it gave the city of London sufficient warning to allow people to take cover, thereby reducing casualties. Radar became essential to Britain's air defence.

In the summer of 1940 Watson-Watt was still working to correct imperfections in the system. Radar, he wrote, was "not yet nearly as good as we would have liked; calibration seldom complete … Range-finding good; direction-finding fairly good; height-finding, as always a delicate and difficult operation."

In Germany Reichsmarshall Hermann Goering assured Hitler that the Luftwaffe would have Britain on her knees in a month, paving the way for invasion of the island. It was not an idle boast—German bomber squadrons had taken

Poland, the Netherlands, Belgium, and France totally by surprise, devastating their military installations and their cities and forcing a swift surrender from each. Given the Third Reich's experience up to that point, there was no reason to believe that conquering Britain would be significantly more difficult.

Saving the worst for last

Shortly before 4:00 in the afternoon of September, 7 1940, what Prime Minister Winston Churchill described as the "banshee wail" of the air-raid sirens shrieked across London, sending pedestrians, office workers and residents scurrying for cellars and Underground stations. Then came the terrifying sound of enemy planes overhead: 348 bombers escorted by 617 fighter planes dropped wave after wave of bombs on the city. At 6:00 in the evening, the Germans flew off. Two hours later the sirens wailed again, announcing the Germans' return, and the bombing kept up until 4:00 in the morning. One thousand fires swept across the city that day; 430 people were killed, and another 1,600 were seriously injured.

American war correspondent Ernie Pyle was in London during the first days of the Blitz. During one of the night-time raids, he and a few brave friends ventured out onto a balcony that overlooked the city. He reported:

> You have all seen big fires, but I doubt if you have ever seen the whole horizon of a city lined with great fires—scores of them, perhaps hundreds. There was something inspiring just in the awful savagery of it ... Into the dark shadowed spaces below us, while we watched, whole batches of incendiary bombs fell. We saw two dozen go off in two seconds. They flashed terrifically, then quickly simmered down to pin points of dazzling white, burning ferociously.

Every day for fifty-seven consecutive days German bombers attacked London. Typically, a single raid dropped 200 tons of bombs and 300 incendiaries.

The worst raid was the last. On May, 10 1941, the Luftwaffe sent 550 bombers armed with 700 tons of bombs and thousands of incendiaries. Nearly 1,500 Londoners died in this raid, and approximately 1,800 were injured. The Chamber of the House of Commons was destroyed. The House of Lords, Westminster Abbey, Westminster Hall, St. James's Palace, Lambeth Palace, the Old Bailey, the British Museum and fourteen hospitals were damaged. But after this raid the Luftwaffe did not return. The war on the eastern front against the Soviet Union required more manpower—Hitler could no longer afford to pummel London at the expense of his troops in the east.

—⁄⁄⁄—

The type of carnage and chaos the Poles, the Dutch, the Belgians, and the French had suffered corresponded very closely to the scenario envisaged by Colonel Fuller in the 1930s. With no warning system in place, these countries, their cities, and their citizens were completely vulnerable to massive bombing raids.

In Britain, however, radar gave the RAF an hour's warning that Nazi bombers were on their way.

Approximately 43,000 Londoners were killed in the Blitz, and about 51,000 were injured, yet the casualty rate would have been much higher had each bombing raid taken the city by surprise. Radar not only saved London from annihilation, it frustrated Hitler's plan to invade Britain.

By the time Hitler called an end to the Blitz, Watson-Watt and his team had invented a small radar transmitter and receiver that could be mounted on a fighter plane. Now, instead of waiting for a radio message from a radar station, every RAF pilot could zero in on the enemy. Watson-Watt took great pride in this achievement, declaring that these small radar devices had increased the effectiveness of British fighter planes "by a factor of three, and perhaps by five."

In 1942 King George VI knighted Robert Watson-Watt. After the war he became a consultant for several government ministries until he moved to Canada. In 1954 he was out driving when a Canadian policeman, armed with a radar-gun, pulled him over for speeding. Soon after the incident Watson-Watt wrote a poem wryly entitled "Rough Justice":

> *Pity Sir Robert Watson-Watt,*
> *strange target of this radar plot.*
> *And thus, with others I can mention,*
> *the victim of his own invention.*
> *His magical all-seeing eye*
> *enabled cloud-bound planes to fly,*
> *but now by some ironic twist*
> *it spots the speeding motorist*
> *and bites, no doubt with legal wit,*
> *the hand that once created it.*

Toward the Moon
Wernher von Braun's V-2 rocket

SCIENTIST: Wernher von Braun

AREA OF SCIENCE: Physics

MAIN INVENTIONS: V-2 rocket and Saturn V
booster rocket

NEAR SCHATTWALD IN THE Tyrolean district of the Austrian Alps, on a day in late April 1945, Private First Class Frederick Schneikert of the 324th Infantry Regiment, 44th U.S. Infantry Division, was on sentry duty when he spotted a young man on a bicycle pedaling toward him. Schneikert ordered him to halt, get off the bike and come forward with his hands up. In mangled English the cyclist introduced himself as Magnus von Braun, whereupon Schneikert cut him off—he spoke German fluently. In fact, Schneikert was the division's interpreter. Relieved, von Braun lapsed back into German and explained that a few hundred yards away, concealed in the forest, was his elder brother, Wernher von Braun, the inventor of the V-2 rocket, along with several other distinguished German scientists who had worked at the Peenemünde research facility in northern Germany. With them was a member of the German General Staff, Major-General Walter Dornberger. The group wanted to surrender to the Americans.

Schneikert could scarcely believe that the notorious Wernher von Braun was nearby, hiding in the underbrush, and he said as much to young Magnus: "I think you're nuts, but we'll investigate."

Since January 1945, when it had been obvious to everyone in Germany that the Third Reich was disintegrating, Wernher von Braun had been making plans to get away from Peenemünde on the Baltic Sea and lead his team of 125 scientists—or at least as many as would come with him—toward the American lines. The Soviet Red Army was rolling across Eastern Europe,

Wernher von Braun in America with a model of the V-2 rocket he helped design and develop for Germany during World War II: "I have learned to use the word "impossible" with the greatest caution."

and von Braun feared what would happen if they captured him. Summary execution in his laboratory, or a show trial in Moscow that would certainly end with a death sentence; at the very least he could expect to "disappear" into the Soviet gulag system. Then again, the Soviets might keep him a prisoner, forcing him to develop new weapons they could use against the West. All these prospects were unthinkable, and so von Braun plotted his escape.

After hearing out the cyclist's story, First Lieutenant Charles L. Stewart issued safe conducts, and on May, 2 Wernher and Magnus von Braun, General Dornberger and a dozen scientists from Peenemünde surrendered to the 44th. With no other place to keep them safe, the Americans locked them up in the standard POW enclosure.

Sputnik *and Muttnik*

Ten years after he sat in that American stockade, Wernher von Braun had undergone an extraordinary transformation. Rather than having to face an Allied war crimes tribunal on a charge of crimes against humanity, von Braun had been taken to the United States to develop new rockets for the military. By 1955 he was so firmly established as one of the great minds of the fledgling American space program that Walt Disney invited him to star in a three-part television series on space exploration, *Man in Space*, *Man and the Moon* and *Mars and Beyond*, which proved enormously popular—40 million viewers tuned in to hear a former Nazi rocket scientist describe the potential of space exploration.

In the final days of the war in Europe, the U.S. military tried to round up or rescue as many Nazi rocket scientists as they could find with the intention of resettling them in America. Operation Paperclip, the code name for the secret program, brought more than 120 German scientists to the United States, including, of course, von Braun. The Soviets had an identical program, and eventually would take more than 270 German scientists to Russia.

Von Braun was assigned to Fort Bliss in El Paso, Texas, where, along with many other German scientists, he worked on rocket technology. He was ambivalent about developing new weapons, but the U.S. Army could not imagine squandering the talents of the man who had invented the deadly V–2 rocket. Then, on October, 4 1957, something extraordinary occurred which altered von Braun's life and career, not to mention the direction of human history. On that day the Soviet Union launched the first artificial satellite into outer space. About the size of a beach ball and weighing 185 pounds, *Sputnik I* orbited Earth for 98 minutes.

Sputnik"s success set off a furore amongst the government, the military, and the American public—the Russians had made it into space first! Less than a month later they did it again, this time sending along a dog named Laika (wits in the United States dubbed her "Muttnik"). The greatest fear in the United States was that the Soviets would arm their satellites and rain down nuclear weapons from space. To make matters worse, America's rushed attempt on December, 6 to send up its first satellite, *Vanguard TV-3*, ended in humiliation—*Vanguard* exploded on the launching pad. Determined to compete in the new space race, in July 1958 the U.S. Congress established the National Aeronautics and Space Administration (NASA), a civilian-run agency for space exploration. Two years later von Braun was offered the position of director of NASA's Marshall Space Flight Center in Huntsville, Alabama. His assignment: to put an American on the Moon before the Russians could get there.

The informants

Wernher von Braun (1912–1977) was born in the town of Wirsitz in what was then Prussia, but today is the town of Wyrzysk in western Poland. His parents were German nobility, Baron Magnus von Braun and Emmy von Quistorp. As a boy he was enthralled by the stories of space travel in the works of Jules Verne and H.G. Wells, but he also read Hermann Oberth's scientific text, *By Rocket into Interplanetary Space*. At eighteen he enrolled at the Charlottenburg Institute of Technology, where he studied everything associated with rocketry; he also joined the Society for Space Travel. This was no science-fiction club, but a group of serious individuals interested in rocket science. In 1931 the society launched its own Repulsor rocket, fueled with liquid oxygen and petrol.

Von Braun was still studying when he met Walter Dornberger, a German army officer who shared the young man's passion for rockets—but as weapons, not as a mode of space travel. Dornberger arranged for von Braun to get a job working for the army as a civilian and to have his educational expenses paid for, including the PhD in physics that he received in 1934 from the University of Berlin. Immediately upon receiving his doctorate, von Braun went to work at Germany's first rocket-development facility, outside Berlin. In 1937 the army transferred the entire staff of eighty scientists to a new research facility, the Liquid Fuel Rocket and Guided Missile Center at Peenemünde, where

Dornberger served as commander and von Braun as technical director. There von Braun and his team designed, tested and produced the V-2 rocket, but they had other weapons in mind as well, including an intercontinental ballistic missile (ICBM) which they hoped could be fired from Germany and strike New York or Washington, DC.

Prisoner of the Gestapo

In March 1944 the Gestapo arrested Wernher von Braun. According to notes made by General Alfred Jodl, chief of the Operations Staff of the German Armed Forces High Command, von Braun was overheard talking with two associates, saying quite plainly that "the main task [of the scientists at Peenemünde] was to create a spaceship." The three men went on to agree that "the war [was] turning out badly." Both statements were regarded as treasonous. Instead of pipe-dreams of a rocket that would travel to outer space, von Braun's job was to build rockets that would defeat the Allies. Furthermore, to complain that the war was not going Germany's way was subversive and disloyal.

At 2:00 in the morning the Gestapo pounded on von Braun's door, and carried him off to a prison in Stettin. Other Gestapo agents arrested the two men with whom von Braun had had his seditious conversation, and his brother Magnus as well.

Later in the morning on the day of the arrests, General Walter Dornberger received a phone call from Adolf Hitler's headquarters in Berchtesgaden in the Bavarian Alps, ordering him to come at once. On his arrival, Dornberger was shown into Field Marshall Wilhelm Keitel's office. "The charges are so serious that arrest was bound to follow," Keitel said. "The men are likely to lose their lives. How people in their position can indulge in such talk passes my understanding."

To his credit, Dornberger went immediately to Gestapo headquarters in Berlin to plead for the release of von Braun, Magnus and the two scientists. Heinrich Mueller, chief of the Gestapo, was far from sympathetic and refused the request. Von Braun was kept isolated in his cell for two weeks; he was not permitted to see or speak with anyone, nor was he told of the charges against him.

Von Braun's most influential ally was his friend Albert Speer, Minister of Armaments and War Production, who the Gestapo believed could do nothing to help von Braun because he was hospitalized and thought to be dying of a severe infection. When Hitler came to visit him, Speer, despite his illness, exerted himself and convinced the Fuhrer to release the men who had served him and the Reich by inventing the V-2 rocket.

By 1942, Peenemünde had nearly 6,000 employees, including 2,000 scientists. Even so, as the facility made the shift from rocket research to rocket production, it required more labor. With most German males in the military and not enough civilian men or women to meet the demand, the Nazis drew on forced labor—in the case of Peenemünde, Russian and Polish prisoners of war from the nearby Karlshagen and Trassenheide camps were put to work in the rocket factory. Two of these slave laborers, both Poles, smuggled word to the Resistance of the types of rockets being manufactured. The Resistance passed the word along to the British, who made their first air strike against Peenemünde in August 1943. Tragically, almost all of the casualties of these air raids were the Russian and Polish POWs, whose barracks had no bunkers where they could take shelter. Amongst the dead were the two Polish informants.

Five times faster than the speed of sound

On a frigid day in March 1926, U.S. scientist Robert Goddard had launched the world's first liquid-fueled rocket. Powered by petrol and liquid oxygen, the rocket shot 41 feet into the air before taking a nosedive into a nearby cabbage field. Von Braun had studied Goddard's work, and his Space Travel club used the same propellant to fire their rockets.

Liquid-propelled rockets pump a fuel such as petrol or (in the case of the V-2) alcohol mixed with water, and an oxidizer such as liquid oxygen, into the combustion chamber where the two liquids burn, generating hot gases which are channeled through a nozzle. The result is a fuel that can send rockets flying at incredible speeds.

The liquid-propelled rocket von Braun developed was named V-2 by Adolf Hitler himself—V stood for Vengeance. It carried a motor seventeen times more powerful than any other rocket. It flew at five times the speed of sound—about 3,479½ miles per hour. It could travel approximately 199 miles. And it carried a 1,984 pound warhead. But the V-2 had a serious disadvantage—it was inaccurate. While this flaw made it useless against long-distance military targets, it could be utilized as a weapon of terror against civilian populations. And that is how it was used: V-2s were simply pointed in the direction of London, or Antwerp, or some other Allied city, and fired. People on the ground had no idea the rocket was coming—unlike the German "buzz" bomb that gave off a weird warning sound, the V-2 was a silent killer.

Nor was there any way to shoot down a V-2. It traveled faster than the speed of sound and at altitudes where ground-based anti-aircraft weaponry could not touch it.

Germany fired its first V-2 at Paris on the morning of September, 8 1944; it struck the south-eastern part of the city, killing six people and wounding some thirty-five others. A few hours later the first V-2 launched against Britain struck London, destroying homes along the Stavely Road. Thousands more V-2s would hit London and Antwerp (a major re-supply depot for the Allies). One came down on a Woolworth's store in Deptford, killing 160 shoppers. Another hit a movie theater in Antwerp, killing 567.

Within days of the first attacks, massed Allied aircraft attacked the rockets' launching bases in Nazi-occupied northern France, Belgium, and the Netherlands. The bases were so heavily defended, however, that only forty-eight V-2s were damaged in the strike, while the Allies lost approximately 450 planes and 2,300 crewmen. Ultimately, V-2 attacks against Allied cities came to an end only when Allied ground forces liberated northern France and the Low Countries between June 1944 and January 1945, and the Germans were obliged to pull back into Germany, taking the rockets with them. And from Germany, the V-2s' targets were out of range.

A man blinded

On June, 25 1944, Barbara McNally was a few days shy of her fifth birthday. That night, as she and her mother looked out a window of the bomb shelter in the cellar below the pub the family owned and operated in the London district of Lambeth, a V-2 rocket struck their front doorstep and brought the house down upon them. Fortunately, heavy timber beams kept the structure from crushing the building's inhabitants; in fact, the only McNally injured was Barbara's father, who was struck on the head by the cash register from the bar. In time, a rescue team pulled the family from the ruins.

The McNallys had been lucky. Eleven of their neighbors were dead and twenty-eight others were injured. The next day they would learn that across London, the death toll from the attack had reached 357. According to Britain's Ministry of Home Security, by the time the V-2s were withdrawn to Germany, V-2 attacks had killed 2,754 civilians overall, and wounded 6,523. As a point of comparison, conventional German bombs took the lives of 51,509 British civilians and seriously injured 61,423.

Long before failing to shut down the rocket launching sites with the mass air raid, the RAF had targeted the facility where the V-2 had been invented and was being manufactured. The air raids on Peenemünde wrought so much damage that Reichsführer-SS Heinrich Himmler decided that construction must be moved to a more secure location.

The site he chose was in the Kohnstein Mountains in central Germany. But isolation was not enough; the rocket factory must be completely secure. So Himmler ordered the construction of a secret subterranean facility beneath the mountains. Thousands of prisoners were brought from the nearby concentration camp of Mittelbau-Dora to chisel tunnels out of the stone in the bowels of the mountains. No one knows how many died of overwork and mistreatment, but by the fall of 1943 Mittelwerk GmbH was open for business. During the final six or seven months of the war in Europe, Mittelwerk produced 4,575 V-2s.

The factory's slave work force numbered 60,000—POWs from across Europe, as well as Jews and Gypsies. Of the 60,000, between 20,000 and 25,000 died of disease, malnutrition, and exhaustion. In a 2002 interview with the Associated Press, Michael Neufeld, a historian and curator at the Smithsonian Air and Space Museum in Washington, DC, addressed the question of von Braun's complicity in the crimes committed at Mittelwerk by the Nazi regime. "I think he blinded himself to the kind of government he was working for," Neufeld said.

A three-stage rocket

Fear of the Soviets had been one of the mainstays of Nazi policy. After World War II ended, the Americans were just as anxious about the power, influence and belligerence of the Communists. And now that they had beaten the United States into space, the Soviets seemed more of a threat than ever.

The situation called for confidence and daring, and Americans found both in their handsome young president from Massachusetts. On May, 25 1961, barely five months after his inauguration, John F. Kennedy issued a challenge to the U.S. scientific community and the American public at large. "Now is the time to take longer strides," he said. "I believe that this nation should commit itself to achieving the goal, before this decade is out, of landing a man on the Moon and returning him safely to Earth."

There was a reason that Kennedy believed it was urgent to get an American on the Moon—only weeks earlier, the Soviet had upstaged the U.S. space program once again. On April, 12 1961, Soviet cosmonaut Yuri Gagarin became

Following pages: At a press conference in 1958, von Braun, now the U.S. Army's chief rocket scientist, describes the Juno II launch vehicle on the Jupiter rocket.

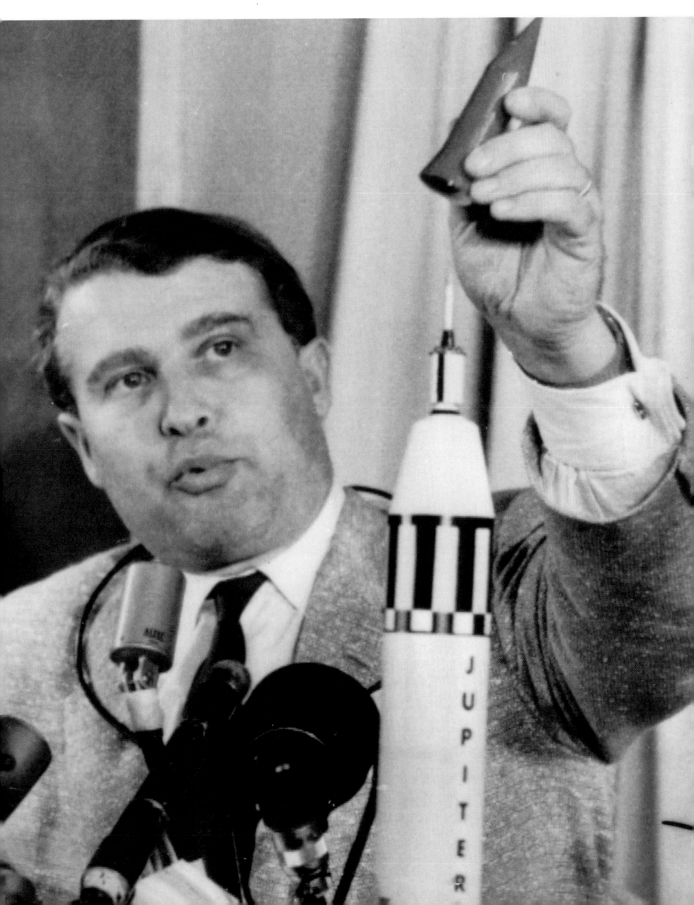

the first man to enter outer space, and the first to orbit Earth. And having made history, he returned home from his mission safely.

Von Braun and his team had been working on a liquid-fueled rocket as early as 1959, but after President Kennedy declared that America must win the space race, the team realized they would need something extremely powerful to carry a flight crew and their equipment to the Moon, and still have enough fuel to bring the crew back to Earth. Their solution was the Saturn V rocket. It was something entirely new, consisting of three stages. The first lifted the rocket off the launching pad and sent it into space; the second fueled the journey to the Moon; the third returned the astronauts to Earth.

Von Braun supervised the test launches of thirty-two Saturn rockets—all of which were a success. In December 1968 the *Apollo 8* astronauts orbited the Moon in a Saturn—the first-ever manned Saturn flight. And in July 1969 a Saturn took the crew of *Apollo 11* to the Moon.

"We would never have made it to the Moon without the Saturn V," said Walter Cunningham, who worked on the Moon mission at NASA in the 1960s. "The Saturn V burned its five million pounds of fuel in such a controlled fashion that it could lift six million pounds sitting still on the ground and place one quarter of a million pounds into an orbit 100 miles high, traveling 25,000 miles per hour."

Unanswered questions

After the Moon landing in 1969, in appreciation of his achievement, NASA promoted von Braun to deputy associate administrator of its headquarters in Washington, DC. He served NASA for two more years before leaving to join Fairchild Industries, a private firm in Maryland, as vice-president of engineering and development. In January 1977 illness forced von Braun to retire from the only private sector job he ever held; six months later he died of colon cancer.

Even in the 1960s, when he was making his greatest contributions to the American space program, von Braun was a polarizing figure. Many Americans could not forget that he had been an officer (albeit an honorary one) of the SS, that he had put his genius at the service of the Nazis, and that his V-2 rockets had cost the lives of thousands of innocent civilians. In 1960, when von Braun published his memoirs, entitled *I Aim for the Stars*, American satirist Mort Sahl suggested the subtitle should be "But Sometimes I Hit London".

Almost all of the American scientists who worked with him at NASA admired von Braun; some even idolized him. In addition to a brilliant mind he possessed an engaging personality. He was a popular man to work for.

Most criticism during von Braun's lifetime concentrated on his rocketry work in Nazi Germany. At the time, few people in America knew about the slave laborers who built the subterranean V-2 factory and then the rockets themselves; fewer still knew of the sufferings of these labourers and the many thousands who died. All this came to light after von Braun was dead, in the early 1980s. Arthur Rudolph was one of von Braun's colleagues in the rocket program in Germany; he also had been brought to the United States after World War II and worked for NASA. In 1982 the Office of Special Investigations suspected Rudolph of war crimes, specifically of mistreating the slave laborers at the Mittelwerk rocket factory. Rather than face the uncertainty of a public trial, Rudolph agreed to renounce his American citizenship and leave the country. In Germany, after a three-year investigation, prosecutors determined there was no basis for charging Rudolph as a war criminal. But the controversy raised once again the question: Was the U.S. military complicit in helping Nazi war criminals escape justice for the sake of their scientific expertise?, a question that has never been answered. To this day Wernher von Braun is remembered as one of the most notorious war scientists, but also as one of the greatest scientists of the space age.

The most moral weapon
Samuel Cohen's neutron bomb

SCIENTIST: Samuel Cohen

AREA OF SCIENCE: Physics

MAIN INVENTION: Neutron bomb

SAMUEL COHEN COULD NOT GET the picture out of his head: Seoul a smoking ruin, survivors of the bombing stumbling through the wreckage and, squatting beside a curb, Korean children drinking contaminated water straight from the gutter. No atomic bomb had done this—Seoul was leveled in 1951 by conventional weapons. As he surveyed the desolated city, Cohen asked himself a question: "If we're going to go on fighting these damned fool wars in the future, shelling and bombing cities to smithereens and wrecking the lives of their surviving inhabitants, might there be some kind of nuclear weapon that could avoid all this?"

It was an odd question. How could nuclear weapons *reduce* suffering?

The more he considered it, the more Cohen believed it was possible to minimize—up to a point—the hellishness of war. Firstly, the notion of total war, which targeted cities and their civilian populations, must be banned and military strikes limited strictly to military targets. Next, he imagined that nuclear weapons could be modified so that they would be no more destructive than conventional missiles. Of course, as long as military installations and the factories that manufactured weapons and other military supplies were in or near cities, cities would come under fire, so Cohen envisioned a type of weapon that would not reduce an entire city to rubble and thus force survivors to try to live on whatever food or water they could find. Finally, there was the question of radiation—the atomic bombs that fell on Hiroshima and Nagasaki had poisoned the cities and their surrounds. Cohen concluded that the dangers of radiation

March 1951: Three Korean children in surroundings ravaged by civil war—the kind of scene that had Samuel Cohen searching for a weapon that could reduce suffering.

might be greatly reduced, perhaps even eliminated, if the bomb produced non-radioactive neutrons.

The audience went wild

Samuel Cohen (1921–) was born in Brooklyn, New York City. His father was a carpenter. In 1923 the family moved to Los Angeles to escape the freezing New York winters and take advantage of a housing construction boom in southern California.

In 1943 Samuel Cohen was studying physics at the University of California at Los Angeles (UCLA) when he was drafted. After he completed basic training, the army sent him to the Massachusetts Institute of Technology to study engineering. He greatly impressed his instructors and the army, and early in 1944 was selected to join the Manhattan Project at Los Alamos in New Mexico. "While at Los Alamos," Cohen recalled in his autobiography, "most of my work involved devising equations on how neutrons would behave in an atomic bomb, and then making detailed calculations by hand about how their behavior would affect the bomb's efficiency."

Only twenty-three when he arrived at Los Alamos, Cohen was one of the youngest scientists working there. Like his colleagues, he was entirely absorbed by the task of designing and building an atomic bomb before the Nazis acquired one. On August, 6 1945, the day the first atomic weapon was detonated over Hiroshima, Cohen joined his fellow physicists in the Los Alamos auditorium, where they waited for a formal announcement of the bombing from their director, Robert Oppenheimer. Cohen remembered the tall, lanky director striding down the aisle, climbing the steps to the stage and in a matter-of-fact tone informing the audience that their work had been an unqualified success. The hall erupted in loud applause, wild cheers, and the stomping of feet. Holding up his hands for silence, Oppenheimer added that he only wished they had had a bomb in time to use against the Nazis (Germany had surrendered to the Allies on May, 7 1945). Once again, the audience, went wild.

Thinking the unthinkable

From Los Alamos Cohen moved to the RAND Corporation, an independent think-tank that focused on military strategy, including nuclear weapons, which had already signed on such world-renowned physicists as John von Neumann,

Herman Kahn, and Edward Teller, who had also worked at Los Alamos. RAND was an acronym for "research and development." According to Cohen, the scientists at RAND regarded it as their mission to bring the Pentagon into the nuclear age, to convince them that the atomic bomb had changed the world—and warfare—forever. From Cohen's point of view, the American military's naïveté was equaled by the RAND scientists' intellectual arrogance, some of whom, such as Herman Kahn, an old college friend of Cohen's, took a perverse pleasure in calculating what the world would be like after a nuclear holocaust. Kahn even published a book on the subject entitled *Thinking About the Unthinkable*.

Science writer Charles Platt explained why contemplating the unthinkable was so popular during the Cold War—especially in Washington, DC:

> *Bad news justified bigger military budgets, which enriched defense contractors, boosted employment in key congressional districts, and increased the influence of cold warriors in the Pentagon. Bad news united the nation and weakened opposition to legislation which rode in on the coat tails of anticommunist hysteria. Most of all, bad news enhanced nuclear drama, which inflated the importance of government in general and the Executive Branch in particular.*

High-ranking military men such as General Curtis LeMay, who had directed the firebombing of Tokyo and other Japanese cities, appealed to the U.S. scientific community to develop a bomb that would, as he said to Cohen, "wipe out all of Russia. That's my number one priority."

In spite of the hawkishness of LeMay and other military brass, think-tanks such as RAND turned their attention to nuclear deterrence. For this reason RAND urged the U.S. government to create a hydrogen bomb, arguing that it was the only way to maintain the balance of power, that the country would be at risk if the Soviets had such a weapon and America did not.

At RAND, Cohen focused his attention on a different problem. Air forces around the world were developing new planes that could fly higher than any of their predecessors—the better to avoid anti-aircraft fire from the ground. In the mid- and late 1950s Cohen envisioned an aircraft that could fly higher than even the highest-flying enemy planes. From this superior height the bombardier could release a bomb that would explode over the enemy planes, destroying the aircraft and their payloads of bombs or ballistic missiles before they reached their targets. Cohen concluded that a neutron bomb would be ideal for such a mission.

"The most moral weapon ever invented"

By December 1958 Cohen had finished his calculations for a neutron bomb, which differed significantly from the bombs built at Los Alamos. The atomic bombs that were dropped on Hiroshima and Nagasaki were fission weapons which derived their power from splitting atoms of uranium or plutonium. As the world learned in 1945, atomic bombs release a great deal of radioactive particles into the ground, water, and air, contaminating a large area. Because of their high level of contamination, atomic weapons are known as "dirty" bombs.

Cohen's neutron bomb would use a different process, known as fission-fusion. A small fission triggered an explosion that generated the heat necessary to get the fusion process started. The energy in the weapon was released by fusing atoms of deuterium and tritium at an extremely high temperature—tens of millions of degrees Fahrenheit. When the deuterium and tritium atoms fused, they formed helium, which released neutrons and a great deal of energy.

Although Cohen's neutron bomb was only one-tenth as powerful as the Los Alamos atomic bombs, it enjoyed three advantages. Firstly, it was a "clean" bomb because fusion did not produce residual radiation to contaminate the ecosystem where the bomb exploded. Secondly, it was an effective "people-killer": everyone within 1¼ miles of ground zero would be killed immediately from the force and heat of the explosion—there would be no wounded. Those close to the perimeter of ground zero would suffer from radiation sickness and die within a matter of hours or, at the latest, a matter of weeks. People who were at some distance from ground zero might fall sick from the neutrons, but after a period of nausea and diarrhea, they would recover. Finally, although every structure within a 1,640½ feet radius of ground zero would be leveled by the explosion, outside ground zero destruction or damage to buildings would be minimal. For the first time in history, science had developed a weapon that could cause tremendous enemy casualties without devastating the surrounding area.

Critics grumbled about the cruel death by radiation sickness those near ground zero would suffer. Cohen replied:

> *I doubt whether the agony an irradiated soldier goes through in the process of dying is any worse than that produced by having your body charred to a crisp by napalm, your guts being ripped apart by shrapnel, your lungs blown in by concussion weapons, and all those other sweet things that happen when conventional weapons (which are preferred and anointed by our official policy) are used.*

Then he went a step further, declaring: "The neutron bomb has to be the most moral weapon ever invented." Over the years this claim has struck some as astonishing, but Cohen was not being cynical—he truly believed that he had invented a moral weapon.

Of course, the fire bombing of German and Japanese cities during World War II produced virtually the same effect as the atomic bombs—it was simply a matter of degree. Nearly 17 square miles of Tokyo were reduced to ashes after one firebombing mission, but it took hundreds of aircraft and thousands of bombs to accomplish this level of destruction. It took only one bomb carried by one plane to utterly destroy Hiroshima.

As nuclear arsenals proliferated during the Cold War, it became possible for an armada of aircraft, each armed with a single nuclear weapon, to attack the NATO nations, or the United States, or the Soviet Empire, and at a single blow wipe countless cities off the map. But the horror would not end with the bombing. The amount of smoke and soot such massive bombings would throw into the atmosphere would obscure the heat and light of the sun, causing a "nuclear winter" that would eradicate the growing season for crops and plunge the world into a global famine.

In spite of these horrifying scenarios, since the 1950s both science and the military have been on a quest to find a tactical nuclear weapon which could be used to great effect in a conventional war without causing carnage or ruin, or disastrously threatening the environment. Samuel Cohen believed absolutely that his neutron bomb was the answer, and beginning in 1959 he tried to make his case to every American president from Dwight D. Eisenhower to Gerald Ford.

"The ultimate capitalist bomb"

Cohen presented his invention formally at the California Institute of Technology (CalTech), where his old boss, Robert Oppenheimer, had once been a professor. He hoped the CalTech physics faculty would use their contacts in Washington, DC to convince the Pentagon to make the neutron bomb part of America's military arsenal. But far from it—the faculty explained that in the wake of Hiroshima and Nagasaki, the American scientific community declined to endorse the use of any kind of nuclear weapon.

So Cohen went directly to the Pentagon, where he hoped to persuade the military to install neutron bombs in Western Europe as a defensive measure in the event the Soviets launched a war against America's NATO allies. But

Following pages: A stockpile of traditional 250 pound incendiary bombs for use by Laotian forces against North Vietnam in 1972. They created carnage of the sort Samuel Cohen believed could be avoided by the use of his neutron bomb.

the Pentagon did not see the advantage in keeping infrastructure intact. From the generals' perspective there was a great tactical advantage in knocking out the enemy's factories, bridges, navy yards, and military installations.

Cohen had no better luck in Congress. Senator Clinton Anderson of New Mexico, who chaired the Joint Committee on Atomic Energy, opposed the neutron bomb because if it won approval it would probably be developed at the Livermore labs in northern California, which would thus be in competition with the Los Alamos National Laboratories in his home state. On the other hand, Senator Thomas Dodd of Connecticut, an ardent anti-Communist, saw promise in its development and urged President John F. Kennedy to make the neutron bomb part of America's nuclear arsenal. Kennedy showed little enthusiasm, but Dodd persisted, making such a nuisance of himself on the subject that the Administration threatened to withdraw its support in his upcoming re-election campaign. Dodd backed away from the neutron bomb project, but he apologized to Cohen, saying, "The first duty of a politician is to get elected."

The press was no help either. Most news stories failed to grasp the difference between the neutron bomb and the atomic and hydrogen bombs. Furthermore, reporters often repeated the charge made by the Soviets, and echoed by American anti-war activists, that because the neutron bomb killed people but spared property it was "the ultimate capitalist bomb."

In the mid-1960s, as the war in Vietnam escalated, the U.S. military unleashed America's overwhelming military technology against civilian targets and civilian infrastructure—bombing the cities, burning villages and farms, and using Agent Orange to defoliate the jungles, thereby giving the Viet Cong no place to hide. Cohen was convinced the Pentagon was making a serious mistake, prolonging the war at the cost of many more lives—American and Vietnamese. After the United States pulled the last of its military, diplomatic, and civilian personnel out of Vietnam in 1975, he said, "I believe that considerably less than 200 neutron bombs could have ended that war."

A slippery slope

In 1976 Jimmy Carter was elected president of the United States, and Cohen's fortunes changed. Carter's Secretary of Defense, Harold Brown, had come to the conclusion that the neutron bomb was a nuclear weapon that could be used on a conventional battlefield. The Carter Administration had a good reason for throwing its support behind the neutron bomb: the Soviet Union had developed armored tanks that were considered the best in the world, and the American scientific community believed the radiation from a neutron bomb could penetrate the tanks' armor and kill or incapacitate the crews. And of course there would be no residual radiation to endanger the lives of American or NATO troops or the local population where the neutron bomb had been detonated.

President Carter planned to arm the W70-3 Lance missile with neutron warheads. A short-range missile, the Lance could strike targets 168 miles distant, and was designed to support conventional, on-the-ground combat forces.

Nonetheless, resistance to using neutron weapons had not gone away. The bomb's critics had two major objections: there was no data on the long-term or delayed effects of neutron radiation on humans or ecosystems, and there was a genuine fear that the use of one type of nuclear weapon in a conventional war might push the nuclear powers over the edge of a slippery slope that would lead to rationalizations for the use of other, more destructive types of nuclear weapons. As a government document entitled "The Neutron Bomb Arms Control Impact Statement" put it: "The principal dilemma for policy-makers considering the W70-3 is whether the perceived gains for deterrence outweigh the perceived risks of a lowered nuclear threshold."

In spite of such opposition, in 1977 Senator Sam Nunn of Georgia, a member of the Senate Armed Services Committee, announced that the United States intended to deploy neutron bombs in West Germany. This created uproar in West Germany, where the government and the people were deeply concerned about their country being the sole location for such a weapon. They argued that it would make them a target if the Soviets decided to "take out" the neutron bombs. Zbigniew Brzezinski, Carter's National Security Advisor, said: "We were quite unprepared for the political storm that hit us."

In a phone conversation with Carter, Helmut Schmidt, Chancellor of West Germany, insisted that he would not accept any neutron bombs on German soil unless the bombs were installed in at least one other NATO country as well; he suggested Belgium, Luxembourg, or the Netherlands.

Carter made the concession, and also won the support of the British government for the deployment of the neutron bomb in Europe. In 1978 he sent a personal emissary to Bonn to formalize the agreement, but before the emissary arrived in the West German capital he did an abrupt about-face, telling his advisers that he had decided against deploying the neutron bomb. The president's sudden reversal was leaked to the press and the first news stories appeared on April, 4 just as Chancellor Schmidt was about to announce that he supported the installation of neutron bombs in West Germany. Three days later Carter admitted publicly what everyone already knew—the neutron bomb program had been derailed. Pressure from demonstrators in the streets of the United States, Germany and other parts of the world, combined with vehement protests from some members of the West German government, led Carter to rethink his decision. He decided to defer deployment indefinitely.

The debacle emphasized the image of Jimmy Carter as indecisive. As for Chancellor Schmidt, the political left in Germany savaged him for caving in to the Americans, while the political right excoriated him for letting Carter withdraw the offer of weapons which the right believed would act as one more deterrent against Soviet and East German aggression.

The inventor rants

In 1979 Samuel Cohen was in France acting as a consultant to the French military, which was building an arsenal of neutron bombs. By chance, U.S. presidential candidate Ronald Reagan was in Paris, one of the stops on a tour of Europe. Cohen managed to arrange a meeting with Reagan during which he discussed the advantages of the neutron bomb. Reagan grasped the concept immediately, and when he became president in 1980 appropriated funds for the manufacture of about 1,000 neutron bombs.

But Cohen was not happy. The Pentagon ordered neutron warheads in two sizes, in a configuration at odds with his idea of a "moral" weapon. Charles Platt, in an in-depth interview with Cohen, wrote:

> Both were configured to explode near ground level, so that instead
> of minimizing blast damage they would maximize it to satisfy the
> enduring military need to blow things up. The larger of the two designs
> was actually so big, Cohen calculated that it would inflict devastation
> on the same scale as the first atomic bomb at Hiroshima.

Once again America's NATO allies refused to allow neutron bombs to be installed on European soil, so the arsenal remained in the United States where, if the Soviet Union did invade Western Europe, they would be useless.

Cohen had been appointed one of President Reagan's policy advisers, but his frequently expressed dissatisfaction—Charles Platt uses the term "rants"— over the way his weapons system was being misapplieddeeply irritated his colleagues in the Administration. In 1985 Cohen's superiors persuaded him to take early retirement.

—⁓—

When George H.W. Bush came to office in 1989, he dismantled America's stockpile of neutron bombs. From Cohen's point of view, $1 billion in military expenditure had been wasted. Speaking in 1997 to a reporter from the *Pittsburgh Tribune-Review*, Cohen stated that he believed China, Russia, and Israel all had stockpiles of neutron bombs.

Samuel Cohen has never regretted inventing the neutron bomb. If anything, he remains frustrated that the U.S. government has never recognized its potential. From his perspective, given the state of scientific research in the 1950s, the development of such a weapon was inevitable. "If I hadn't figured out the neutron bomb," he wrote in his autobiography, "somebody else would have."

Catching bullets

Stephanie Kwolek's bullet-proof fabric

SCIENTIST: Stephanie Kwolek

AREA OF SCIENCE: Chemistry

MAIN INVENTION: Kevlar body armor

SINCE DAYBREAK THE SKY had been overcast and threatened rain. As the battalions lined up on the Plains of Abraham on September, 13 1759, a splatter of raindrops speckled the blood-red coats of the English and the tartan kilts of the Scots Highlanders. Their objective, the great graystone city of Quebec, lay less than 1¼ miles distant, but the French, under the command of the Marquis de Montcalm, would not surrender this bastion of New France without a fight. By 6:00 a.m., French troops in white uniforms were massed before the city walls to check any British advance. Out from the gates of St. Louis and St. Jean poured more French troops, along with colonial troops, Canadian woodsmen and their Indian allies, their faces and bodies streaked with warpaint.

The battle began when three pieces of French field artillery began to shell the British lines with canister-shot while, from the cover of rocks and shrubs and cornfields, 1,500 Canadian and Indian snipers picked off the English and the Highlanders. At 10:00 in the morning, the English commander, General James Wolfe, led a foot charge against the French and Canadians who had taken position on a ridge called Anse du Foulon. As Wolfe advanced a bullet struck him in the wrist. He bandaged it with his handkerchief and pressed on. A second shot struck him in the arm, a third hit him in the chest. Staggering backwards, he sat heavily on the ground. Four soldiers rushed to the general's side, lifted him, and carried him to the rear.

A U.S. Marine on patrol in Iraq, protected by bullet-proof armor made from Kevlar, the extraordinarily strong polymer fiber discovered by Stephanie Kwolek in 1965.

Wolfe, in great pain, begged the men to let him lie on the grass. As they lowered him gently to the ground, one of the men asked if he should fetch a surgeon. "There's no need," the general replied. "It's all over with me."

The officers and men who had gathered around their fallen general were still trying to absorb what he had said when one of the men cried, "They run! See how they run!"

Wolfe, drifting toward unconsciousness, revived enough to ask, "Who run?"

"The enemy, sir," the trooper replied. "Egad, they give way everywhere!"

"Go, one of you, to Colonel Burton," Wolfe said. "Tell him to march Webb's regiment down to Charles River to cut off their retreat from the bridge."

In a sudden spasm of pain he rolled over on his side and whispered, "Now, God be praised, I will die in peace!" A moment later he was dead. Dangling from a black ribbon around his neck was a silver crescent engraved with the coat of arms of Great Britain; it was a gorget, a symbol of the general's office, a token of the age of chivalry and a symbol of the heavy steel armor that once protected the warrior aristocrats of the Middle Ages. Artillery and firearms such as were thundering all around the body of General Wolfe had made such armor obsolete, so now fighting men, for the first time in tens of thousands of years, went into battle entirely unprotected.

The death of General James Wolfe during the battle that captured Quebec from the French in 1759.

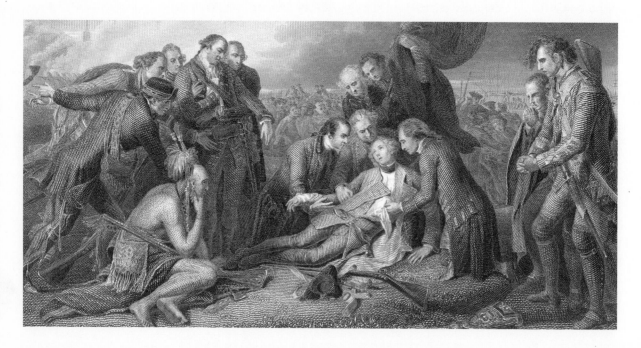

A brief history of armor

"Humankind, perhaps the most aggressive of species, differs from others in the animal kingdom—from the crab to the rhino, in being soft-bodied," writes arms and armor consultant Robert Woosnam-Savage. "We do not possess a natural outer shell or thick hide to protect us from attack." So what nature failed to provide, humankind created for itself. Woosnam-Savage estimates that our prehistoric ancestors devised some type of protective device some time between approximately the fourth millennium BC, when the spear was developed, and approximately 30,000 BC, when the bow and arrow were invented. Most likely the first piece of armor was a hand-held shield, an object found in virtually all societies. The oldest surviving depiction of a shield in the Mediterranean world, found on the wall of a tomb in Egypt, also dates from the fourth millennium BC.

Technically a shield is not armor since it is carried rather than worn. The first body armor was developed no later than 2525 BC in ancient Sumeria, a kingdom that covered modern-day Iraq. In or about that year Sumeria's king, Eannatum, erected a limestone stele, or slab, to commemorate his victory over a rival, the king of Umma. It is known as the Stele of the Vultures because it depicts vultures and lions devouring the corpses of fallen soldiers. While such grisly scenes alone make it memorable, what makes the Stele of the Vultures important is that it is the earliest depiction we have of how Sumerian troops were equipped. Sumerian infantrymen wore thick tunics, long leather cloaks studded with little metal spikes, and helmets made of copper lined with leather. This was the world's first body armor.

In ancient Egypt noblemen and pharaohs wore scale armor, small bronze plates laced together with leather straps. This forerunner of chain mail offered the wearer protection while being sufficiently flexible to not inhibit his mobility in battle. A lowly Egyptian infantryman wore a sleeveless padded linen cuirass that covered his chest and back. It wasn't much protection against a sword blow, a javelin thrust, or a speeding arrow, but it was better than nothing at all. Similarly inexpensive, minimal armor for the rank and file would be the norm for at least the next 3,500 years.

The first metal plate armor was developed in the ancient Greek kingdom of Mycenae in the Peloponnese, about 1400 BC. A sleeveless bronze cuirass covered the chest and back. Riveted to the cuirass were three pairs of horizontal, curved bronze bands, each about 8 inches deep, which covered the groin and the legs to just below the knees. More bronze plates were worn over the shoulders; a high bronze collar protected the neck and chin. Assembled, the armor looks like a bronze tube. It would have been heavy and unwieldy on the battlefield, which has led many military historians to surmise that it was worn by men fighting from a chariot. Given the massive protection of the body armor, it is strange that the Mycenaean helmet was lightweight—a leather cap onto which boar's teeth were sewn. Of course, only a Mycenaean king or nobleman could afford such armor; ordinary fighting men went into battle wearing a sleeveless leather corselet.

Chain mail, made of small metal rings linked or riveted together, was worn by the ancient Celtic nations of Europe. The Romans certainly encountered it in their wars against the Gauls, and they recognized the advantages of chain mail immediately; it was lighter than plate armor and infinitely more flexible. Beginning in the first century BC, all Roman legionnaires were outfitted with a chain-mail shirt that covered the body from the neck to just below the groin; hanging from the shoulders were short chain-mail sleeves that protected the biceps. Beneath the chain mail the soldier wore a short-sleeved leather shirt to give his body a little extra protection.

The first effective "soft" armor was invented in Asia. By the ninth century AD, the Chinese had developed armor made up of interwoven sheets of mulberry paper, fifteen layers thick. It was said to be able to deflect an arrow.

In Europe, long after the fall of Rome, chain mail remained the preferred type of armor. By AD 1000, knights were wearing long-sleeved chain mail. By 1200 a knight could purchase chain-mail armor that covered every part of his body—including his hands and feet. Only his face was exposed, and to protect that he wore a helm, a solid helmet shaped like a bucket with long narrow eye-slits so he could see (somewhat) and perforations so he could breathe (barely).

In the fourteenth century full-body chain mail was replaced by steel plate armor that was not only costly but also restricted the knight's mobility. Some medieval suits of armor consisted of 170 separate pieces and took up to four months to make. Much is made of the weight of medieval armor, but a suit of armor in the fifteenth century on average weighed from 59½ to 70½ pounds. Compare that to the 110 pound kit an infantryman carried in World War I, or the 121 pounds of gear that British Marines carried during the Falklands War.

Infantrymen and archers in the Middle Ages were lucky if they had a leather or quilted linen shirt to protect them. Officers wore chain-mail collars that protected their necks, and helmets, and perhaps steel gloves known as gauntlets.

Japanese armor of much the same period generally consisted of metal plates over the chest and back, supplemented over the legs and arms with metal scale armor laced together with colored silk cords. The armor of a samurai could be incredibly elaborate, with festoons of gorgeous silk, brightly colored silk tassels, lacquered and inlaid sheaths and scabbards, and, for warriors of the highest caste, helmets that featured grotesque face masks and gilded animal horns. The result was both spectacular and unnerving.

Beginning in the fourteenth century, when artillery and firearms arrived in Europe, metal armor began its long journey into obsolescence. It hung on into the seventeenth century, when steel breastplates and helmets were still worn in battle. They could deflect a sword blow, but they were useless against a musket ball or shrapnel from a cannon. By the eighteenth century, armor had essentially vanished in the West. Some regiments might sport a steel cuirass, but it was entirely decorative. In Great Britain, armor had been reduced to a trinket, a pretty silver gorget suspended from a silver chain or a silk ribbon around an officer's neck.

Five times stronger than steel

Stephanie Kwolek was born in New Kensington, Pennsylvania, in 1923. Her father, John Kwolek, worked as a mould maker at a local factory. After his death in 1934, Kwolek's mother, Nellie Zajdel Kwolek, went to work to support herself and her two children.

As a child Stephanie Kwolek had a gift for sewing—she created elaborate outfits for her dolls, and for a time thought she might be a fashion designer. By the time she completed high school she still enjoyed sewing, but her interests had shifted to the sciences, and in 1942 she enrolled at the Carnegie Institute of Technology (now Carnegie Mellon University) in Pittsburgh, where she studied chemistry and biology. Kwolek hoped to go on to medical school, but she could not afford the tuition fees, so she put her plans on hold and in 1946 took a job at the DuPont Company, intending to save her money and apply to medical school later.

Kwolek arrived at DuPont at an interesting time, when chemists were learning to create fibers from petrochemical compounds. A few years earlier, in 1939, Dr. Wallace Hume Carothers of DuPont had invented nylon. DuPont scientists would go on to invent other synthetic fabrics, including Dacron polyester, Orlon acrylic and Lycra spandex.

With her dual interests in fabrics and chemistry, Kwolek should have been a welcome addition to the DuPont laboratories, but in the 1940s very few women worked in chemical research, and those who did found that their male colleagues made them feel distinctly unwelcome. In an interview she gave in 1986 Kwolek recalled, "Women I knew, even PhD women, lasted about two or three years, and then went back to teaching, frequently at a women's college. But there were some of us who decided to stick it out, and I was one."

Kwolek worked with aromatic polyamides, trying to develop a resilient new synthetic fiber. Originally she was searching for a strong, lightweight fiber that could replace the steel in radial tires. There was talk of a petrol shortage in the early 1960s, and it was thought that if manufacturers could reduce the weight of each car—including tyres—they would burn less fuel. While working with the polyamides she discovered a solvent unlike anything anyone in the DuPont lab had ever seen before. It was pearl-colored, opaque and had the consistency of watery milk. "Ordinarily these solutions would have been discarded," Kwolek recalled in a 2003 interview published in *Invention & Technology Magazine*. But she believed she was onto something.

Instead of throwing out the strange, cloudy substance, she brought it to the head of DuPont's spinning unit. Taking just one look, he refused to put it in the spinneret to see whether it would form a fiber. In the first place, all the polymers that so far had yielded synthetic fibers were clear as glass, not opaque like this one. To form a fiber, the polymer solution was forced through the tiny holes of the spinneret—and he feared that Kwolek's substance would clog the holes.

It took a lot of persuading, but ultimately he placed Kwolek's substance in the spinneret. To his surprise, it did not damage his machine. To Kwolek's surprise, the fibers proved to be incredibly strong—five times stronger than steel.

Concerned that it might be a fluke, or that the fiber might deteriorate over time, or disappoint in some other way, Kwolek continued to experiment with her discovery. She patented her fiber, then assigned the patent to DuPont (in return, the company gave her a promotion and a generous bonus). In 1971 Kwolek's fiber, now known as Kevlar, was introduced to the market.

Catching bullets and arrows

Unlike other synthetic fabrics such as nylon, Kevlar does not drape over the body of the person wearing it. It is stiff, in some ways reminiscent of the metal plate armor of the Middle Ages. Since it requires up to forty layers to stop a

Ned Kelly's armor

Australia's most infamous bushranger, Ned Kelly (c. 1854–1880) began his life of crime by the time he was fourteen. For the next ten years, he was in and out of prison, usually for assault or possession of stolen property.

By the time he reached his twenties, Kelly had assembled a small gang that included his younger brother Dan and their friends Joe Byrne and Steve Hart. In October 1878 the Kelly Gang committed their most daring and most notorious crime—at Stringybark Creek, in Victoria's Wombat Ranges, they ambushed and murdered three police officers. Declared outlaws by the colonial government and in danger of being shot on sight by any honest citizen, Kelly and his gang decided they needed some extra protection. In or about 1879, they commissioned a blacksmith to make each of them a suit of armor. Hammered out of iron ploughshares and held together with leather laces and iron bolts, the armor consisted of breastplate and backplate, a helmet, shoulder guards, and a curved plate that hung in front of the groin. To test its effectiveness, Kelly fired a stolen police rifle at one of the armor suits—it dented, but did not penetrate, the breastplate.

In June 1880 the Kelly Gang entered the little Victorian town of Glenrowan and killed a police informant. As the police converged on them, the gang took refuge inside a hotel. In the gunfight that ensued, Dan Kelly, Joe Byrne and Steve Hart were killed, and Ned was wounded and captured. It's said that he was wearing his armor, and the only way the police could bring him down was by shooting him in his unprotected legs.

We know that the police confiscated the gang's four suits of armor at Glenrowan, although in the years that followed pieces of it were dispersed across Australia. Ned Kelly's suit survived intact and is displayed today in the State Library of Victoria.

bullet, Kevlar body armor is not only rigid, it is also heavy—a Kevlar vest weighs more than 10 pounds. Today, for added protection, the U.S. military issues its troops with large ceramic armor plates, which are inserted into front and back pockets in a Kevlar vest and which, of course, increase the weight of the vest.

When a bullet or a piece of shrapnel strikes Kevlar armor the fabric stretches but it is not pierced—it is said to "catch" the bullet. Furthermore, it spreads the force of impact over a large area of the body. A soldier whose Kevlar vest is struck by a bullet will feel the impact and will probably come away with a large bruise and perhaps a broken rib or two, but will not suffer a from bullet wound.

It's interesting that about seven hundred years before Kwolek invented Kevlar, Chinese physicians had discovered a similar principle. In the first decades of the thirteenth century, as Genghis Khan extended his empire across Asia, he made a point of sparing the lives of engineers, artisans, physicians, even chefs, and musicians—anyone he considered useful and thought would improve the life of the Mongol nation. Every time the Mongols went to war, medical units staffed by Chinese physicians rode with them. A few Mongol warriors owned chain mail, some wore a leather tunic for protection in battle, but most had no armor at all. Some time about 1220, the physicians discovered that thick, tightly woven raw silk could diminish the injury inflicted by an arrow.

Arrow wounds had always been difficult to tend. If the arrow was deeply buried, the physician might be compelled to make a large incision with a knife to dig out the arrowhead. If the arrowhead was barbed and could not be cut out, the physician or even the warrior's comrades would push it through the torso or limb, a process that caused terrible pain and did even more damage.

But the Mongols' Chinese physicians discovered that if a warrior wore a shirt of thick raw silk, the fabric would obstruct an arrow and prevent it from causing a deep wound. To remove the arrow, the physician pulled gently on the silk until the arrowhead popped out. There would still be a wound, of course, but a much less serious one than if the warrior had been unprotected.

Silk armor succeeded in reducing the number of serious arrow wounds, but not the rate of infection. Although the physicians had convinced the Mongols to wear silk armor, they could not persuade them that they would suffer fewer infections if they washed their bodies and laundered their clothes.

"Chicken jackets"

When the United States was fighting the war in Vietnam in the 1970s, the military did not rush to adopt Kevlar body armor for the troops. Some officers believed that protective gear would undermine a soldier's natural aggression, and perhaps even his courage—they took to calling body armor "chicken jackets." After the Vietnam War, Dr. James E.T. Hopkins, who had served as a combat surgeon in the South Pacific and South-east Asian theaters during World War II, claimed that the lives of 15,000 American troops could have been saved if the military had equipped all its men with protective jackets and better helmets.

In 1976, after American troops had been withdrawn from Vietnam, the military earmarked $3.5 million for the development of a Kevlar helmet.

Lawrence R. McManus and Philip Durand of the Natick Research and Development Command in Natick, Massachusetts, were asked to create the new helmet. Their first model weighed nearly 15½ pounds, but eventually they pared it down to a helmet that weighed little more than 3 pounds.

The old steel helmet wobbled when a soldier walked and often flew off his head when he ran. The new Kevlar helmet was more comfortable and a better fit because it was modeled to the contours of the human skull. It passed all the army field tests, and even the economic test—the Kevlar helmet was a bargain at only $92 apiece. And it saved lives. To cite just one example, during the U.S. invasion of Grenada in 1983, a shell from an AK-47 struck the helmet of paratrooper Brent Taylor; he survived.

Kevlar also attracted the attention of police officers and prison guards. The lightest Kevlar vests, known as concealable body armor, cannot be detected when worn under clothing, but there is a trade-off—the lightest vests provide the least amount of protection. A concealable vest will shield the wearer against a bullet fired from a .22 caliber handgun and similar low-caliber firearms, but not against shotguns, automatic weapons or a police officer's own service weapon.

While on duty most law enforcement personnel wear heavier Kevlar vests that provide much better protection than the concealable variety. In 1987, the International Association of Chiefs of Police teamed up with DuPont to form the IACP/DuPont Kevlar Survivors' Club to encourage police officers to wear body armor and to pay tribute to police officers whose lives were saved or who were spared from suffering a serious injury because they were wearing Kevlar body armor. To date, more than three thousand survivors have been honoured by the club.

The use of Kevlar is not limited to body armor. Because it is so strong, Kevlar cables support suspension bridges and elevator cars. Because it is 95 percent lighter than steel, Kevlar ropes are used at sea as tow and salvage lines. Kevlar is used for inflatable boats, kayaks, and parachutes. Hiking boots, bicycle helmets, tennis rackets, motorcycle tires, baseball bats, and hockey sticks are made of Kevlar. It is even used to make fire-resistant mattresses.

In 1986, after forty years at DuPont, Stephanie Kwolek retired. In recognition of her achievements, in 1995 she was inducted into the National Inventors Hall of Fame, and in 1997 was awarded the Perkin Medal from the American Chemical Society. Such recognition from her colleagues in the scientific community must have been gratifying, but certainly it takes second place to the countless lives that have been saved thanks to her discovery.

Bibliography

A heaven-sent weapon: Callinicus' liquid fire

Diodorus Siculus (1st century BC). *The Library of History*, vol. 209, trans. C.H. Oldfather. Loeb Classical Library, Harvard University Press, Cambridge, MA, 1933.

Lifshitz, Felice, ed. *Dudo of St Quentin's Gesta Normannorum: An English Translation*. www.the-orb.net

Lucan (39–65 AD). *The Civil War*, trans. Sir Edward Ridley. Longmans, Green & Co., London, 1896.

Mayor, Adrienne. *Greek Fire, Poison Arrows and Scorpion Bombs: Biological and Chemical Warfare in the Ancient World*. Duckworth/Overlook, New York, 2003.

Norwich, John Julius. *Byzantium: The Early Centuries*. Alfred A. Knopf, New York, 1989.

Catapult, claw, death-ray: Archimedes' strange war machines

"Archimedes' Weapon", *Time*, November, 26 1973.

Biello, David. "Fact or Fiction?: Archimedes Coined the Term 'Eureka!' in the Bath", *Scientific American*, December, 6 2006.

Plutarch's *Lives*. www.fullbooks.com

Stein, Sherman. *Archimedes: What Did He Do Besides Cry Eureka?* The Mathematical Association of America, Washington, DC, 1999.

Titus Livius Livy (59 BC–AD 17). *The War with Hannibal: Books XXI–XXX of the History of Rome from its Foundation*, trans. Aubrey De Sélincourt. Penguin Classics, London, 1965.

First biological weapons: Hannibal's pots of serpents

The Book of the People: Popul Vuh, trans. Delia Goetz and Sylvanus Griswold Morley, Plantin Press, 1954.

Cornelius Nepos (c. 100–24 BC). *Lives of Eminent Commanders*, trans. Rev. John Selby Watson. Hinds & Noble, New York, 1886.

Herodian of Antioch (c. 170–240). *History of the Roman Empire*, trans. Edward C. Echols. University of California Press, 1961.

McNamee, Gregory. *A Desert Bestiary: Folklore, Literature, and Ecological Thought from the World's Dry Places*. Big Earth Publishing, Neenah, WI, 1997.

Pliny the Elder (23–79 AD). *The Natural History*, trans. John Bostock and Henry Thomas Riley, H.G. Bohn, London, 1855.

Flying, dancing powder: Wei Boyang's heaven-shaking thundercrash bomb

Breuer, Hans. *Columbus Was Chinese: Discoveries and Inventions of the Far East*, trans. Salvator Attanasio. Herder & Herder, New York, 1972.

Crowley, Roger. "The Guns of Constantinople", *Military History*, September 2007.

Kelley, Jack. *Gunpowder: Alchemy, Bombards, and Pyrotechnics— The History of the Explosive that Changed the World*. Basic Books, New York, 2004.

Kierman, Frank A. Jr. & John K. Fairbank, eds. *Chinese Ways in Warfare*. Harvard University Press, Cambridge, MA, 1974.

Hateful to God: Zhuge Liang's new, improved, repeating crossbow

Chu-ko-nu: The Manchurian Repeating Crossbow. www.arco-iris.com/George/chu-ko-nu.htm

Comnena, Anna (1083–1153). *The Alexiad*, trans. Elizabeth A. Davis. Routledge Kegan Paul, London, 1928.

Frankland-Payne-Gallwey, Sir Ralph William. *The Crossbow: Its Military And Sporting History, Construction And Use* [1848]. Skyhorse Publishing, New York, 2007.

Horn, M.E. Zhuge Liang (Kong Ming) The Original "Hidden Dragon". www.jadedragon.com/history/liang1.html

O'Connell, William. "The Life and Hard Times of the Crossbow", in Robert Cowley, ed., *The Experience of War*. W.W. Norton, New York, 1992.

Renaissance tinkerer: Leonardo da Vinci's machine-guns

Bertelli, Carol. "The Restoration of *The Last Supper*", *National Geographic*, November 1993.

Ellis, John. *The Social History of the Machine Gun*. Pantheon Books, New York, 1975.

Hart, Ivor B. *The World of Leonardo da Vinci: Man of Science, Engineer and Dreamer of Flight*. Viking Press, New York, 1961.

Heydenreich, Ludwig, H., Bern Dibner & Ladislao Reti. *Leonardo the Inventor*. McGraw-Hill Book Co., New York, 1980.

White, Michael. *Leonardo: The First Scientist*. St. Martin's Press, Gordonsville, VA, 2000.

Massed firepower: Marin le Bourgeoys' flintlock

Abels, Robert. *Early American Firearms.* The World Publishing Co., New York, 1950.

Baumgartner, Frederic J. *From Spear to Flintlock: A History of War in Europe and the Middle East to the French Revolution.* Praeger, New York, 1991.

Hughes, Major-General B.P. *Firepower: Weapons Effectiveness on the Battlefield, 1630–1850.* Sarpedon, New York, 1997.

Marvick, Elizabeth Wirth. *Louis XIII: The Making of a King.* Yale University Press, Newhaven, CT, 1986.

An effort of genius: David Bushnell's submarine

Submarine History Timeline 1580–1869. www.submarine-history.com/

Swanson, June. *David Bushnell and His Turtle: The Story of America's First Submarine.* Atheneum, New York, 1991.

Turtle. www.navsource.org/archives/08/08441.htm

A very immoral act: William Congreve's rockets

Fort McHenry. www.nps.gov/fomc/historyculture/index/htm

Potts, J.R. "Congreve Rocket", *Military Factory.* www.militaryfactory.com/munitions/detail.asp?munitions_id=Congreve-Rocket

Seringapatam 1799: Letters and Journals of Lachlan Macquarie in India. www.lib.mq.edu.au/digital/seringapatam/intro.html

"Star-Spangled Banner and the War of 1812", *Encyclopedia Smithsonian.* www.si.edu/Encyclopedia_Si/nmah/starflag.htm

Safe and nutritious: Nicolas Appert's canned goods

Can Manufacturers Institute. www.cancentral.com/

Shephard, Sue. *Pickled, Potted, and Canned: How the Art and Science of Food Preserving Changed the World.* Simon & Schuster, New York, 2000.

The equalizer: Samuel Colt and the revolver that won the West

Grant, Ellsworth S. *The Colt Legacy: The Story of the Colt Armory in Hartford, 1855–1980.* Mowbray Co., Providence, RI, 1982.

Russell, Carl P. *Guns on the Early Frontiers: A History of Firearms from Colonial Times through the Years of the Western Fur Trade.* University of Nebraska Press, Omaha, 1980.

Texas Ranger Hall of Fame. www.texasranger.org

Texas Rangers. www.forttours.com/pages/ranger.asp

Wilson, R.L. *Colt: An American Legend.* Artabras, New York, 1985.

The merchant of death: Alfred Nobel and dynamite

Brown, G.I. *The Big Bang: A History of Explosives.* Sutton Publishing, Stroud, UK, 1998.

Fant, Kenne. *Alfred Nobel: A Biography*, trans. Marianne Ruuth. Arcade Publishing, New York, 1991.

Gleasner, Diana C. *Dynamite.* Walker & Company, New York, 1982.

Hoosac Tunnel. www.hoosactunnel.net/index.php

Nobel Prize. nobelprize.org/nobelfoundation/index.html

Making armies obsolete: Richard Gatling's machine-gun

Bilby, Joseph G. "Load the Hopper and Turn the Crank: Rapid-Fire Guns of the Civil War". www.historynet.com/load-the-hopper-and-turn-the-crank-rapid-fire-guns-of-the-civil-war.htm

Keller, Julia. *Mr Gatling's Terrible Marvel: The Gun That Changed Everything and the Misunderstood Genius Who Invented It.* Viking, New York, 2008.

Wahl, Paul & Don Toppel. *The Gatling Gun.* Arco Publishing Company, New York, 1965.

Slow but effective: Robert Whitehead's torpedo

Cumming, E.M. *A Short History of Torpedoes, 1866 to 1944.* www.weymouthdiving.co.uk/torphist.htm#WHITEHEAD

Holings, D.F. *The Centenary Story of Robert Whitehead and the Whitehead Torpedo and Engineering Works.* www.users.globalnet.co.uk/~wykedh/rwbook/rwcover.htm

Kirby, Geoff. "A History of the Torpedo: the Early Days", *Journal of the Royal Navy Scientific Service*, vol. 27, no. 1, 2009.

Like a pomegranate: William Mills perfects the hand grenade

Botsford, Charles Alexander. *Fighting with the U.S. Army.* The Penn Publishing Co., Philadelphia, 1919.

Empey, Arthur Guy. *Over the Top.* The Knickerbocker Press, New York, 1917.

Morton, Desmond. *When Your Number's Up: The Canadian Soldier in the First World War.* Random House of Canada, Toronto, 1993.

Weapons of War—Grenades. www.firstworldwar.com/weaponry/grenades.htm

Weir, William. *50 Weapons That Changed Warfare.* Career Press, Franklin Lakes, NJ, 2005.

Perverting chemistry: Fritz Haber's poison gas

"Battles: The Battle of Loos, 1915." First World War.Com. www.firstworldwar.com/battles/loos.htm

Hager, Thomas. *The Alchemy of Air: A Jewish Genius, a Doomed Tycoon, and the Scientific Discovery That Fed the World but Fueled the Rise of Hitler.* Harmony Books, New York, 2008.

"Memoirs and Diaries: The First Gas Attack." First World War.Com. www.firstworldwar.com/diaries/firstgasattack.htm

"Phosgene: Military History." web1.caryacademy.org/chemistry/rushin/StudentProjects/CompoundWebSites/2003/phosgene/history.htm

Sinnott, John P. "Use of Chlorine Gas Cylinders in World War I", *Military History*, April 1994.

"Weapons of War: Poison Gas." First World War.Com. www.firstworldwar.com/weaponry/gas.htm

The flaming coffin: The Wright brothers build the first military aircraft

Coggins, Edward V. Jr. *Wings That Stay On: The Role of Fighter Aircraft in War.* Turner Publishing, Paducah, TX, 2000.

Crouch, Tom. *The Bishop's Boys: A Life of Wilbur and Orville Wright.* W.W. Norton & Co., New York, 1989.

"De Havilland DH-4", National Museum of the U.S. Air Force. www.nationalmuseum.af.mil/factsheets/factsheet.asp?id=324

Gordon, Arthur. *The American Heritage History of Flight.* American Heritage Publishing, Rockville, MD, 1962.

Traveling caterpillar fort: Lancelot de Mole's tank

The Chariot in Ancient Egypt. www.reshafim.org.il/ad/egypt/timelines/topics/chariot.htm

Fleming, Thomas. "Tanks", *Invention & Technology Magazine*, Winter 1995.

Fournie, Daniel. "Second Punic War: Battle of Zama." *Military History*. www.historynet.com/second-punic-war-battle-of-zama.htm

Gray, E. Dwyer. "Story of the Tanks; De Mole's Travelling Caterpillar Fort; Remarkable Letter From Perth in 1914", *The Argus*, 9 August 1924.

Kiester, Edwin, Jr. *An Incomplete History of World War I.* Murdoch Books, Sydney, 2007.

Motavalli, Jim. "Rolls-Royce Armored Car: The Bulletproof Ghost", *Military History*. www.historynet.com/rolls-royce-armored-car-the-bulletproof-ghost.htm

Suhr, Robert Collins. "Battle of Kadesh", *Military History*, August 1995.

White, Niles. "From Tractor to Tank", *Invention & Technology Magazine*, Fall 1993.

Wright, Patrick. *Tank: The Progress of a Monstrous War Machine.* Viking, New York, 2002.

The plague zone: Ishii Shiro and the germ warfare scientists

Croddy, Eric & James J. Wirz. *Weapons of Mass Destruction: An Encyclopedia of Worldwide Policy, Technology, and History.* ABC-CLIO, Inc., Oxford, UK, 2005.

Gill, Harold B., Jr. "Colonial Germ Warfare", *Colonial Williamsburg Journal*, Spring 2004.

Maksel, Rebecca. "An American waged germ warfare against U.S. in WWI", *San Francisco Chronicle*, 14 January 2007. www.sfgate.com/cgi-bin/article.cgi?f=/c/a/2007/01/14/RVG6SNFRVL1.DTL

The destroyer of worlds: Robert Oppenheimer, father of the atomic bomb

Hiroshima & Nagasaki Remembered. www.hiroshima-remembered.com

J. Robert Oppenheimer (1904–1967). *The Atomic Archive.* www.atomicarchive.com/Bios/Oppenheimer.shtml

Los Alamos National Laboratory. www.lanl.gov

Maddox, Robert James. "The Biggest Decision: Why We Had to Drop the Atomic Bomb", *American Heritage*, June 1995.

"Race for the Superbomb", *The American Experience.* www.pbs.org/wgbh/amex/bomb

Rhodes, Richard. "The Experiment of the Century", *American Heritage*, April 1999.

For rescue missions: Igor Sikorsky builds the first helicopter and invents vertical flight

Cochrane, Dorothy, Von Hardesty & Russell Lee. *The Aviation Careers of Igor Sikorsky.* University of Washington Press, Seattle, 1989.

Day, Dwayne A. "Helicopters at War." U.S. Centennial of Flight Commission. www.centennialofflight.gov/essay/Air_Power/Heli_at_War/AP42.htm

The First Helicopter Combat Rescue. www.hmfriends.org.uk/combatrescue65th.htm

McGowen, Stanley S. *Helicopters; An Illustrated History of Their Impact.* ABC-CLIO, Inc., Oxford, UK, 2005.

Verne, Jules. *The Clipper of the Clouds* [1887].

BiblioBazaar, 2009.

Waiting for an echo: Robert Watson–Watt invents radar

Brown, Louis. *A Radar History of World War II: Technical and Military Imperatives*. Institute of Physics Publishing, Bristol, UK, 1999.

Brown, R. Hanbury. "Robert Watson-Watt, the Father of Radar", *Engineering Science and Educational Journal*, February 1994.

Clarke, David & Andy Roberts. "Radar and the Death Ray", *Fortean Times*, October 2003.

Commager, Henry Steele. *The Story of the Second World War*. Little, Brown & Co., Boston, MA, 1945.

Hough, Richard Alexander & Denis Richards. *The Battle of Britain: The Greatest Air Battle of World War II*. W.W. Norton, New York, 2005.

Rose, Alexander. "Radar Saves the Day." *American Heritage*. www.americanheritage.com/articles/web/20090806-Radar-World-War-II-Chain-Home-Low-Churchill-Blitz-Battle-of-Britain-Air-Force-RAF-Britain.shtml

Toward the Moon: Wernher von Braun's V-2 rocket

Adams, Guy B. & Danny L. Balfour. *Unmasking Administrative Evil*. M.E. Sharpe, Armonk, NY, 1998.

Bryan, Dave. "Remembering Wernher von Braun's German Rocket Team", Associated Press, posted August, 13 2002.

Day, Dwayne A. "The V-2 (A4) Ballistic Missile Technology". U.S. Centennial of Flight Commission. www.centennialofflight.gov/essay/Evolution_of_Technology/V-2/Tech26.htm

Dr. Wernher von Braun. MSFC History Office. history.msfc.nasa.gov/vonbraun/bio.html

Heppenheimer, T.A. "Lost in Space: What Went Wrong with NASA?", *American Heritage*, November 1992.

Stocker, Jeremy. "Missile Defence—Then and Now." *Officer Magazine*. www.cdiss.co.uk/Documents/Uploaded/Missile%20Defence%20-%20Then%20and%20Now.pdf

Young, Anthony. "Remembering Wernher von Braun", *The Space Review*, 10 July 2006.

"I think you're nuts, but we'll investigate." 44th Infantry Division. efour4ever.com/44thdivision/vonbrauncapture.html

"Sputnik and the Dawn of Space Age." NASA. history.nasa.gov/sputnik/

The most moral weapon: Samuel Cohen's neutron bomb

Brown, G.I. *The Big Bang: A History of Explosives*. Sutton Publishing, Stroud, UK, 1998.

Cohen, Sam. *The Truth About the Neutron Bomb: The Inventor Speaks Out*. William Morrow & Co., New York, 1983.

Conrad, William. "The Future of Tactical Nuclear Weapons", *Air & Space Power Journal*, June, 26 2001.

Newhouse, John. *War and Peace in the Nuclear Age*. Alfred A. Knopf, New York, 1989.

Platt, Charles. "The Profits of Fear", posted August 2005.

Snow, Donald M. "Strategic Implication of Enhanced Radiation Weapons". *Air University Review*, July–August 1979.

Catching bullets: Stephanie Kwolek's bullet-proof fabric

Andrews, Peter. "The New Army Helmet", *American Heritage*, August/September 1984.

Gabriel, Richard A. & Karen S. Metz. *A Short History of War: The Evolution of Warfare and Weapons*. Strategic Studies Institute, U.S. Army War College, Carlisle, PA, 1992.

Parkman, Francis. *France and England in North America, Vol. 2: Count Frontenac and New France under Louis XIV, A Half-Century of Conflict, Montcalm and Wolfe*. The Library of America, New York, 1983.

Quinn, Jim. "I was able to be creative and work as hard as I wanted", *Invention & Technology Magazine*, Winter 2003.

Vare, Ethlie Ann & Greg Placek. *Women Inventors and Their Discoveries*. The Oliver Press, Minneapolis, MN, 1993.

Woosnam-Savage, Robert & Anthony Hall. *Body Armor*. Brassey's, Washington, D.C., 2001.

Welcome to Kevlar. www2.dupont.com/Kevlar/en_US/index.html

Acknowledgments

Writing a book is often considered a solitary occupation. In fact, every writer needs a small army of allies, and I have been very fortunate in mine. My heartfelt thanks to my publisher, Diana Hill, and my editors Anne Savage and Paul O'Beirne—it is always a joy to work with all. Furthermore, I am very grateful to the staff members of the libraries at the University of Connecticut, Fairfield University, and the Connecticut state library system.

Index